Petrochemica

The New World of Synthet

by Ray T. Wendland

A broad but concise survey of the petrochemical industry that has produced a multitude of modern miracles —from the gas engine and anti-freeze to films and fibers. The author traces the development of the industry from Colonel Edwin Drake's discovery of oil in the hills of Western Pennsylvania in 1859 to the modern technique of catalytic cracking, a picturesque word for the process that breaks down the big molecules of heavy oil into the smaller molecules used with other materials to form what chemists call petrochemicals and what we know as plastics, nylons, and no-knock gasoline. This is a lively introduction to the technology that has put men into space and children into portable, backyard swimming pools.

s
l
e
l
t
i-
g
y
s
l-
e
:s
es

have each been written by distinguished authorities in the field, and cover such various topics as agricultural chemistry, chemicals from the atmosphere and from the ocean, and the chemistry of paints, the soil, water purification, sulfuric acid, the silicon compounds, synthetic textiles, drugs, and antibiotics.

PETROCHEMICALS

Ray T. Wendland is Professor and Chairman of the Department of Chemistry at Carroll College, Waukesha, Wisconsin. A graduate of Carleton College, Professor Wendland received his doctoral degree from Iowa State University. Thereafter he gained experience in petroleum chemistry in the research laboratories of the Universal Oil Products Company, and at the Mellon Institute, Pittsburgh, as a Research Fellow in Petroleum with the Gulf Oil Corporation. During World War II he worked on problems of rubber synthesis at the University of Minnesota under the War Production Board. Formerly Professor of Chemistry at North Dakota State University (Fargo), he established courses there in petroleum chemistry when North Dakota became an oil-producing state.

He is the author of a number of technical papers and articles on various aspects of science education, and acts as a consultant in chemical industry.

The *Chemistry in Action Series* has been designed to give the interested layman a thorough introduction to the many different sides of the chemical industry. Prepared under the joint supervision of the Education Activities Committee of the Manufacturing Chemists' Association and Doubleday & Company, Inc., each volume focuses on a particular segment of the chemical industry and relates the pure chemical science to the final products met in everyday life. The volumes have each been written by distinguished authorities in the field, and cover such various topics as agricultural chemistry, chemicals from the atmosphere and from the ocean, and the chemistry of paints, the soil, water purification, sulfuric acid, the silicon compounds, synthetic textiles, drugs, and antibiotics.

PETROCHEMICALS

The New World of Synthetics

RAY T. WENDLAND

PREPARED UNDER THE SPONSORSHIP OF
THE MANUFACTURING CHEMISTS' ASSOCIATION

Garden City, New York
DOUBLEDAY & COMPANY, INC.
1969

Library of Congress Catalog Card No. 68-12771
Copyright © 1969 by Ray T. Wendland
All Rights Reserved
Printed in the United States of America
First Edition

PREFACE

Within these pages is a chemical short story, a story about a determined band of men who worked through science and industry to generate a revolution which in effect teaches how to transform muck into miracles.

In the course of their actions, these investigators learned how to change something which is black and repelling, namely crude oil, into a mine of great treasures. For their purpose they contrived a "Golden Cat," a monstrous machine that breaks apart the largest molecules of the petroleum conglomerate—those responsible for its sticky and tarry character—and converts them into liquid fuels and gases. The fuels make it possible for people to enjoy the benefits of engine power—to move swiftly on wheels and on wings, and do the heavy chores around them with ease. The gases, made up of small lively molecules called "olefins," are ideal building blocks for transmutations that would have been incredible to the ancient alchemists; through the wonders of precise chemical synthesis these olefins are guided through an array of complex processes from which they finally emerge in new form. Then we see them as solvents and as pure chemicals, or as structural materials like films and fibers, plastics, adhesives, and rubbery products.

This story is written to appreciate the labors, the struggles, the brilliant ideas and flights of fancy of scientists who made all this possible—in short, how they wrought a modern miracle in the transformation of crude resources into products of beauty and utility.

CONTENTS

PETROCHEMICALS

Chapter 1

IN THE BEGINNING

When the North American continent was still new to the explorers who had barely begun to penetrate its depths and mysteries, the few people who lived here were scattered widely across the abundant land. Its primeval forests were dense and filled with all manner of animals, while great herds of buffalo roamed over the lush, unbroken prairies covered with tall waving grass. Thousands of lakes teeming with fish sparkled in the dazzling sunshine, and the air was crisp and clear, as yet undimmed by smoke. Of resources there was such an abundance that one might imagine life in that time to be filled with gentle ease and comfort and well-being.

But if you ponder this for a while, you will see that these resources were rarely in a state ready for direct use; they needed to be refined, reshaped, or transformed into clothing, fuel, lumber, brick, mortar, or useful devices before they could be beneficial. In that era of virgin forests, trackless prairies, buried minerals, and onrushing rivers, man was more dominated by than dominant over natural forces. Moreover, there was a great amount of work to be done—more than enough for every living person who inhabited the land. People contrived to get work from every living creature that looked strong enough to be useful. They harnessed horses, mules, dogs, oxen—yes, they even harnessed people at times to do some of the enormous amount of work that faced them.

The land was also filled with ideas of freedom, but men knew that they could not be very free when their days were so filled with toil, when all their working hours were spent in chopping, sawing, building, hoeing, harvesting,

harnessing and unharnessing, pumping, scrubbing, cooking, rendering, spinning, mending, caring for the sick, and
burying the dead. It seemed that people were free only to
work; a few even thought this was good. After all, men
and women became toughened by hard work and were
not easily discouraged when their pathways became difficult and painful.

On the other hand, there were those not naturally born
to this heavy toil—poets, musicians, artists perhaps, who
went to untimely graves under burdens they could not
bear. For all but a few, the unceasing struggles to stay
ahead of want, ahead of disease, ahead of the encircling
forest, ahead of the onrushing night and the encroaching
winter, and away from the fury of nature's upheavals—
exacted a toll and shortened their lives.

In the precious little time left to men for reflection (or
in time snatched from an onerous task), they took to in-
venting, testing, and experimenting in order to find ways
to lessen their toil, so that they might have freedom *from*
work, as well as freedom *for* it, and freedom to enjoy
the fruits of their labor.

To this end, little by little, they developed better ways
to lift a load, to move a boat, to harness a waterfall or a
windmill in order to grind their grain or to pump water
into a convenient reservoir. However, all of these methods were nothing compared to the wonders of load-lifting
and muscle-sparing that became possible when *engine
power* appeared on the world stage. Engine power—the
ability to do useful work by the burning of a fuel—had a
humble beginning in the form of some heavy machines
built by the Englishmen Newcomen and Watt in the mid-
1700s. These early engines, in which the expansion of
steam from a water boiler moved a piston back and forth
and slowly turned a wheel, revealed a revolutionary new
force that was to transform the working habits of mankind,
and make possible activities and explorations only

dreamed of by the boldest thinkers. The steam engine was a fascinating device that attracted a host of experimenters and inventors who sought to improve it in numerous ways and apply it to working situations of all types. Before long, the steam engine was the motive power that pulled trains across the continents, drove ships up and down the great rivers and across the oceans, lifted stone and steel to great heights so that men could erect buildings and useful structures like bridges, dams, and levees, and pulled the plows in the spring and turned the harvesters' wheels in the fall. It needed only coal or wood as its fuel, water for its boiler, and grease for its gears and bearings.

In the 1800s a rival appeared on the scene, a compact little device with remarkable efficiency, that spun at high speed and needed no coal, wood, or water—only electrical energy that could be carried in slender wires. The steam engineers could afford to be haughty about this rival, however; after all, it took a *steam* engine to drive a generator to activate an electric motor. So long as this was true, the steam engine was still the prime mover, and its status was secure.

However, with invention went discovery and learning. When engine power was used to drill wells for water it was found that in going down to deeper levels than were previously accessible, one sometimes brought up water that was contaminated by an odorous dark oil. Those who wanted water were dismayed by this pollution, but a few were challenged by the discovery. They wanted to know more about this mysterious, smelly stuff that was locked up deep in the subterrane. First, enough of it must be gotten from the earth to have a good look at it and investigate its behavior. To this end, an adventurous band of men, backed by the newly formed Seneca Oil Company of New Haven, Connecticut, and led by a forceful pro-

moter, one Colonel Edwin Drake,* drilled into an oil field
in the rugged hills of western Pennsylvania. Colonel
Drake's men brought up oil in quantity—more than
enough to satisfy the uses they found for it at that time.
The year was 1859, a date to be remembered in the industrial life of America, the year when petroleum or "rock
oil" was discovered on this continent and made available
to man as a new natural resource.

It was a most unpromising kind of material, almost as
unaesthetic a resource as could be imagined. Crude it was,
and "crude" it is, and everyone in the business of finding
or using oil still speaks of "crude oil" when he describes
this fluid as it comes from the ground.

However, this new oil intrigued the early investigators,
first, because it would burn easily and provide abundant
heat, and second, because gentle heating in a simple retort
caused a volatile, practically colorless fluid to emerge from
it. Stronger heating drove out more "distillate" material,
and when the heating was prolonged, the last bit of material to distill was viscous and colored, while the residue
turned darker and took on the character of pitch or tar.
The first distillate fraction was called gasoline; it was
found to be quite unsafe to handle for it caught fire easily
and produced a variety of disasters for its handlers. The
second distillate was less volatile and less easily ignited;
called kerosene, this fraction was much safer to handle,
and though it had to be coaxed to ignite, it would burn
very readily after it was once set afire. Furthermore, its
flame was quite luminous compared to the pale blue flame
of burning gasoline. Finally, it occurred to someone that
this was a real benefit! Here was the substance for a whale
oil lamp without the hazards of hunting the whale! And so
kerosene went into lanterns to light the night and make
life after sundown more hospitable and comfortable. Colo-

* The title of "Colonel" was self-imposed by the intrepid
Drake.

nel Drake's bold venture of drilling for rock oil began to pay off, and handsomely too, for everybody soon wanted kerosene.

Because a kerosene lamp produced heat as well as light, it wasn't long before other inventive minds produced kerosene cookstoves and burners. The use of kerosene spread rapidly, for here was a fire that could be turned on and off at will. Imagine the benefit on a cold winter morning of having a cooking fire ready immediately; likewise on a hot summer day, contrast a roaring wood or coal fire in a cookstove with the compact flame of the kerosene burner that could be promptly turned off after the food was heated.

The wonders of kerosene lamps and burners spread so rapidly around the world that before long American producers were getting rich exporting the precious fluid and providing oil for the lamps of China and many other lands. Drilling rigs sprang up all over western Pennsylvania, and in fact in any place where prospectors, promoters, or speculators thought that oil could be found.

Pennsylvania was the source of the nation's oil until 1885; in 1882 it reached its peak with the production of 30 million barrels. In 1885 oil was discovered near Lima, Ohio, and this field produced a million barrels in 1886. Fortunes were made and lost in the mad scramble for oil, because oil was not always found where men said it ought to be. Many companies were made, broken, or absorbed in the struggle for survival and profits. A phenomenon of the times was the formation of the Standard Oil empire, an amazing collection of companies in which John D. Rockefeller was the leading personality.* But it was clear

---

* The Standard Oil Company of Ohio was formed in 1870 by Rockefeller and his associates, a brother William, Henry Flagler, Samuel Adams, and Stephen Harkness. In rapid succession followed Standard of Iowa (1885), Standard of Kentucky and Standard of Minnesota, both in 1886, Standard of Indiana

that a new industry—the petroleum industry—had been forged out of the excitement of discovery and the utilization of a new resource, and the roots of this industry were in solid ground by the 1880s.

However, in the late 1800s, despite electricity, steam engines were still the prime movers. They had, in truth, undergone remarkable improvements, and the marvelous steam turbine was now supplementing and even replacing the reciprocating steam engine. Steam was supreme and kerosene had affected it not at all.

Nevertheless, thoughtful people were not satisfied to

(1889), and Standard of Illinois (1890). They were all controlled by the Standard Oil Trust organized in 1879.

Competition in oil production, refining, and distribution was fierce, and the methods involved were not always laudable. Rockefeller and the various Standards became storm centers of controversy for their efforts to monopolize and dominate the oil business. For instance, Standard of Ohio, which refined only 4 per cent of U.S. crude production in 1870, succeeded in acquiring 90 per cent of production for its refineries by 1880. Favored treatment that the Standard companies acquired from the railroads in regard to freight rates on oil shipments was a large factor in their success and expansion.

However, as the oil business grew larger, new factors came into play. Oil production was moving westward, and federal as well as state laws became operative to break up monopoly practices in business.

In 1895 Ohio exceeded Pennsylvania as the nation's leading oil producer with an outpouring of 19.54 million barrels. Indiana began producing oil in 1891, Kansas in 1892, Oklahoma in 1900. Texas excited world attention with its spectacular gusher at Spindletop, which erupted in 1901. New oil companies capitalized on the Western production. Among these were Sun Oil, Texaco, and Gulf, companies that are now among the strongest in the industry. A little later came Phillips, Sinclair, Cities Service, Shell, and Skelly, also very prominent. The net effect of the growth of strong new companies outside the Standard system was to ensure vigorous competition throughout the entire petroleum industry—a condition that has certainly prevailed since the mid-twenties or earlier.

ignore that highly flammable gasoline that accompanied the kerosene in petroleum and they were horrified to see producers burn it just to get rid of it. In time, their efforts to contrive new forms of heat engines bore fruit. The new engines, despite early American hopes, came from Germany. Otto invented the gasoline-consuming internal-combustion engine, the so-called four-cycle engine, in 1866; and Rudolf Diesel invented a two-cycle engine, the first of which blew up in 1892, while a second model ran successfully in 1897. It was soon discovered that Diesel's engine could burn high-boiling *less* flammable fuels as well as gasoline. In fact, because of the fuel ignition system of the Diesel, it actually ran better on high-boiling fuels than on gasoline. (Its compression of air was so great that the high temperature produced induced spontaneous ignition of the injected fuel.) This engine, however, had to be of heavier construction than the gasoline-burning engine of Otto; hence it was not well suited for easy mobility. But as a stationary power plant or mounted in heavy vehicles like ships, locomotives, or trucks, the Diesel engine rapidly gained favor among industrial users.

The Otto and Diesel engines, competing against a well-established steam-engine business, had a formidable struggle before they gained full respect as reliable power plants. Although these two engines were of foreign birth, they were quickly adopted by Americans, who in turn effected numerous improvements while applying them to mechanical systems requiring new forms of power. It was in automobiles that the inherent advantages of the Otto four-cycle engine appeared most clearly. Here was a lightweight power plant that needed no water supply or heavy boiler to accompany it; its fuel was a liquid easily carried in a small tank, and—in contrast to an electric motor—its life did not depend on a ropelike cord bearing a pair of wires. It was, indeed, the ideal mobile power pack, provided that it ran according to plan.

The twentieth-century history of the gasoline engine has been one of phenomenal growth and expansion of usefulness. From the early Model T automobile, by which Henry Ford and company put America on wheels,* to engines for boating and giant transport airplanes, we see the gasoline engine as a prime mover without a peer. Without it, our present mobility on land, on the sea, and in the air would be difficult. Moreover, the incessant toil, labor, sweat, and struggle of our forebears have been practically banished, at least in the Western world. The steam engine is still with us, but its role has been taken over largely by the gasoline engine, the oil-burning Diesel engine, and electric motors which run because electricity has been generated by some other prime mover.

This amazing world of engines and machines, which we take so much for granted as though it were a natural heritage, rests squarely on the petroleum industry. Without the continual production of crude oil and its refinement into gaseous and liquid fuels and lubricants, the world of engines would quickly grind to a halt.

* "In 1909 Henry Ford sold over ten thousand Model T's—a staggering figure in those days, but he was just getting started. In the next half dozen years, by 1915, his sales reached a quarter of a million cars a year. And the interesting thing was that simultaneously the price of the Model T had dropped from the 1908 price of $950 to the 1914 price of $490! It confirmed the conviction of R. E. Olds and taught the rest of America the fundamental lesson which has turned out to be our guiding principle in achieving prosperity and plenty—namely, that in order to place articles in reach of the average man's pocketbook, you have to produce them in large quantities. In other words, mass production is the key to quality and quantity at a low price. Mass production is to the inventor and engineer what the printing press was to the writer." (The above is a verbatim quote from *The American Battle for Abundance—A Story of Mass Production* by Charles F. Kettering and Allen Orth, published in 1947).

For those who might not recognize the name of Kettering, he was anything but a Ford publicity agent—he was in fact one of the giant leaders in the opposition party, General Motors!

The petroleum industry has been notable for its production of fuels for energy purposes. However, in recent years it has gone beyond fuels, and has taken on a new role as a producer of chemicals and intermediates for chemical synthesis. (Synthesis is a chemical building-up process in which complex structures are compounded from simpler molecules easily available, such as natural gas, benzene, alcohol, and nitric acid. Examples of synthetic products are rubber, dyes, and "miracle" drugs.) This development was in part forced upon petroleum processors, but it was also a natural outcome of their efforts to know more about petroleum in order to use it more efficiently. Before about 1920, for instance, when those who drilled for oil found natural gas instead, the event was regarded as something of a calamity. The gas might even have contained a fair amount of so-called "light gasoline" or "naphtha"; nevertheless, there was little demand for the gas. So it was set afire like a giant torch right at the well site. Other oil wells gushed out under great gas pressure; a rough separation of liquid from gas was made in the field, and the gas, unwanted again, was burned. Indeed, it was a dangerous material to have around. Many of the rich oil fields of Texas and Oklahoma glowed like furnaces because of the incessant burning of gas from one year to the next.

Naturally, many people deplored this wasteful burning of a natural resource. However, before the gas could be turned into useful channels, the chemistry and physics of the hydrocarbons (the hydrogen-carbon compounds in gases) had to be worked out. As knowledge accumulated in these matters, natural gas was put to work as an additional valuable fuel in the national economy, and also as a source of chemical products.

By far the greatest advances in the chemistry of petroleum arose from the continual demands of the motor industry for more gasoline and better gasoline. The natural

gasoline, obtainable directly from crude oil by simple distillation, was entirely inadequate to satisfy the expanding
motor industry. Accordingly, gasoline had to be *made
chemically* from petroleum, not merely distilled from it.
These efforts to make more and better gasoline required a
special kind of chemical study. New research was begun
on reactions of hydrocarbons, and processes were devised
for transforming the hydrocarbons in petroleum* into new
hydrocarbons needed by the motor industry. The practical
consequences of this research were the following:

1. The need for more and better gasoline was abundantly satisfied and, in fact, great reserve capacity
   was built into new refineries to satisfy expanding
   needs far into the future.
2. By-product gases were formed in addition to gasoline. These highly reactive gases, called "olefins,"
   now available for the first time at low cost, became
   ideal building stones for synthesis of useful chemical
   products—the so-called "petrochemicals."
3. Petroleum chemists learned also how to separate pure
   liquid hydrocarbons from complex mixtures. Among
   these were five valuable aromatic compounds, benzene

toluene and the three xylenes

---

* The composition of most crude oils is such that carbon and
hydrogen together compose 97 per cent or more of the entire

(In each of these formulations the hexagon with the letter "B" inside represents a benzene ring of six carbon atoms. Thus, benzene itself—with its six hydrogen atoms—has the molecular composition C_6H_6.) Each of these compounds is useful in itself, either as an ingredient in high-quality gasoline, or as a solvent, and each has unique reactivities which lead to further petrochemical syntheses.

4. Mass production *day and night,* month after month without a shutdown, was realized on an immense scale which, before this time, was hardly conceivable as a practical attainment. This introduced a new economy factor into the oil industry by which its products could be turned out in large quantities and at low costs. They could therefore enter competitively into all areas of the fuel and chemical markets.

This new role of petroleum as a base for a chemical industry will recur frequently in the remaining chapters of this book. The process of converting crude oil into quality gasoline, while at the same time producing great quantities of gaseous olefins—those primary building blocks for synthesis of petrochemicals—will appear in the next several chapters. Thereafter, the individual products made from olefins and aromatic hydrocarbons will be described.

Meanwhile, it must be remembered that petroleum, a smelly, unaesthetic crude resource, could hardly have entered the era of pure chemicals without its history of developing hand in hand with the era of engines and machines. The knowledge gained in that century-long de-

---

mass. The remaining elements are accounted for by traces of sulfur, nitrogen, and oxygen, and even some metals, e.g. vanadium and nickel. Natural gas likewise is almost entirely hydrocarbon in nature, except for an occasional trace of sulfur compounds. Some natural gases—fortunately for us—contain also a significant amount of helium (and thus serve as a commercial source of helium).

velopment has paid off well—in lightening the burdens of man, and now in producing things of beauty and utility, such as Dacron fibers and Butyl rubber, which we describe as "petrochemicals."

Chapter 2

PETROLEUM AND A NEW AGE FOR MAN

In the long history of people on this planet, there have been many stages of development. Historians frequently speak of them as "Ages," and they have made us aware of the Stone Age, the Bronze and Iron Ages, the Middle Ages, the Renaissance Age, the Elizabethan Age, and so on. Much of the nineteenth century might be called the "Age of Steam"; but the twentieth century with its complexities seems to defy any simple characterization. However, I propose to call it the "Fluid Age," or the "Age of Liquids and Gases."

Except for wind and water, ancient man (and modern man until the 1800s) had little to do with gases and liquids.* Then came petroleum, a great new source of flowing materials. The merging of petroleum with physical science not only elevated machines to enormous prominence, but the merger introduced a new principle into the economy of materials processing. More than any other enterprise, the petroleum industry has *fluidized* the operations of industrial science.

The advantage of liquids and gases is so obvious that it frequently escapes notice—they are free-flowing, and therefore can be piped and pumped and moved around

* One of the gases that intrigued him most was that which arose from the alcoholic fermentation of fruit juices and the gas which raised the bread dough after inoculation with yeast (carbon dioxide). The lively effervescence of champagne became almost a symbol of gay living and social affluence.

Other liquids which were common in various places were olive oil, whale oil, turpentine, and resin from trees.

literally for thousands of miles, quickly, easily, and economically. Because most of what we use and consume is manufactured, it becomes apparent that the procession of raw materials into the factory and their movement inside the plant are enormously assisted by moving them as liquids or gases. Finally, if a liquid or gaseous product can be delivered to the ultimate consumer, for instance as fuel for the furnace or cooking gas for the kitchen range, then the cycle of free-flowing materials from field or mine to the factory and from factory to home is complete.*

Now, a chemist should be the last to minimize the importance of the solid state, which certainly will be with us for a long time to come. But at this point in history the chemist has achieved a fair mastery of those forces by which he reduces solid matter to liquids and gases—and then reverses the process, converting gases to liquids, liquids to solids, or in a single stroke even changes gas to solid matter. There is no miracle or hocus-pocus about this—it is all in accordance with natural laws.

The newest of the chemical engines by which one can convert high-boiling petroleum distillates, or even nondistillable residues, into *gases* and low-boiling liquids which make a superior gasoline is the *fluidized catalytic cracker*. This complex device is known in petroleum circles as the "cat cracker." Because the cat cracker has unlocked a golden storehouse and released substances that contribute immeasurably to our material well-being, we shall call this fantastic machine the "Golden Cat." Through its pipes and reactors, heavy oils in amounts as great as

---

* Can you think of any other substance that is *unseen,* and *untouched* by human hands from the time it leaves its natural habitat until it is delivered to the ultimate consumer, the man with an engine or a furnace? He likewise gets full benefit from the fuel he buys with no necessity to see it or touch it. He only needs to set fire to it!

60,000 barrels per day* flow continuously for as long as two years, while hundreds of tons of "fluidized" catalyst circulate with that river of oil, transforming it to gasoline and olefinic gases suitable for synthesis of plastics, rubber, alcohols, and other valuable chemical products. The cat cracker is truly a revolutionary invention that has elevated the techniques of mass production to a new level. How the cat cracker works, and how it has become the foundation stone for the petrochemical industry, will be described in Chapter 6.

Before we go to that point, however, it is advisable to examine the meaning of various technical words, which will be used more frequently as the story unfolds. Some of those most common in petroleum technology and chemistry are defined in the chapter that follows.

* Cat crackers vary upward in capacity from a minimum of about 10,000 barrels per day.

Chapter 3

A BRIEF INTRODUCTION TO
TECHNICAL TERMS

DESCRIPTIONS AND DEFINITIONS*

We shall begin with *hydrocarbons,* the foundation stones of petroleum composition. A hydrocarbon is a chemical compound made up only of hydrogen and carbon, for which the symbols are H and C. The versatility of carbon is such that carbon atoms may be joined to each other in an enormous variety of forms. For instance, the following hydrocarbons are well known:

Group I
(linear)

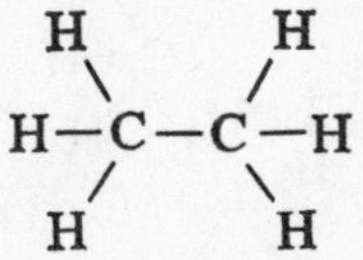

ethane 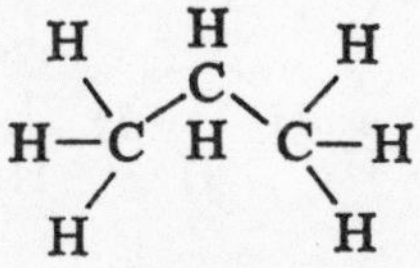   propane

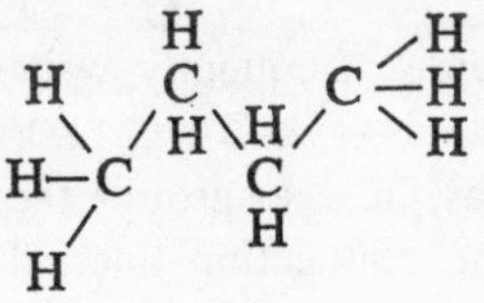

butane

* In this chapter the meaning of various scientific and technical words will be presented in a fashion like that of a dictionary. A clear understanding of these words will be necessary before one is able to read about the chemical processes that follow. For those who know these words, there is no need to stop here, in which case Chapter 4 is the next station.

(The connecting lines represent a pair of electrons combined in such a way as to form a chemical bond—the covalent single bond—between two atoms.)

Group II
(branched)

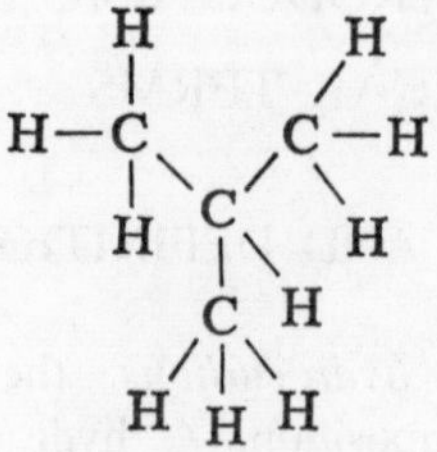

isobutane 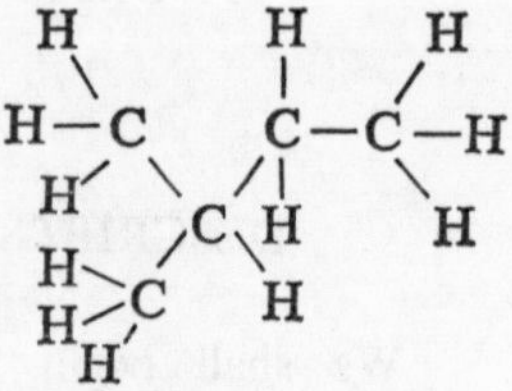   isopentane

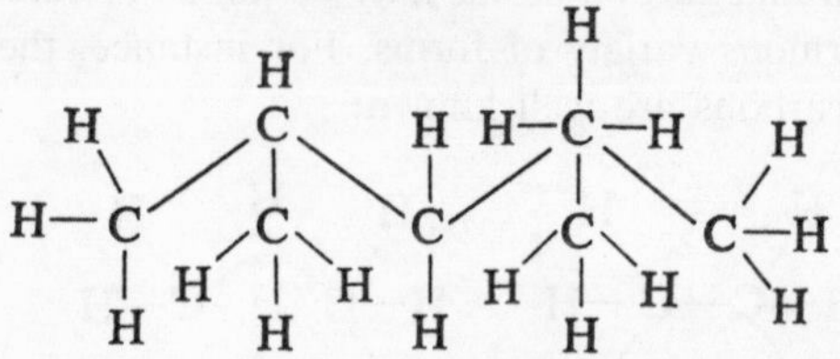

iso-octane

Carbon atoms in long chains are actually linked together in a zig-zag fashion,

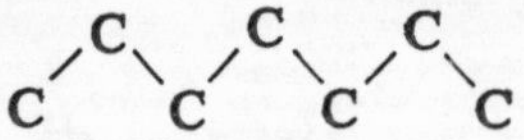

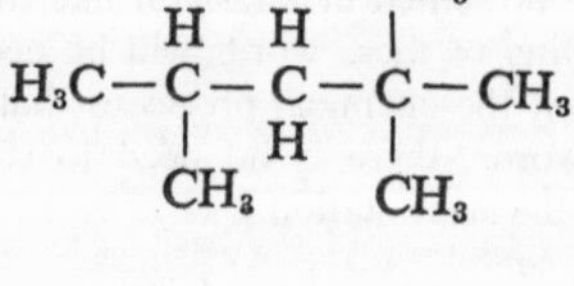

, but for simplicity's sake the chemist frequently writes them in a linear fashion, thus $C-C-C-C-C$. Also to simplify the writing of formulas, he also groups the H atoms together, and leaves out the connecting lines. Thus for iso-octane we will usually find

but one should never forget that the zig-zag representation is better, because this reflects the *tetrahedral* nature of the carbon atom when it is bonded to four other atoms —all H's as in methane:

(here H⌃C⌄H lies in the plane of the paper, while

means that the H is *behind* the paper, and

means that the H is in front of the paper) or combinations of C and H, as in ethane

Chemists frequently think of carbon atoms as little pyramids with the corners representing the geometric locations

where other atoms, like hydrogen and carbon, may be attached through formation of single bonds.

Carbon atoms may be joined in rings, of which the commonest have five or six carbon atoms, thus:

Group III
(cyclic)

$$H_2C \overset{\overset{\displaystyle H_2}{\displaystyle C}}{\diagup} \diagdown CH_2$$
$$H_2C \text{——} CH_2$$

cyclopentane

$$H_2C \overset{\overset{\displaystyle H_2}{\displaystyle C}}{\diagup} \diagdown CH_2$$
$$H_2C \qquad CH_2$$
$$\diagdown \underset{H_2}{C} \diagup$$

cyclohexane

and the rings may contain side chains, as in

$$H_2C \overset{\overset{\displaystyle H_2}{\displaystyle C}}{\diagup} \overset{H}{\underset{|}{C}} - CH_3$$
$$H_2C \qquad CH_2$$
$$\diagdown \underset{H_2}{C} \diagup$$

methylcyclohexane

and

$$H_2C \overset{\overset{\displaystyle H_2}{\displaystyle C}}{\diagup} \overset{H}{\underset{|}{C}} - \overset{CH_3}{\overset{\diagup}{CH_2}}$$
$$H_2C \qquad CH_2$$
$$\diagdown \underset{H_2}{C} \diagup$$

ethylcyclohexane

where $-CH_3$ is methyl, and $-CH_2-CH_3$ is ethyl, two very common atom groupings known as "radicals."

Carbon atoms may be joined not only by single bonds, but by double or even triple bonds, as in acetylene

$$H-C \equiv C-H$$

Examples of double-bonded compounds are

Group IV
(olefinic)

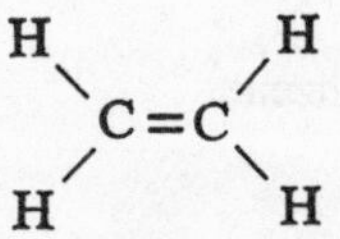

$$\underset{H}{\overset{H}{\diagdown}} C = C \underset{H}{\overset{H}{\diagup}}$$

ethylene

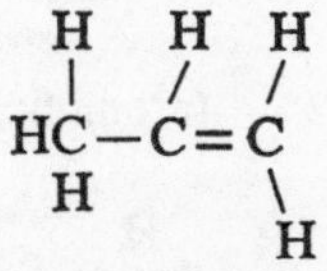

$$HC - C = C$$

propylene

$$HC - C = C - CH$$

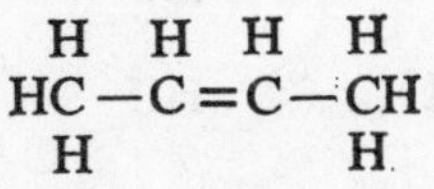

butylene (2—butene)

which are known as unsaturated, or olefinic, hydrocarbons. Here the double link between carbon atoms, $C = C$, stands for two pairs of electrons joined in a covalent double bond.

Another prominent group of hydrocarbons is that known as the aromatic compounds, in which there appear to be both double and single bonds alternating around six-membered rings, as below.

The compounds in Group I are called saturated hydrocarbons because the *bond* that holds the carbon atoms together is a *single* bond; the remaining bonding capability of carbon is "saturated" with hydrogen. (This "bonding capability," called "valence," is always *four* for carbon.) In other words, a saturated hydrocarbon, no matter how

Group V

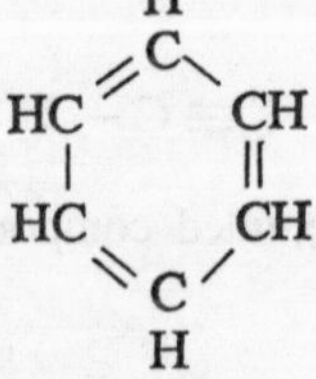

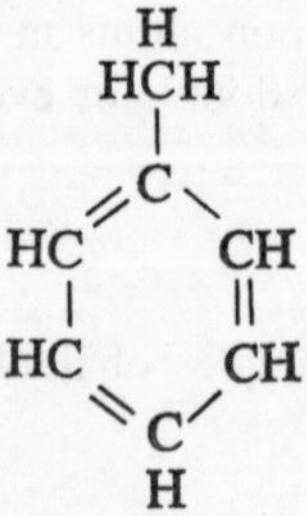

(aromatic)   benzene   toluene

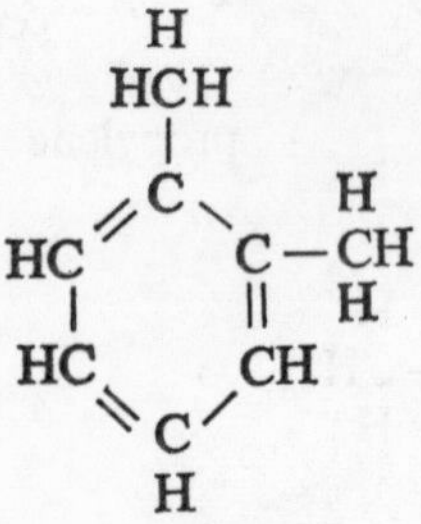

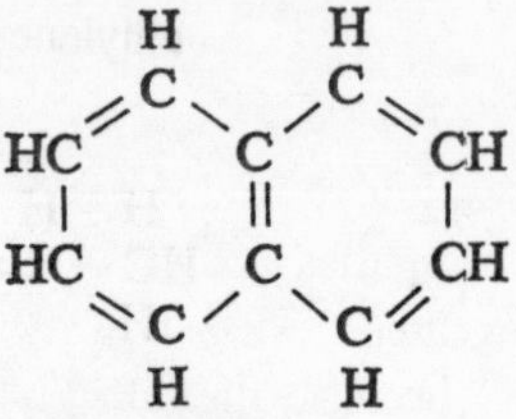

xylene   naphthalene

many C atoms it contains, always has its C atoms joined by single bonds.

According to this definition, the compounds in Groups II and III are also *saturated* hydrocarbons. However, those in Group I are *linear,* while Group II compounds are nonlinear, that is, they carry branches, and Group III compounds are ringlike or cyclic. Accordingly, we can define these three groups more specifically as follows:

Group I are unbranched saturated hydrocarbons
Group II are branched saturated hydrocarbons
Group III are cyclic saturated hydrocarbons.

Groups I and II also go by the name "paraffins" or paraffinic hydrocarbons; Group III compounds are commonly called "naphthenes," particularly in the petroleum industry.

Compounds in Group IV, the unsaturated ones, may react with more hydrogen to reach full saturation with respect to hydrogen. Each compound containing a carbon — carbon double link ($C = C$) can react with an H_2 molecule (in the presence of a suitable "catalyst"—see page 25) and absorb hydrogen into its structure. Unsaturation in general lends to the molecule a high degree of activity, making it susceptible to many transformations that are not possible among the saturated hydrocarbons.

Compounds in Group V, the aromatic hydrocarbons, have this name because of their rather pleasant odors. Their structures are characterized by alternating single and double bonds around a ring of six carbon atoms. The aromatics are unique and different from all the preceding types. Although they appear to be highly "unsaturated" because of the numerous double links between C atoms, in reality they behave much like the saturated hydrocarbons, and show a low order of activity compared to compounds in Group IV. This stability feature* makes them valuable in certain ways, but is not easy to explain in the small space available here.† We shall not attempt

* Stability and reactivity can be equated with familiar terms such as these:

(a) High stability means low reactivity, and *resistance* to chemical change.

(b) High reactivity means low stability, and *susceptibility* to chemical change.

† Like the olefinic compounds of Group IV, the aromatic hydrocarbons will combine with additional hydrogen to form *saturated* rings, in which case they become compounds like those in Group III, the "naphthenes." However—note well—this hydrogen reaction (promoted by catalysts, of course) requires a higher temperature and pressure than in the case of the more reactive olefins.

to do so except to say that the normal energetic quality of the double bond is somehow swallowed up and dissipated in the ring system. The phenomenon is referred to as "resonance." Some chemists give it a romantic sort of name, "aromaticity," and we shall accept this for the present.[*]

The remaining technical terms for this chapter will appear in alphabetical order.

ALPHABETICAL LISTING OF TECHNICAL TERMS

Antiknock agent. An additive for gasoline that reduces the tendency of a gasoline engine to "knock" under a heavy load, or under increased compression. The principal material used for this purpose is tetraethyl lead, $Pb(C_2H_5)_4$, frequently called "TEL." (See also *engine knock* and *octane number*.)

Antioxidant. A chemical agent that protects another material from attack by oxygen. Antioxidants are put into lubricating oils, for instance, to prevent their deterioration at the high temperature and oxidizing conditions of the automotive engine. Antioxidants are also put into "cracked" gasolines to prevent formation of sludge during storage, and into rubber and other polymeric materials

---

[*] In spite of the pleasing odor of many aromatic hydrocarbons, they are not acceptable for frequent inhalation. In fact, they can produce serious poisoning and their vapors should be avoided. Benzene is worse in this respect than the others named. As for contact with skin, *all* hydrocarbons may remove fatty components of the tissue and cause trouble in varying degree. It is best not to permit frequent contact of hydrocarbon liquids with the skin.

containing double bonds in order to prevent breakdown by oxygen.

Catalysis (Catalysts). The use of catalysts to promote chemical transformations that otherwise would proceed too slowly to be useful. Catalysis is also used to describe a situation where the catalyst, or promoter, induces a transformation that otherwise would not occur, provided, however, that the catalyst must be substantially unchanged when the transformation is finished. An example of a process that occurs slowly is the breakdown of fatty materials, e.g. butterfat or lard, into fatty acids and glycerol when they are heated in water. However, if either alkali or acid are added, the breakdown occurs very rapidly. The use of alkali for breakdown of fats is one that people have practiced for a long time in the preparation of soap. In this example, the acid, or the alkali, has "catalyzed" the transformation, that is, has accelerated it to a useful rate.

Another example is the fermentative breakdown of sugars into acids and alcohols induced by the enzymes of bacteria and yeasts. Although enzymes have very complex structures, they behave like catalysts in that they induce a specific transformation and afterward still retain their identity. By this is meant that they can continue to induce more of the original transformation. Thus there appears a second characteristic of catalysis, namely that a small amount of catalyst can effect a large amount of chemical change.

Catalysts are very diverse in character. For instance, a variety of ordinary acids and bases serve as catalysts for the breakdown of fat mentioned above, and for similar transformations where water is involved. In petroleum chemistry, the catalysts that induce the breakdown of large hydrocarbon molecules are usually metal oxides, particularly aluminum and silicon oxides. Chromium oxide and platinum metal are used to induce cleavage of carbon-hydrogen bonds in order to promote dehydrogenations.

Cracking. A chemical reaction induced by heat (in the absence of air) or by heat with the assistance of catalysts whereby high-boiling components of petroleum are broken down into lower-boiling materials suitable for gasoline. The materials to be cracked would be those with boiling points over 200° C. or even non-distillable materials left in the residue from petroleum distillation. Cracking is described more completely in Chapter 5.

Dehydrogenation. The process for removing hydrogen from organic compounds, whereby saturated hydrocarbons are converted to unsaturated ones or to aromatic hydrocarbons. The process requires an elevated temperature and an appropriate catalyst. Platinum, palladium, nickel, and chromium oxide are commonly employed.

Desulfurization. Catalytic processes that cause the removal of chemically combined sulfur from petroleum or its fractions. The sulfur thus split out usually appears as hydrogen sulfide, a gas with a characteristic odor of rotten eggs. Desulfurization is frequently an accompaniment of other processes, e.g. cracking; thus when these processes are operating on petroleum fractions that contain appreciable sulfur, foul odors become noticeable. The removal of sulfur is, of course, desirable as an improvement in the materials which are thus rendered sulfur-free.

Distillation. The process of heating a mixture containing volatile materials until vapor is formed, then allowing the vapor to pass into a condenser (cooler), thereby causing it to liquefy. See Figures 1 and 2. When the heating is done slowly, and the vapor passes through a long tube, partial condensation of the highest-boiling components takes place, while the lowest-boiling components pass through and finally emerge via the condenser. Thus a separation of low-boiling material from high-boiling material occurs during such a controlled distillation. Dis-

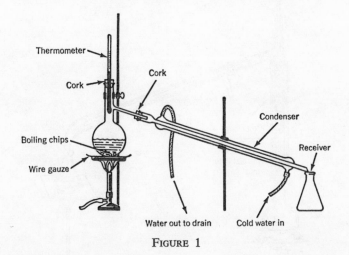

FIGURE 1

Apparatus for simple distillation of volatile liquids. The mechanics of distillation in the apparatus of Figures 1 and 2 permit only batch operation, that is, the boiler must be drained and refilled after each performance. This is acceptable for small-scale laboratory operations, but is wasteful of time, labor, and heat on a large industrial scale. Figure 3, which follows, shows a *continuous* operating fractionating tower. Feed stock flows into it continuously, while the tower is maintained at graded temperatures: hottest at the bottom, and coolest at the top. Distilled fractions emerge continuously at various levels after having undergone thorough fractionation due to the refluxing action that occurs by passage through the trays and the bubble caps.

tillation is practiced on a giant scale in the petroleum industry to accomplish these separations of materials boiling at different temperatures. See *Figure 3*.

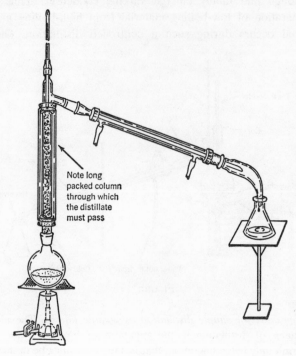

Note long
packed column
through which
the distillate
must pass

FIGURE 2
Apparatus for fractional distillation.

Engine knock. The hammering noise that occurs in a gasoline engine when it is operating under a heavy load, or when the fuel is inferior and unable to withstand the compression of the engine. The phenomenon, fortunately, is rare nowadays, because the fuels have been improved to the point where they burn smoothly with the compressions common to modern engines. The use of the

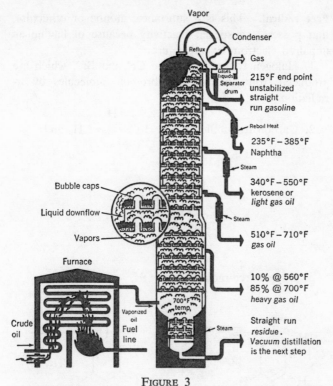

FIGURE 3

Typical modern fractionating tower. Courtesy of the American Petroleum Institute.

antiknock agent, tetraethyl lead, has greatly helped to suppress this knock, which is due to pre-ignition of the fuel-air mixture in the engine cylinder. By the use of special test engines that have adjustable compressions, any fuel can finally be made to knock when the compression is *increased* up to the *critical tolerance level*. This critical compression is correlated with the so-called "octane number" of the fuel through use of appropriate tables. See *octane number*.

Free radical. This is a substance, atomic or otherwise, that possesses a special reactivity because of having an unpaired electron. Examples are:

1. Halogen free-radicals, like Cl˙ and Br˙, which are produced from chlorine and bromine molecules by irradiation.

2. Carbon free-radicals, e.g. $H_3C - \overset{\displaystyle H}{\underset{\displaystyle \bullet}{C}} - CH_3$ and

3. Oxygen free-radicals, e.g. ˙OH,

and

Numerous reactions are induced by free radicals, of which the commonest are:

(1) Removal of H atoms from other molecules, thus forming new free radicals.

(2) Addition to C=C double bonds, thereby inducing polymerization of unsaturated hydrocarbons.

(3) Combination of one free radical with another to form a neutral molecule.

The promotion of polymerization is one of the most important reactions of free radicals, and will appear in the chapter on polyethylene, polystyrene, and the rubber polymers. Equally important, frequently because of its degrading effect, is promotion of oxidative breakdown, beginning with reaction (1) above.

Halocarbon. A compound in which the carbon atoms are linked only to halogen atoms (and to themselves). Note that hydrogen is absent. Many of these compounds have high stability, particularly the fluorocarbons. Examples are:

F_2CCl_2 Freon
Cl_3C-CCl_3 Hexachloroethane
CCl_4 carbon tetrachloride
$F_2C=CF_2$ tetrafluoroethylene

Halogen. One of the nonmetallic elements of Group VII in the periodic table: fluorine (F_2), chlorine (Cl_2), bromine (Br_2), or iodine (I_2).

Halohydrocarbon. A compound that contains carbon, hydrogen, and a halogen. Very often these compounds are made by the direct reaction of elemental halogen on a hydrocarbon. Examples are:

$HCCl_3$ chloroform
H_3C-CH_2Cl ethyl chloride
H_3C-CH_2Br ethyl bromide
BrH_2C-CH_2Br 1,2 dibromoethane (ethylene
                  dibromide)
H_3C-CH_2I ethyl iodide

Inhibitor. A material that hinders or stops some undesirable chemical process that might otherwise occur. Inhibitors are used in petroleum to protect materials against the action of oxygen, either at ordinary temperature or at elevated temperature, such as encountered with lubricating oils for the cylinder walls of the automobile engine.

Such inhibitors would probably be called antioxidants. Many inhibitors are able to combine strongly with free radicals.

Lewis acid. A substance that is acidic but that lacks the protons characteristic of ordinary acids like HCl, H_2SO_4, etc. Examples of Lewis acids are aluminum chloride, $AlCl_3$, boron trifluoride, BF_3, and phosphorous tribromide, PBr_3. In common with protons, they are electron-seeking agents and combine strongly with electron-donating groups. Very often Lewis acids are used as catalysts in processes where acid is needed but proton acids are undesirable. They are named for G. N. Lewis, who first clearly recognized their character.

Octane number. This is a rating of a fuel on a scale from zero to about 115 that indicates approximately the maximum compression that an internal-combustion engine can tolerate when burning the given fuel. If the engine has a higher compression than this value, the engine will knock (see *engine knock* above). The standard fuel for *100* octane rating is 2,2,4-trimethyl pentane, the so-called iso-octane of commerce. The standard fuel for *zero* octane rating is normal heptane, $CH_3 - CH_2 - CH_2 - CH_2 - CH_2 - CH_2 - CH_3$, a fuel that knocks very badly in an engine unless the fuel compression is reduced to 2.8/1,* a value so low that the engine will operate at extremely low efficiency. Mixtures of normal heptane and iso-octane will show intermediate octane numbers, e.g. 25 per cent of the former and 75 per cent of iso-octane will give a mixture with octane number of 75, corresponding to an engine compression about 5/1. Gasolines with 75 octane rating were considered quite good in 1940 (prewar), but now they would be unacceptable, for present-day engines demand gasolines with octane numbers 90 and above.

* This figure expresses the ratio of the maximum cylinder volume (2.8) to the minimum cylinder volume (1).

Polymerization and Polymers.   Polymerization is a chemical process in which many molecules are linked together to form one large molecule. Molecules of a *single* substance may be involved to form a *homo* polymer, or, molecules of *two* or *more* substances may interact to form a *hetero* polymer.

Two kinds of *addition* polymerization may occur, thus:

    (1) A adds to A molecules many times.

        The product is A-A-A-A-A- etc.

    (2) A and B molecules interact by addition.

        The product is A-B-A-B-A-B- etc.

Besides processes where molecules *add* to each other, there are other processes where small molecules unite to form large molecules, but in the course of their reaction, some second substance is split away. For instance suppose *A* and *B* molecules contain reactive functions like $-OH$.* Then the following is possible:

$$HO - A - \textbf{OH} + \textbf{HO} - B - \textbf{OH} +$$
$$\textbf{HO} - A - \textbf{OH} + \textbf{HO} - B - OH \text{ yields}$$
$$HO - A - O - B - O - A - O - B - O - A -$$
$$O - B - O - A - O - B - OH + \textbf{n}\textbf{H}_2\textbf{O}$$

Note that H_2O (water) is split out as a secondary product, while the molecules *A* and *B* are linked by oxygen atoms to form a new large molecule. (In the above example, the process of water elimination is usually catalyzed by addition of an acid. See *catalysis* above.)

What is the reason or the necessity for making large molecules of the type shown? The answer is found in the properties of various "large molecule" substances that are polymers of small molecules. Consider cellulose, for instance, which is a polymer of the sugar glucose. Cellulose as a structural material of plants is best known to us as

---

* The symbol O stands for an oxygen atom; hence OH is a group in which hydrogen is linked to oxygen.

cotton—a fibrous material of great utility and durability that enters widely into clothing and high-grade permanent papers.

Large molecules of these types, with molecular weights of 100,000 or more, usually display properties that cannot be found in small molecules, e.g. the ability to form fibers or films of high strength, "rubberiness," plasticity, "stickiness" (adhesion), and in some cases extraordinary chemical stability and resistance to solvents and corrosive agents.

Stereo-isomerism. The variations in structure of a molecule that occur as a result of altering the *spatial* disposition of its component parts. The definition is better understood by reference to diagrams. Consider the structures represented by *A* and *B:*

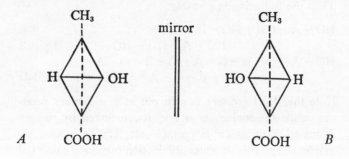

The tetrahedron figure represents a carbon atom, and each of the four corners represents a valence bond. (See page 19.) To the four valences of carbon are attached *H, CH₃, OH,* and *COOH* groups and the result is formation of the well-known substance lactic acid, which occurs in sour milk and sauerkraut. Note that the two arrangements are possible, *A* and *B*. *A* is not identical to *B,* because it could not be superimposed on *B*. Despite lack of identity, *A* and *B* are obviously much alike—they differ by only a little "space" factor. If a mirror M is placed between A and B, one quickly notes that the mirror image of A is B, and vice versa. A and B are described as stereo-isomeric compounds of the type called "mirror-image isomers."

In physical and chemical properties, the molecules A and B are nearly identical but there are a few subtle differences, for instance in optical properties, which distinguish one from the other. Larger molecules than A and B may contain several carbon atoms each of which contains *four* different attached groups. The differences between the "stereo" isomers of such molecules become greater, until finally there may be large differences in such properties as melting point and solubility in various solvents.

When one deals with the giant molecules composing polymers like rubber and polypropylene, stereo-isomerism becomes a major factor in the effort to construct a synthetic material identical to any given model.

Vinyl Group.   This is the characteristic unsaturated group

$$\underset{\substack{\Large| \\ H}}{\overset{\substack{H \\ \Large|}}{C}}=\underset{\substack{\Large| \\ H}}{\overset{\substack{H \\ \Large|}}{C}}$$

comprising one part of a larger molecule, e.g. styrene, which is properly called "vinyl benzene":

The characteristic high reactivity of vinyl compounds is due to the double bond between C and C (C=C), and a common reaction observed in many cases is polymerization. Polymerizable compounds of this type are frequently called "vinyl monomers," or sometimes simply "monomers." Other examples are:

$$H_2C=CHCl \quad \text{vinyl chloride}$$

$$H_2C=CH{-}OC({=}O){-}CH_3 \quad \text{vinyl acetate, and}$$

$$H_2C=CH{-}CH=CH_2 \quad \text{butadiene (which might be called a "double vinyl").}$$

Unfortunately, in the business world, the word "vinyl" means a *polymer* produced from a vinyl *monomer,* but in the polymer the vinyl group no longer exists because its double bond has been used up during the polymerization.

Chapter 4

PROPERTIES OF PETROCHEMICALS

In this chapter are tabulated the basic structures and properties of the most common petrochemicals. By reading through it quickly, you will get a good foundation by which to better recognize and understand the terms when they are used in subsequent chapters.

A. MONOMERS

The common physical and thermal properties of a variety of monomers (starting materials for chemical synthesis) are listed in Table I. The list is not exhaustive but includes compounds whose uses are described in this book. The arrangement is alphabetical. Commercial products from the monomers are also listed.

B. POLYMERIC MATERIALS

Polymeric, or macromolecular products, exhibit properties of a plastic, rubbery, or fibrous character and are valued for their suitability as *structural* materials. Accordingly, their mechanical, electrical, and thermal characteristics are matters of concern to the fabricators of the end products. Practical tests of great variety have been applied to polymers. Among them are the following:

Softening and/or crystalline melting temperatures
Ignition temperature
Specific heat (calories per gram per degree C. elevation
    of temperature)

Table I

A. Hydrocarbon Monomers, and Structures	m.p. °C	b.p. °C	T_c^* °C	P_c^* atm	n_D	d	ΔH_{comb} Kcal. Mole
1. Acetylene $HC \equiv CH$	−81.8		+36	62	gas	gas	310.6
2. Benzene	+5.5	+80.1	+288.5	47.7	1.5011/20°	0.8790/20°	782.3
3. Butadiene $H_2C = C - C = CH_2$ H H	−108.5	−5	+162	42.7			597
4. Isobutane $(CH_3)_3CH$	−145	−10	+134	37			683.4
Butenes							
5. Butene-1 $H_3C - CH_2 - CH = CH_2$	−180	−5	146	39.5			649.7
6. Butene-2 $CH_3CH = CH - CH_3$	−138	+1, +3	155	40.0			
7. Isobutene $(CH_3)_2C = CH_2$	−147	−5.5	+151	39.2			647.2

8.	Cyclohexane	+6.5	+82	+281	40.4	1.4290/15	0.7791/20°	937.8
9.	Divinylbenzene $H_2C=CH-\!\!\!\bigcirc\!\!\!-CH=CH_2$	+31	distillable only under vacuum			(1.5820 | 0.913)40°	
10.	Ethylene $H_2C=CH_2$	−169	−103.9	+9.7	50.9		gas	337.7
11.	Isoprene $H_2C=C-C=CH_2$ (H, H)	−145	+34			1.4194/20	0.6806/20°	
12.	Isopropylbenzene $(CH_3)_2\,C\!-\!\!\!\bigcirc$ H	−96.9	152.4			(1.4914 | 0.8618)20°	1247.3
13.	Methane CH_4	−184	−161.4	−82.5	45.8	gas	gas	210.8
14.	Propylene $CH_3-C=CH_2$ H	−185	−47	+92.3	45.0	gas	gas	490.2
15.	Styrene $H_2C=C\!-\!\!\!\bigcirc$ H	−32	+146			(1.5454 | 0.9074)20°	1047.1

* T_c and P_c are critical temperature and pressure respectively. The values are given if they are known; if the compound polymerizes or decomposes before reaching T_c, then, of course, no value can be given.

Hydrocarbon Monomers, and Structures	m.p. °C	b.p. °C	T_c °C	P_c atm	n_D	d	ΔH_{comb} Kcal. Mole
16. Toluene H₃C— (benzene ring)	−95	+110.6	320.6	41.6	(1.4969	0.8669)20°	934.2
17. Xylene; dimethylbenzene							
ortho	−29	+144			(1.5045	0.8802)20°	1091.7
meta	−53.6	+139.1			(1.4972	0.8642)20°	1088.4
para	+13.2	+138.3			(1.4958	0.8610)20°	1089.1

B. Oxygen containing Monomers	m.p. °C	b.p. (760 mm)	T_e	D_e	n_D	d 20° or otherwise	ΔH_{comb}
1. Water*	00	100	374.2	217.7	1.333	1.000	
Adipic acid HOOC−(CH₂)₄−COOH	+151						669.0

No.	Compound							
2.	Bisphenol-A	156–7	250/13 mm					
	HO—⬡—C(CH₃)₂—⬡—OH							
3.	Ethylene glycol $HOCH_2 - CH_2OH$	−13	+197			1.4300/25	1.113/25°	281.9
4.	Ethylene oxide $H_2C{-}CH_2$ (O)	−111.3	+10.7	196	70	(1.3598	0.887)8°	302.1
5.	Phenol	+40.7	182			(1.5403	1.054)45°	732.2
6.	Terephthalic Acid $HOOC{-}⬡{-}COOH$	300°						770.4

* Constants for water given as a basis for comparison.

C. Monomers with additional elements

	m.p. °C	b.p. (760 mm)	T_c	D_c	n_D	d 20° or otherwise	ΔH_{comb}
1. Allyl chloride $H_2C=CH-CH_2Cl$	−135	+46			(1.4154)	0.9379)20	
2. Caprolactam	68–70	139/12					
3. Chloroprene $H_2C=C-C=CH_2$ with H, Cl	−130	59.4 33/300 mm	261.7		(1.4583)	0.9585)20	
4. Epichlorohydrin $H_2C-C-CH_2Cl$ with H, O	−57.2	116.1			1.4358/25	1.1745/25	420.7
5. Ethyl chloride	−139	+12.2	187.2	52			

6. Hexamethylene diamine	42	204 100°/20 mm

D. Common products derived from the monomers in A, B, and C above

MONOMER	PRODUCTS
A Group	
Acetylene	Chloroprene, and neoprene rubber; also Orlon
Benzene	Styrene, polystyrene, phenol, phenolic polymers
Butadiene	Polybutadiene rubber, neoprene rubber, ingredients for nylon synthesis, SBR rubber
Isobutane	High-octane gasoline ("alkylate")
Butene-1 and -2	Gasoline, alcohols
Isobutene	Butyl rubber
Cyclohexane	Ingredients for synthesis of Nylon 6 and 6/6
Divinylbenzene	Cross-linked non-fusible, non-soluble polystyrene, e.g. for ion-exchange resins
Ethylene	Polyethylene, ethylene glycol antifreeze, Mylar (Dacron), ethyl alcohol
Isoprene	Synthetic rubber ("natural synthetic")
Isopropylbenzene	Acetone, phenol, bisphenol-A, epoxy resins, and polycarbonates
Methane	Formation of acetylene
Propylene	Isopropylbenzene, isopropyl alcohol, polypropylene
Styrene	Polystyrene, SBR rubber
Toluene	Cresol for phenolic plastics, antioxidant (di-tert. butylated paracresol)
Xylenes	Di-acids, particularly terephthalic acid for Mylar, poly-para-xylylene ("Parrylene")

MONOMER	PRODUCTS
B Group	
Adipic acid	Nylon
Bisphenol-A	Epoxy resins, polycarbonates (e.g. Lextan)
Ethylene glycol	Mylar, antifreeze fluid
Phenol	Epoxy resins, phenolic resins, salicylic acid, aspirin, dyes, etc.
Terephthalic acid	Mylar
C Group	
Allyl chloride	Epichlorohydrin (see below), glycerol, allyl ethers
Caprolactam	Nylon 6
Chloroprene	Neoprene rubber
Epichlorohydrin	Epoxy resins, glycerol
Ethyl chloride	Tetraethyl lead (antiknock fluid)
Hexamethylene diamine	Nylon

Coefficient of thermal expansion (change in volume per unit volume per degree C.)

Thermal conductivity

Tensile strength (lb/in^2) versus elongation, and tensile strength at the ultimate elongation, or "break"

Tensile impact strength, and compressional strength

Dead load "creep" tests (measuring the yield of a material under prolonged stress)

Glass to rubber transition temperatures

Electrical insulating character—volume resistivity, dielectric constant, and dielectric strength

Density; optical clarity or opacity

Gas permeability through thin films

Water vapor absorption

Solvent resistance, or solubilities in solvents

Resistance to chemical attack by various corroding agents, e.g. strong acids, strong bases, oxidizing agents

Resistance to oxygen, ozone, ultraviolet light. (Accelerated aging tests are frequently employed)

The tests chosen for a given material will naturally vary depending on the intended end use; rarely are all of the above applied to a given material. Some materials are intended for either very high or very low temperature applications, under which conditions mechanical or thermal properties might be quite changed from those at ordinary temperatures.

Some of the more common tests applied to polymers are listed in Table II.

In examining and comparing properties, one must be aware of the known fact that polymeric products are practically always complex mixtures—mixtures of materials very closely similar chemically but differing in molecular weight, or even mixtures in which chemical structures differ considerably because of some secondary reactions im-

TABLE II—PROPERTIES OF POLYMERS

	THERMAL PROPERTIES			
	Melting (M) or Softening (S) Temp.	Ignition Temp.	Spec. Heat C/g/°C	Coeff. Thermal Expan.
Polystyrene (Dow-oriented Trycite)	95 (S) 240 (M)			$4.3 \cdot 10^{-5}$
Polyethylene				
Hi pressure	110–115 (M)		0.55	$8.3 \cdot 10^{-5}$
Lo pressure	132–37 (M)			$1.8 \cdot 10^{-6}$
Phillips "Marlex" 50	110 (S)			
Polypropylene (Hercules)	168–71 (M)			$1.4 \cdot 10^{-5}$
Parylene (UCC)	280–400 (M)			
Mylar (du Pont)	250–260 (M)	560	0.315	$1.5 \cdot 10^{-5}$
Lexan polycarbonate (GE)	220–230 (M)	self-exting.	0.3	$3.75 \cdot 10^{-5}$
Nylon 6/6 (du Pont)	295 (M)	532		
Nylon 6 (du Pont)	220 (M)			
Orlon (du Pont)	Indeter.	530		
Teflon	Becomes rubbery 327	Does not ignite	0.25	$5.5 \cdot 10^{-5}$
Kel-F (3M)			0.24	
Polysulfone (UCC)		self-exting.		3.10^{-5}
Polyimide–Kapton (du Pont)	non-melting	self-exting.	0.261	$2 \cdot 10^{-5}$
Polyphenylene oxide (GE)	1.06–1.27	self-exting.		$1.5–3 \cdot 10^{-5}$
Epoxy polymers (Dow) from bisphenol-A	non-melting	>500		$5 \cdot 10^{-6}$
Rubbery products, each one with carbon black and vulcanized				
Cis polybutadiene (Goodyear)	Indeter.			
Polychloroprene (Neoprene)	Indeter.			
Cis polyisoprene (Goodrich; Firestone)	Indeter.			
Butyl rubber	Indeter.		0.464	
Styrene-butadiene copolymer	Indeter.			
Natural rubber	Indeter.	>400	(0.50	$6.7 \cdot 10^{-5}$)
Wool	Indeter.	590		
Cotton	Indeter.	390		

MECHANICAL				ELECTRICAL			OTHER
Tensile Strength (psi)	Ultim. Elongation %	Breaking Tenacity g/denier	Tensile Impact Strength	Volume Resist ohm/cm.	Dielectric Constant	Dielectric Strength	Density g/cm.
9–10,000	10–20		2.9 Izod	10^{16}	2.54	2500	1.05
1800–2200	400–700		>16 Izod	>10^{15}	2.3	480	0.92
2500–5000	100–700		1–7 Izod	10^{15}	2.33	500	0.94–0.96
4000–4500			3 Izod	>$6 \cdot 10^{15}$	2.34	510	0.96
5000	>200		1 Izod	$2 \cdot 10^{17}$	2.25	520	0.901
9–13,000	200			$8{-}10 \cdot 10^{16}$	2.6–3.0	3700–6500	1.10–1.29
25,000	30	8.0		10^{15}	3.9	5000	1.39
9500	110		16 Izod	$2 \cdot 10^{10}$	3.17	3900	1.2
$66{-}88 \cdot 10^3$	26	4.5–8		$4 \cdot 10^{14}$	4–7	3000	1.14
$60 \cdot 10^3$		4–5		10^{14}	3.4–4.5	400–500	
$40{-}45 \cdot 10^3$		5.5		10^{14}	4–6	450	1.15
3000	100–200	1.68	3 Izod	10^{19}	2.0	2000	2.15
6200	200		7.3 Izod	>10^{18}	2.5	1500	2.12
10,200	50–100		1.3 Izod	$5 \cdot 10^{16}$	3.14	425	
14–21,000	80–100		7–14 Izod	$10^{17}{-}10^{18}$	3.5	4000–7000	1.42
14–18,000	4–6		10	$10^{17}{-}10^{18}$	2.6–3.0	1000	1.06–1.27
7–11,000	5–17		0.5–1.1	$1{-}9 \cdot 10^{15}$	3–4		1.15–1.25
2650	650						1.09
22–2500 (no carbon)	700–900						1.23 (No vulcan.)
34–4100	550–850						>1
3–4000	900–1100						>1
2500–3000	800–900				2.11	600	
3000–4000	300–500						1.14
3500–4100	570–700			$4 \cdot 10^{15}$			0.93 (raw)
$17{-}28 \cdot 10^3$		2.0					1.32
$66{-}90 \cdot 10^3$		3.0					1.54

posed on primary materials. For instance, natural rubber from trees, which is quite homogeneous, may be vulcanized according to different recipes, or an "epoxy" primary polymer may be "cured" by use of various agents in varying amounts for shorter or longer times; in both cases, end products, although related, will vary in chemical nature, and will be comprised of a mixture of different structures.

For these reasons, the data on properties found in Table II are only representative of a named article,* and the article will vary in its properties from one manufacturing treatment to another. More than that, it will frequently change with age, for we should be well aware of the continuing influence of the atmosphere upon all structural materials around us. Sunlight, oxygen, water, and incessant temperature changes have much to do with the behavior of structural materials. It is a matter of professional pride with polymer chemists to produce materials that will defy the ravages of time by building structures of increasing durability. But it is not easy to outwit nature in this strenuous game.

* Manufacturers of primary polymers will always furnish extensive data on their products, and their bulletins should be studied carefully before anyone makes extended use of the products. Companies which are prominent in the kinds of polymers described here are du Pont, Dow, Union Carbide, General Electric, Phillips Petroleum, Shell Oil, Hercules, Monsanto, 3M (Minnesota Mining and Manufacturing), and all the major tire and rubber companies.

Chapter 5

THE FLUIDIZED CATALYTIC CRACKER

A. WHAT IS CRACKING?

As natural gasoline production expanded, and as the market diminished for kerosene (Thomas Edison's electric light bulb was gaining rapidly in popularity), petroleum technologists tried to find a means of converting the large amount of residue remaining after gasoline was distilled from petroleum into gasoline for the growing motor industry.

The answer was "cracking," a picturesque word for a process in which the big molecules of heavy oils are broken down into smaller molecules that have boiling points in the gasoline range.* This breakdown is induced by heating the heavy oils to the decomposition point (in the absence of air, of course). A breakdown by heat alone is called "pyrolysis" (splitting by fire); a breakdown assisted by chemical promoters, catalysts, is called catalytic cracking. Pyrolysis begins slowly at temperatures of 400–450° C., depending on the particular oil; catalytic cracking occurs at somewhat lower temperatures, and proceeds much more swiftly.

The catalysts that are most effective in this process are solids: the refractory oxides of aluminum, silicon, and magnesium, along with traces of other metal oxides, e.g. Fe_2O_3 and CaO.

How can catalytic cracking, which involves solid materials, be fluidized?

* The molecular size required for gasoline (boiling point 40–200° C.) is that of hydrocarbons with five to twelve carbon atoms.

The answer to that question was not so obvious to early investigators, but it grew out of some common observations. Everyone has poured white sand from one container to another, and is familiar with fine powders like cement, which likewise can be poured back and forth. Everyone is familiar too with wind-blown dust storms, in which a fast-moving air stream picks up fine particles of dry clay or soil. These dusts sometimes remain suspended in air for a long time. For instance, some great volcanic explosions have thrown up dusts into the air that drifted thousands of miles before settling back to earth. A moving stream of water can carry a considerable burden of silty solids out to sea, but these solids finally settle out as river "deltas" when the water is still.

Now, petroleum processing involves fast-moving streams of *liquids* and *gases*. Isn't it possible that these streams of liquids and gases could also pick up fine dusts and move them along, just as water and wind can? Careful research showed clearly that the answer was "yes." Furthermore, the catalyst oxides just mentioned were found (luckily) to be easily reducible to fine powders that would flow along readily with streams of hydrocarbon liquids and gases.

However, one problem remained. The large molecules, breaking down into smaller ones under the combined influence of heat and catalysts, were also undergoing some mysterious reactions that produced "coke," a material approaching elemental carbon in composition. Furthermore, this coke adhered to the catalyst particles, blackening them and deactivating them. Catalytic cracking stopped, and the whole process came to a halt.

There was an obvious solution—sift out the coked-up catalyst, add fresh catalyst, and start all over again. But this stopping and starting, *ad infinitum,* was not an operation to be proud of. Worse than that, the catalyst was an expensive material and could not be thrown away lest the operators go bankrupt in the process. Clearly the catalyst had to be restored to its original active condition and used over again. Because the carbon could not be extracted by any known process, the answer appeared to lie in burning the carbon away as carbon dioxide; hydrogen, if any, formed water, while the metal oxides (hopefully) were left intact and as active as before. Burning at moderate temperature was required; otherwise the catalysts lost their activity. Thus the process of "regeneration" was worked out finally to complete satisfaction.

One needs to bear in mind also that cracking breaks up the large molecules into some very small ones containing only one, two, three, and four carbon atoms, as well as the medium-size molecules, those with five to twelve carbon atoms that comprise gasoline. The former are gases; accordingly, a considerable stream of mixed gases emerges from the cat cracker, along with liquid products. These gases must be handled apart from the liquid products that go into great distilling columns called "fractionators." The bulk of these gases is made up of highly reactive compounds—the olefins, ethylene, propylene, and butylenes. These are the materials so highly desired for petrochemical synthesis; hence they are carefully saved and put to use later.

This brief description of catalytic cracking includes the main factors that must be accounted for in the working of a practical *continuously operating* fluidized catalytic cracking machine. Now, if the reader is inclined to be an inventor along chemical lines, he might try to set up the principal outlines of the process. He may be assured this is an intriguing problem but a heavy challenge to his imagination.

The successful solution to the problem is shown in the next section.

B.   HOW DOES IT WORK?

After some ten years of concentrated efforts, the pioneers of petroleum catalysis succeeded in devising a commercial fluidized catalytic cracking process, and they put the first unit into operation in 1942. In 1943, three large units were in operation, and were contributing substantially to the wartime demand for high-octane gasoline.

A flow diagram of the essential operating features in catalytic cracking is shown in *Figure 4*. Gas oil, a frac-

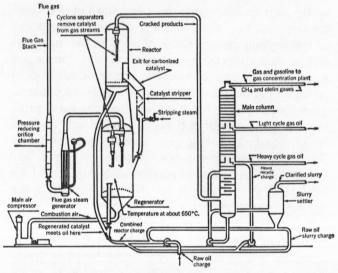

FIGURE 4

Simplified flow diagram of fluidized catalytic cracking system (heat exchange circuits and control systems have been omitted). Courtesy of Universal Oil Products Company.

tion of crude oil with a substantially higher boiling temperature than gasoline, enters the system at the lower left of the figure. It is first preheated and partially vaporized. Into the stream of this feed stock flows hot, finely divided catalyst—about eight times the weight of the oil. This catalyst has come down through a standpipe from the "regenerator" above, which is at a temperature of over 1000° F. (about 550° C.). The heat in the catalyst is sufficient to vaporize the oil completely and to initiate the cracking action. The catalyst-vapor mixture then blows like a dust-laden gas into the reactor, which is about half full of a turbulent mass of catalyst. The turbulence and agitation inside the reactor are equivalent to a violent storm which promotes intimate contact of catalyst particles with the oil vapors. These vapors, as they rise through the fluidized catalyst mass, are cracked into lighter materials (lower molecular weight), which enter a "cyclone" separator before passing overhead into a fractionating tower. The "cyclone," a centrifugal device, recovers the catalyst that otherwise might escape with the hot gas. In the fractionating tower the gaseous products, beginning to liquefy, are separated into gasoline, into several higher-boiling fractions corresponding to furnace oils, and into a heavy residual oil. The remaining material, which is still gaseous at ordinary temperature, is made up of compounds with one to four carbon atoms. Among these are ethylene, propylene, and the butylenes—olefins that will be separated more completely in a later operation and then used for syntheses of petrochemicals.

During the cracking operation, coke is deposited on the catalyst; this must be burned off in order to restore the catalyst to full activity. The catalyst settles down and flows from the reactor continuously. It contains not only coke at this point, but also some absorbed liquids; hence it passes to a "stripper" where volatile hydrocarbons are removed by steam. The catalyst, still containing coke, is then carried by a stream of air to a large vessel called the regenerator, where another fluidized bed is maintained, and where the coke is burned off. This burning, of course, generates heat that sustains the high temperature in the regenerator. The hot catalyst finally settles down and flows through the standpipe to the incoming gas-oil stream to complete the cycle of operations.

Flue gases from the regenerator pass out through the chimney at the top. Catalyst dust entrained in these gases (mostly CO_2, CO, and steam) is removed by another cyclone separator.

Huge quantities of materials are involved in fluid cracking operations; no other catalytic reaction is carried out on such a scale. A typical unit handling 25,000 barrels per day of charging stock contains about 700 tons of catalyst, which circulates at a rate of a *carload* every two minutes. The coke burned from the catalyst each day amounts to more than 200 tons; the heat produced in the regenerator is more than enough to heat the charge stock up to reaction temperature; hence the excess is used to generate steam needed elsewhere in the process. From 25,000 barrels of gas-oil feed, about 12,000 barrels of high-quality motor gasoline are produced.* Variations in feed stock and operating conditions will change the yield of gasoline somewhat, but it is common to obtain 40 to 50 barrels of gasoline per 100 barrels of charge. The yield of gas is in the range of 6 to 9 per cent by weight of charge, and the coke yield is 4 to 6 per cent.

* After one has examined all the fascinating features of a catalytic cracker, he is tempted also to inquire, "What does machinery like this cost the refiner?"

Obviously, a cat cracker must not be thrown together in a crude fashion; therefore one does not spare expense in making sure that durability and reliability are built into it. Costs of cat crackers are not usually published, and they vary considerably depending on the accessory equipment involved. However, a 25,000-barrel-per-day unit will require an investment of seven to ten million dollars.

C. MORE ABOUT THE PRODUCTS—
QUALITY OF THE GASOLINE

Catalytic cracking greatly increased the *quantity* of gasoline that could be produced from a given amount of crude oil. What now about the *quality* of this gasoline?

First, it is necessary to consider what is meant by *quality* in any gasoline. Five factors are of great importance:

(*a.*) Octane rating, or antiknock value;

(*b.*) Sulfur content, which also governs two other factors—corrosivity to metals, and odor;

(*c.*) Tendency toward sludge formation;

(*d.*) "Lead susceptibility," meaning its improvement in octane rating by addition of tetraethyl lead; and

(*e.*) Vapor pressure relative to the climatic conditions in which it will be used.

These will be discussed briefly.

(*a.*) The *octane rating* of a gasoline by actual test is probably the most important single quality feature. Octane rating is correlated with the ability of a gasoline to burn smoothly without knocking as the engine compression is increased. Thus the higher the octane rating of a gasoline, the higher the compression it will withstand in the automotive engine. An 85 octane gasoline will just begin to knock at a fuel compression of 7/1; 100 octane gasoline withstands a compression of about 8/1 in a standard test engine. Compression is a key factor in the thermodynamic efficiency of a heat engine—the higher the allowable compression, the higher the efficiency of converting heat energy of the fuel to mechanical energy (work) in the engine.

Modern automotive engines and also aviation engines

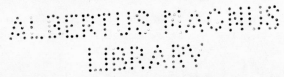

of the piston type (now somewhat outdated by jets) are designed for high compressions, 8/1 or more, in order to get the most mechanical energy out of a given amount of fuel. Accordingly, the gasolines must have a high octane rating, 90 and above.

(*b.*) *Sulfur content* is a critical feature of all fuels— the *less* sulfur the better! Sulfur burns to sulfur dioxide, perhaps some of it even to sulfur trioxide. These are highly corrosive to exhaust pipes and all engine parts; to human beings they produce a choking irritation of the throat and lungs. Even before the sulfur burns, it may cause trouble. If it is present as "mercaptan," a sulfur alcohol with the type formula R-S-H,* then the sulfur is doubly obnoxious. Mercaptans are among the vilest-smelling compounds on earth and, secondly, they are acidic enough to cause corrosion of many metals. Accordingly, gasoline containing mercaptan sulfur must be treated to destroy the mercaptan, or to eliminate the sulfur altogether. It is fair to add, however, that there are other types of sulfur compounds that might be in gasoline without producing either a bad odor or corrosivity toward metals. Nevertheless, sulfur compounds in gasoline or in other fuels are a general liability. They are responsible also for another detrimental action in that they reduce the "lead susceptibility" of gasolines, as we shall see in point (*d.*) below.

(*c.*) *Sludge formation.* "Natural" gasoline contains saturated hydrocarbons only, along with aromatics, and is free of olefins, the unsaturated hydrocarbons. Certain other gasolines derived from cracking processes have been *hydrogenated,* hence are free of olefins too. Consequently, these two types of gasolines are free of the reactivity of olefinic compounds; one of such reactivities is the tendency to polymerize and form sticky resinous materials known as "sludge." Gasolines from cracking processes contain

* R is an organic radical, like CH_3-, C_2H_5-, etc.

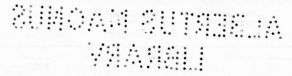

olefins, and therefore might form sludge during storage. There must be efforts then to build into such gasolines *resistance to sludge formation*. This is accomplished by addition of polymerization inhibitors and "stabilizers," an important part of the preparation of cracked gasolines for commercial use.

(*d.*) *Lead susceptibility*. Tetraethyl lead fluid, $(C_2H_5)_4Pb$, has been an important additive for gasolines since the early twenties when it was discovered by Midgley and Boyd to be a powerful knock suppressant.* The effect of adding about three cubic centimeters of tetraethyl lead (TEL) to a gallon of "natural" gasoline is to increase the gasoline's octane rating 10 to 13 points. This is known as high susceptibility. Although cracked gasolines already have fairly high octane ratings, they also respond to addition of TEL, rising in octane rating by 5 to 15 points. However, the presence of sulfur compounds in gasolines *decreases* this susceptibility to TEL. This is true whether the gasoline is derived from cracking, or directly from petroleum by ordinary distillation. It is clear then that, so long as TEL is employed as an additive, the sulfur present is an added detriment.

(*e.*) *Vapor pressure*. Gasoline will explode in the internal-combustion engine only because its *vapors* have been drawn into the cylinders and mixed with air. Vapor pressure is a measure of the tendency of a liquid to enter the gaseous state; hence a gasoline at any *given operating temperature* must have sufficient vapor pressure to generate vapors that can be ignited. Ordinary gasoline chilled in dry ice ($-110°$ F.) would not ignite; warmed back to

* This story of efforts to prevent engine knock and to find an additive for gasoline that would fulfill this purpose is one of the most fascinating facets in all petroleum history. It was also one of the most difficult. The story is beautifully told by S. P. Nickerson in "Tetraethyl Lead, a Product of American Research," *Journal of Chemical Education,* 31 (1954), 560.

TABLE III—PRODUCTION AND QUALITY OF
MOTOR GASOLINE FROM FLUID
CATALYTIC CRACKING
(Reactor at 900° F., Regenerator at 1100° F.)

Properties of Feed Stock*	Source of Feed Stock			
	East Texas	West Texas A	B	Gulf Coast
Sulfur content, wt. %	0.48	1.80	2.49	0.63
Spec. gravity	0.86	0.89	0.92	0.925
Distillation test; temp. at which 50% has distilled	680° F.	710	825	781
Products formed				
(a) Motor gasoline: b.p. 115–400° F. yield, vol. %	45	43.2	46.0	46.2
Sulfur, wt. %	0.03	0.18	0.246	0.044
Octane no.	92	91.9	91.3	94.3
Octane no. after addn. of 1.5 cc TEL/gal	97	95.9	95.3	98.1
(b) Gas C_4 and below, wt. % of feed	4.3	6.3	5.6	5.4
(c) Carbon formed, wt. %	3.1	4.3	3.3	2.6

room temperature its response to a flame would be obvious. Accordingly, gasolines intended for the arctic and for wintry conditions have to be built up by inclusion of easily volatile materials, e.g., the gases, propane and butane, and pentane, boiling point 96° F. If this same gasoline were sidetracked to a hot desert or tropical area, these highly volatile materials would actually boil out of the storage tank, and their vapors would constitute a serious fire hazard. One can see then that a summer or tropical gasoline must differ from a winter gasoline in that its *lowest*-boiling components should begin to boil at temperatures of 110–120° F. or even higher.

These examples illustrate the importance of proper

* The "feed stock" for cracking is the material known as "gas oil" in the refinery. It is that part of crude oil that remains after

volatility or vapor pressure. The problem is readily solved these days by the refiner as he tailors the gasolines according to the hot or cold areas where they will be used.

Let us now examine the quality of gasolines obtained from the cat cracker.

Examination of Table III shows that two quality factors stand out prominently:

1. The gasoline produced is high-octane material (octane numbers 91–94) even before addition of tetra-

---

the natural gasoline and kerosene fractions have been removed by distillation up to about 500° F. (260° C.).

The above examples were taken from an early review of fluidized catalytic cracking, mentioned below. Improvements have appeared since then, but most of these have been directed toward removing harmful materials from the feed stock, stabilization of the cracking catalysts so that they will last longer, and increased automation of operation to improve overall operating economy. The products have remained much the same *within a prescribed set of operating conditions.*

Source: E. V. Murphree, C. L. Brown, H. G. Fischer, E. V. Gohr, and W. J. Sweeney, "Fluid Catalyst Process; the Catalytic Cracking of Petroleum," *Industrial and Engineering Chemistry,* 35 (1943), 626–30, 768. This is a prime reference because of its clear outline of the essential principles involved (which have changed little since 1943) as well as the techniques employed and results obtained. The illustrations are excellent, and the writing style makes the material intelligible to any interested reader.

The magnitude of the subject is revealed by the number of authors' names appearing on the article (all of whom were members of the Standard Oil Development Co. of New Jersey) and the acknowledgment made by these authors, as follows: "The process represents a contribution of the Standard Oil Development Company to a cooperative study on catalytic refining participated in by the Angle-Iranian Oil Co., Ltd., M. W. Kellogg Company, Shell Oil Company, Standard Oil Company (Indiana), Texas Company and the Universal Oil Products Company." In other words, the combined efforts of *seven* major oil companies appear in the successful end result! More about the people involved will appear in Section E of this chapter.

ethyl lead. Addition of a very small amount of TEL
(1.5 cc per gal) raises these numbers 4 to 5 points.
2. Despite sulfur contents of .5 to 2.5 per cent in the
feed stocks, the gasolines produced contained only
0.03 to 0.25 per cent sulfur, amounts that are regarded as very low. The tetraethyl lead susceptibility is relatively low; however, the initial high octane rating makes the response to TEL addition a
matter of minor importance. The low sulfur content
is a good factor relative to odor and to corrosive
action on metals. However, cracked gasolines usually have a mercaptan "flavor" if their sulfur exceeds
about .25 per cent. Treating to remove mercaptan
is then in order; this process also reduces corrosivity
practically to zero.

What about the tendency to sludge formation?

Cracked gasolines (those derived from thermal as well
as catalytic cracking) contain *unsaturated* hydrocarbons,
in contrast to natural gasoline, which is free of olefins.
The amount of olefins in fact is considerable. They are in
part responsible for the high-octane quality, so it would
be a backward step to remove them. However, the olefins
in contact with air slowly react with oxygen to form peroxides,* and in time undergo "polymerization," or molecular
growth. One olefin molecule activated by peroxide adds
to another olefin, which then adds to another olefin, on
and on, until very large molecules are formed; these become sticky and sludge-like. This property of cracked
gasolines is no problem when the material is used within
a couple of weeks of production, but if the gasoline is
stored for several months, polymerization and sludge formation become really troublesome.

The solution to the problem came with the discovery of
"antioxidants," materials that inhibit the reaction by

---

* These peroxides contain a C-O-O-H group of atoms.

which peroxides were formed. These *antioxidants,* or inhibitors, were studied intensively to find those which are most effective in preventing the gasoline from forming sludge and "gums." The studies were successful, and gasolines now are well protected by these additives. One of them is a compound derived jointly from a coal-tar product, para cresol

$$HO \left\langle \underline{} \right\rangle CH_3$$

and a refinery gas, isobutylene

$$H_2C = C \begin{smallmatrix} CH_3 \\ \\ CH_3 \end{smallmatrix}$$

These two have been combined chemically to form the interesting structure

$$\begin{array}{c} H_3C \\ H_3C - C - CH_3 \\ HO \left\langle \right\rangle CH_3 \\ H_3C - C - CH_3 \\ CH_3 \end{array}$$

which is called "di tertiary butyl para cresol"* (the actual inhibitor), and which we shall call "DTBPC" for short. The reader will probably be surprised to learn that this "protector" of gasolines is equally effective in protecting

* The preparation of this compound and its ultimate uses were described by Dr. Donald Stevens. See *Industrial and Engineering Chemistry,* 35 (1943), 655.

vegetable oils, lard and peanut butter from becoming rancid.*

In summary, we see that the fluidized cat cracker has greatly increased both the quality and the quantity of motor gasoline. Furthermore, the gasoline can be had at reasonable prices, because of the remarkable economy inherent in this machine's day-and-night productivity on a massive scale.

D.   VARY THE OPERATING CONDITIONS AND VARY THE PRODUCTS

The principal variables at work in a cat cracker were described briefly in Section B above. These include the *ratio of catalyst to feed*, the *temperature* in the reactor, the residence *time* of the oil vapors in the reactor (contact time), and the *temperature of the preheated oil* at the moment the hot catalyst makes contact with it. These so-called operating conditions (process variables) determine the nature and amounts of products formed in the cracking process. If they are changed, then the amounts of products will change—sometimes, with drastic changes, altogether new products may be obtained and some of the originals may disappear. Another variable is the catalyst itself. If one were to replace a typical cracking catalyst (silica-alumina) by one that contained chromium oxide or platinum, for instance, then only a minor amount of cracking would occur, but much *dehydrogenation* of

* Strange that the solution to a gasoline problem should also be the answer to a problem in food biochemistry! Of such is the quality of imaginative research that it reaches far beyond its original intentions. Accordingly, at this date, sludge or gum formation in cracked gasolines is no longer a matter of concern. Neither is rancidity in peanut butter, in salad oils, or in shortening for apple pies. Petroleum antioxidants have solved the problem.

hydrocarbons would occur, and hydrogen gas in abundance would appear in the gaseous products. However, we shall assume here that an active cracking catalyst is employed, which is regenerated repeatedly during the operating cycles so that its activity remains practically constant.

What happens in the cat cracker if the temperature is raised? What happens if the contact time is increased?

Increased temperature* and increased contact time, singly or together, increase the "severity" or extent of cracking of the oil. This seems altogether logical; therefore, one will naturally inquire, "Why not increase the severity to the point where practically all of the feed stock is cracked to gasoline and gas?" (See Table III.) Why settle for only 45 per cent gasoline and 5 per cent gas?

The answer is found in Table IV.

TABLE IV—EXPERIMENTS IN WHICH THE
SEVERITY OF CRACKING IS INCREASED
ABOVE STANDARD CONDITIONS†

Product Yields	Experiments		
	A	B	C
Gasoline, Vol. % of feed	49.6	50.1	51.2
Gas, C_4 and lighter;			
Wt. % of feed	16.4	16.4	16.8
Coke (carbon);			
Wt. % of feed	9.4	8.6	7.9

† These were actual commercial operations on a large cracker in which the conditions were varied in a complex manner, including increased temperatures for the preheated oil and reactor, and increased temperature in the regenerator so that the catalyst was hotter than usual upon first contact with the incoming oil.

Source: J. B. Pohlenz, Universal Oil Products Co., "Effect of Operational Variables in Fluid Catalytic Cracking of Petroleum."

* Two temperatures may be involved here, either the reactor temperature or the temperature of the oil as it first makes contact with the hot catalyst from the regenerator.

Inspection of the table shows clearly:

(a) The gasoline yield is increased but only up to about 50 per cent of the charge stock.

(b) Much more gas is produced than in standard operations—about 16 per cent vs. the usual 5 to 6 per cent.

(c) The coke (carbon) deposited on the catalyst is greatly increased, 8 to 9 per cent vs. the usual 3 to 5 per cent.

Accordingly, changes have occurred, but are they desirable? If one wants a great deal more gas for ensuing petrochemical synthesis, the answer is "yes." However, the *gasoline yield* is increased very slightly, but *carbon on the catalyst* is increased greatly (relative to standard results shown in Table III).

These are the usual results of increasing severity of cracking. Any carbon produced beyond that needed to keep the regenerator operating at a proper temperature and producing the heat required to bring the catalyst up to the desired reaction temperature is a total loss. Furthermore, with excessive carbon production, the regenerator, in burning so much carbon, will have to be cooled by external means. It is easy to see that when carbon is produced above a certain level (usually about 3 to 4 per cent), the process becomes uneconomical.

These are some of the factors that an expert manager of a catalytic cracking process must consider when he undertakes to vary the conditions in order to vary his products. Frequently, others are involved too, but we shall not take time for them now. The common situation is that once a great cat cracker has been put into operation and everything is running smoothly with satisfactory yields of desired products, practical judgment dictates "Let well enough alone."

E. WHO INVENTED CATALYTIC
CRACKING? A TRIBUTE

The fluidized cracking process is a creation of modern catalytic chemistry and advanced engineering. Because of its magnitude, flexibility, and efficiency, it represents a truly revolutionary advance in mass production on a gigantic scale; because of its contribution both to our needs for energy at low cost and for chemicals in an age of chemical synthesis, the great cat cracker is now a cornerstone of material progress in Western civilization.

Who invented catalytic cracking?

The answer is that no one person did it alone. Many were involved in its final perfection, but some were outstanding in their creative contributions to this difficult art. It is fitting that we should recognize and pay tribute to several of those men who pioneered and led the way to this heroic achievement.

First, we know that catalytic cracking could hardly have been developed without the prior recognition of *thermal cracking* as a fact, and of the successful development of thermal cracking on a large commercial scale. During the twenty-five years before the advent of catalytic cracking, thermal cracking processes had converted millions of barrels of low-grade residual oils into good-quality gasoline.

Three men were most prominent in the development of the technique of thermal cracking: William Burton of the Standard Oil Company (Indiana), and Carbon P. Dubbs and Gustav Egloff of the Universal Oil Products Company.

At Standard Oil, in 1913, after four years of intensive development studies, Dr. Burton, ably assisted by Drs. Rogers and Humphreys, put into operation a series of basic cracking units, which came to be known as "Burton Stills" (U. S. Patent No. 1,049,667). They operated at

5–6 atmospheres pressure and 750–800° F., and contained about 8250 gallons of "gas oil"; about forty-eight hours were needed to process a batch, clean out the still, and get ready for another run. Coke formation and resultant overheating of the flame-fired bottoms of the stills created enormous technical problems. Nevertheless, the difficulties were overcome and the process became a large success factor in the prominence of Standard Oil as a major refiner, because it doubled the production of gasoline from a given crude and formed a higher-octane fuel as well.

Dr. Burton was named president of the Standard Oil Company in 1918 and he occupied that position until 1927. For the cracking process, as well as for other contributions to petroleum chemistry, Burton received the Willard Gibbs Medal of the American Chemical Society (1918) and the Perkin Medal of the Society of Chemical Industry (1922); late in life (1947) he received from the American Petroleum Institute its Gold Medal for Distinguished Achievement. Dr. Humphreys became manager of the Whiting Refinery, and Dr. Rogers chief chemist—both in 1914.

A few years later than Burton, but operating essentially in a pioneering period of petroleum advances, Egloff and Dubbs at Universal Oil Products Company continued with innovations and improvements on thermal cracking. In a company then very small and without the financial backing that major oil companies could offer, they nevertheless succeeded in developing and licensing unique processes that were notably successful on a large commercial scale. Their successes, in fact, served to establish Universal Oil Products Company as a major power in the oil world. In later life, Dubbs remained mostly the practical engineer, while Egloff—with managerial talent and promotional flare—entered the front ranks of those who pushed petroleum into every level of mid-century American chemical industry. As a director of chemical research at UOP, Dr. Egloff kept in close touch with a broad front of petroleum advances, published a great variety of books and reviews, and for his zeal and enthusiasm for his work was generally known as "Mr. Petroleum."

EUGENE J. HOUDRY

Eugene J. Houdry, known in petroleum circles as the "father of catalytic cracking," was born in France (1892) and educated there as a mechanical engineer. He came to this country in 1930 and formed the Houdry Process Corporation in order to develop his inventions in catalytic cracking. For the necessary financial backing and business know-how required to translate speculative developments of this nature into workable commercial processes, Houdry owed much to Mr. Arthur Pew, Jr., of the Sun Oil Company.

The first commercial Houdry cracking unit went on-stream in 1936, and the process was an immediate success—so successful in fact that it produced a sensation in the American petroleum industry. By 1941 sixteen Houdry units were producing, or under construction. Before the original process was rendered obsolete by the development of fluid and moving-bed processes, twenty-nine units had been built with a combined capacity of 375,000 barrels throughput per day.

The early Houdry process employed several fixed-bed catalyst chambers operating in cycles of 30–135 minutes' duration. Carbonaceous deposits, accumulated on the catalyst during the on-stream cycle, were burned off during regeneration; thus the beds alternated between on-stream cracking and off-stream regeneration. Heat from the regeneration was utilized for steam production. The original catalysts were activated clays, and these had a short useful life. Later, Houdry developed synthetic catalysts with longer lives and perfected a moving-bed catalytic system that competed successfully with fully fluidized units.

In 1939, as a result of war in Europe, Houdry was recalled to France to consult with the government on processes for making aviation gasoline. When the Nazis overran France, Houdry rallied American sympathies for the cause of the Free French, becoming the first president of France Forever, Inc., in 1940. That same year the National Association of Manufacturers awarded him the honor of Modern Pioneer, and the Pennsylvania Military College conferred upon him the honorary degree of doctor of science, as did Grove City College in 1941.

During World War II he pioneered the development of the Houdry single-step butane dehydrogenation process—a catalytic route to butenes for aviation fuels and for butadiene, essential for rubber syntheses.

In 1959, "Mr. Catalysis," as he was frequently called, was given the Perkin Medal of the Society of Chemical Industry's American section, and, in April 1962, he received the American Chemical Society Award in Industrial and Engineering Chemistry sponsored by Esso Research and Engineering.

Dr. Houdry died at the age of seventy, on July 18, 1962. His last activities were directed in a beneficial war against air pollution—especially from engine exhausts. Only a month before he died, he was awarded a patent on an anti-smog muffler, a device to burn up exhaust carbon monoxide so that only harmless gases would emerge from the automobile tail pipe.

TEAMWORK

At Universal Oil Products Company, Chicago, an imaginative group of young men (carrying on some earlier explorations of Hans Tropsch) made great strides in developing synthetic silica-alumina catalysts of the type now almost universally accepted in the catalytic cracking industry. These men were Drs. Charles L. Thomas, Elston Ahlberg, Herman Bloch, Joseph Danforth, Edward Lee, and Julian Mavity. Together they put UOP into a very prominent position in the cracking art. Thomas, who was group leader, left later and joined the Sun Oil Company. The team's successes led to the entrance of UOP into the massive combination of efforts among several companies that finally produced the fluidized cat cracker in the early forties, and assured for UOP a prominent place in catalysis of petroleum processes.

EGER V. MURPHREE

E. V. Murphree, born in 1898 in Bayonne, New Jersey, graduated from the University of Kentucky and later entered Massachusetts Institute of Technology for advanced studies. There he had the good fortune to become a student of the distinguished professor of chemical engineering, Dr. Warren K. Lewis. From Lewis, Murphree developed a comprehension of large-scale chemical engineering problems, an area in which he was later to achieve high distinction. In 1930 Murphree became director of a new group formed by Standard Oil Company (New Jersey) to develop chemical processes utilizing petroleum raw materials. In 1934 he became manager of development and research for the Standard Oil Development Company, in which capacity he participated in many high-level accomplishments in the fluidization of catalytic cracking, and syntheses of toluene and butadiene. In 1943, as co-author with C. L. Brown, H. G. Fischer, E. V. Gohr, and W. J. Sweeney, he published a comprehensive description of the new fluid-flow catalytic cracking process.* This milestone of chemical and engineering achievement, a cooperative work of many individuals, was intended first as a competitive answer to Houdry's new processes. However, it was greater than that, for it established a revolutionary new mode of materials handling on a massive scale never before achieved.

The development of this new cracking process was most timely, for the nation was already embroiled in the titanic struggles of World War II. The flood tide of high-quality aviation gasoline that followed was one of the major factors in the success of the Allied air fleets as they finally subdued the German *Luftwaffe,* and then struck across the Pacific at the shores of Japan.

In 1950, Dr. Murphree received the Perkin Medal of the Society of Chemical Industry.

* See footnote at bottom of page 58.

Chapter 6

THE LIVELY GASES: ETHYLENE, PROPYLENE, BUTYLENES, ISOBUTANE

Ethylene, propylene, the butylenes, and isobutane have been mentioned several times before, and a brief description of their structures and reactivity was presented in Chapter 4. Now we shall examine them in more detail to learn how their reactions can lead to products of great interest and value.

All of these hydrocarbons are found among the products arising from the cracking of larger hydrocarbons, such as those in the high-boiling fractions (fuel oils) derived from petroleum. They are obtainable in other ways too, for instance from common alcohols, but no other source equals that of cracking petroleum fractions for mass production and low cost. Even natural gas becomes a good source of some, if not all, of them. For instance, the

$$2 \times \text{H}-\overset{\overset{\displaystyle \text{H}}{|}}{\underset{\underset{\displaystyle \text{H}}{|}}{\text{C}}} \quad \overset{\text{H}}{\underset{\text{H}}{\text{C}}} \quad \overset{\overset{\displaystyle \text{H}}{}}{\underset{\underset{\displaystyle \text{H}}{|}}{\text{C}}} -\text{H} \xrightarrow{500°\text{C}} \quad \text{H}_2\text{C}=\text{CH}_2$$
(ethylene)

propane

$$+\text{H}_2\text{C}=\text{C} \overset{\displaystyle \diagup \text{H}}{\diagdown \text{CH}_3}$$
(propylene)

$$+ \text{CH}_4$$
(methane)

$$+ \text{H}_2$$
(hydrogen)

(Note that the products add up exactly to two units of propane.)

thermal cracking of propane* produces ethylene, propylene, hydrogen, and methane as shown above.

The butylenes, containing four carbon atoms, necessarily come from larger molecules. There are three of these butylene compounds, each with four carbon atoms and one double bond, as shown below:

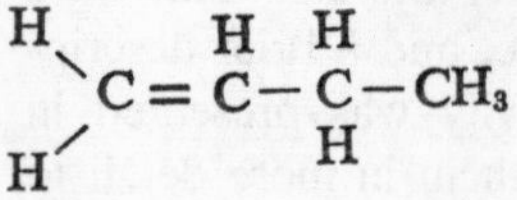

$$\begin{array}{c} H \\ \diagdown \\ \diagup \\ H \end{array} C = \overset{H}{\underset{}{C}} - \overset{H}{\underset{H}{C}} - CH_3 \qquad \text{1–butylene (1 butene)}$$

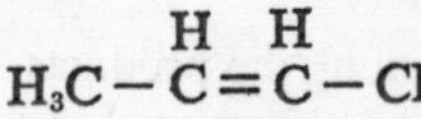

$$H_3C - \overset{H}{\underset{}{C}} = \overset{H}{\underset{}{C}} - CH_3 \qquad \text{2–butylene (2–butene)}$$

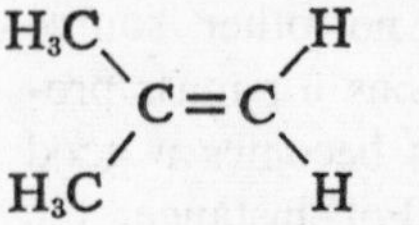

$$\begin{array}{c} H_3C \\ \diagdown \\ \\ H_3C \diagup \end{array} C = C \begin{array}{c} H \\ \diagdown \\ \\ \diagup H \end{array} \qquad \text{isobutylene (2–methyl propene).}$$

The final compound of this series has the structure

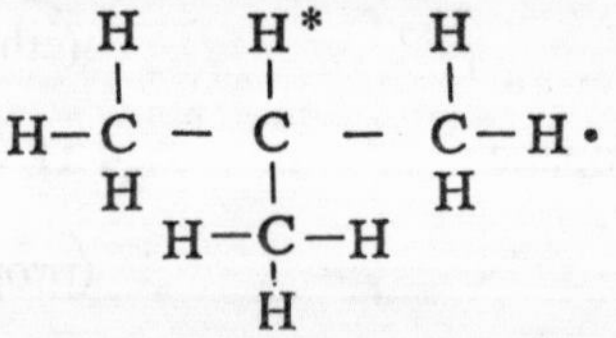

$$H - \overset{H}{\underset{H}{C}} - \overset{H^*}{\underset{\overset{\displaystyle |}{H - \underset{H}{C} - H}}{C}} - \overset{H}{\underset{H}{C}} - H \cdot$$

---

* Propane is one of two easily liquefied components of natural gas; the other is butane ($H_3C - CH_2 - CH_2 - CH_3$). Upon compression and cooling, these two liquefy and are widely used as fuels for portable cookstoves and in rural areas. As such they are referred to as "LPG" (liquefied petroleum gas). Many people know them as "Skelgas" and "Philgas" in pressurized gas cylinders.

This compound is called *isobutane,* an *isomer,* or variant, of the original "normal" butane, which is linear. It is of special interest because the lone H atom on the central carbon (marked by a *) is more reactive than the others. It can be detached in various ways to leave a reactive carbon radical, which can be of two types as shown:

(a) isobutane minus an H atom (H·)

$$CH_3$$
$$|$$
$$H_3C - C \cdot \qquad \text{tert. butyl free radical}$$
$$|$$
$$CH_3$$

(b) isobutane minus a hydride ion (H⁻)

$$CH_3$$
$$|$$
$$H_3C - C^+ \qquad \text{tert. butyl cation}$$
$$|$$
$$CH_3$$

Both free radicals and carbon cations (carbonium ions) enter into a great variety of synthetic processes. For that reason isobutane becomes one of the main characters in this story.

In these formulas a single line connecting the C atoms symbolizes the covalent *single* bond, a *pair* of electrons shared between the two C atoms. Carbon atoms may be joined by *double* bonds, and also by triple bonds, the remaining valences of carbon being satisfied by union with H atoms. Thus we have $H_2C=CH_2$, ethylene, and $HC\equiv CH$, acetylene, where the double line (=) stands for a group of four electrons, and the triple line ($\equiv$) stands for six electrons. The question naturally arises —can C atoms be joined by four bonds? The answer is "no," and we need not concern ourselves about quadruple bonds.

Compounds with three or more carbon atoms may contain combinations of single, double, or triple bonds. They may, in fact, contain two or more of these multiple bonds. For instance, three compounds of great importance in synthetic rubbers are

$$
\begin{array}{c}
H \\ \diagdown \\ C = C \\ / \diagdown \\ H C = C \\ H H
\end{array}
$$
Butadiene,

$$
\begin{array}{c}
H H \\ \diagdown / \\ C = C \\ / \diagdown \\ H C \equiv CH
\end{array}
$$
vinyl acetylene, and

$$
\begin{array}{c}
H CH_3 \\ \diagdown / \\ C = C \\ / \diagdown \\ H C = CH_2 \\ / \\ H
\end{array}
$$
isoprene .

One sees in these examples a great variety of structures. There is also a great variety of chemical reactivities in the hydrocarbons with double or triple bonds. The increased reactivity of these unsaturated hydrocarbons (above those that are single-bonded) lies in these multiple bonds, which possess higher energy than single bonds. That this is true can be shown by simple experiments in which the heats of combustion of the compounds in question are measured and then compared with the sum of the heats of combustion of the elements contained in the compounds.

In a heat measuring device, known as a bomb calorimeter, containing excess oxygen, imagine that the following reactions are examined:

(a) The gas ethane, $H_3C - CH_3$, is burned completely to form carbon dioxide and water. For the purpose, take one gram molecular weight, (one mole) equal to 30.0 grams of ethane. When the burning is finished and the products brought back to standard temperature (20° C.), measure the heat liberated by the reaction, for which the symbol $\triangle H$ is used. The reaction is represented by the equation:

$$C_2H_6 \text{ (ethane)} + O_2 \text{ (excess)} = 2CO_2 + 3H_2O_{\text{(liquid)}}$$
$$30.0 \text{ grams} \qquad\qquad\qquad + \text{Heat}$$

(Note that the water formed is now in the *liquid* state.)

The experimentally obtained $\triangle H_1$ is −373 Kcal.* That is, the $\triangle H$ of combustion of ethane is −373 Kcal per mole, with the water product recovered as a liquid.

(b) In place of ethane, substitute the *same* mass of elemental carbon and hydrogen as one would find in one mole of ethane. That is, use 24.0 grams of graphite and 6.0 grams of hydrogen gas. Burn them in the same calorimeter completely to carbon dioxide and water; measure the heat liberated as before, *after* the products have cooled to 20° C. The reaction is represented by the equation:

$$2C + 3H_2 + O_2 \text{ (excess)} = 2CO_2 + 3H_2O_{\text{(liquid)}}$$
$$24.0 \text{ grams} + 6.0 \text{ grams} \qquad\qquad + \text{Heat}$$

* Kcal is a kilocalorie, equal to 1000 small calories. The negative sign (−) is adopted for this reason: the burning mass of material produces heat (exothermal process), but after the burning is finished and the enclosed mass is restored to the original temperature, that heat is now *lost* from the system. Hence, the loss is represented by the negative (−) sign. Contrariwise, if one must *add* heat to a system (endothermal process) to promote a chemical reaction, the heat input is expressed by a positive (+) sign.

The experimentally obtained $\triangle H_2$ for this combustion of the elements is -393 Kcal.

The two experiments are summed up in the following manner:

For Process (a), $\triangle H_{(ethane)}$ $= -373$ Kcal/mole
For Process (b), $\triangle H_{(2C + 3H_2)}$ $= -393$ Kcal
(b) $-$ (a) $= -393 - (-)273$ $= -20$ Kcal

Conclusion: The burning of the elements alone* produces 20 Kcal more heat energy than the burning of an equivalent weight of ethane. This means, in fact, that ethane is at a *lower* energy level than the equivalent weight of elemental carbon and hydrogen.

These results now justify us in writing a hypothetical reaction to form ethane from carbon and hydrogen:

(c) $\quad 2C + 3H_2 = C_2H_6 \qquad \triangle H_f = -20$ Kcal
$\quad 24.0\,g + 6.0\,g = 30.0\,g$

In this case $\triangle H$ is given the special symbol $\triangle H_f$, which means that the heat of *formation* of ethane *from the elements* is equal to 20 Kcal per mole with a negative sign (energy is *lost* in the process).

Consider now a similar experiment where we examine the combustion of ethylene and measure the heat liberated with the following results:

* The burning of elemental carbon and hydrogen has been studied in great detail and the experimental values for the combustion are now well known. Hence, there is no need to repeat experiment (b).

The accepted values for carbon and hydrogen combustion are the following:

$C(12.0$ grams of graphite$) + O_2 = CO_2 \quad \triangle H = -94.05$ Kcal
$H_2(2.0$ grams of gas$) + O_2 = H_2O_{(liquid)} \quad \triangle H = -68.3$ Kcal

The most precise determinations of atomic weights for carbon give 12.01, and for hydrogen give 1.0078. For ordinary calculations, one usually rounds off these numbers to 12 and 1.

(d) C_2H_4 (ethylene) + O_2 (excess) = $2CO_2 + 2H_2O$ (liquid)

$$\triangle H_4 = -337.7 \text{ Kcal}$$

$(2 \times 12 \text{ g} + 4.0 \text{ g} = 28 \text{ g})$ Expt. 2

(e) $2C + 2H_2 + O_2$ (excess) = $2CO_2 + 2H_2O$ (liquid)

$$\triangle H_5 = -324.7 \text{ Kcal}$$

24 g of graphite plus 4 g of hydrogen   Calc.

Note in this case that the elements combined in the form of ethylene produce more heat than they do if uncombined.

How is this possible?

Clearly it is only possible if the elements receive outside energy during the course of their combining to form ethylene.

These results mean that the molecule ethylene stands at a *higher* energy level than the equivalent amount of carbon and hydrogen, the difference being 13 Kcal. Ethylene is thus spoken of as an *endothermal* compound.

We turn now to a similar experiment on combustion of acetylene, $H-C\equiv C-H$. Its heat of combustion is 310.6 Kcal/mole, while heat of combustion of the equivalent amount of elemental carbon and hydrogen is only 256.4 Kcal, 54.2 Kcal less than the former.

Obviously acetylene is packed with energy above that contained in the starting carbon and hydrogen. It follows that if a mole of acetylene were to be formed from 24.0 grams of carbon and 2.0 grams of hydrogen, 54.2 kilocalories would have to be *absorbed* from an external source. Accordingly, we say that acetylene is an endothermal compound (like ethylene) and its heat of formation is +54.2 Kcal.

Quantitative experiments like those above have been performed on pure hydrocarbons of many types; from the results one can compare the heats of formation and combustion and come up with predictions for the heat changes in new reactions without actually measuring them. Examples of these studies are shown in Table 5.

Table V—Comparison of Heats of Formation of Single- and Double-Bonded Hydrocarbons*

Saturated Hydrocarbon	A ΔH_f Kcal	Unsaturated Hydrocarbon	B ΔH_f Kcal	Diff. $(B-A)$
Ethane H_3C-CH_3	-20.2	Ethylene $H_2C=CH_2$	+12.5	32.7
Propane $H_3C-CH_2-CH_3$	-24.8	Propylene $H_3C-\overset{H}{C}=CH_2$	+4.9	29.7
Butane $H_3C-CH_2-CH_2-CH_3$	-30.1	Butylene $H_3C-CH_2-\overset{H}{C}=CH_2$	-0.03	30.0
Pentane $H_3C-(CH_2)_3-CH_3$	-34.9	Pentene $H_3C-(CH_2)_2-\overset{H}{C}=CH_2$	-5.0	29.9

* The heat of formation of a compound from the elements contained in it is represented by the symbol ΔH_f. The unit commonly employed is kilocalorie (Kcal) per mole.

From Table V one can readily see that on the energy scale the *unsaturated* hydrocarbons on the right all stand at a *higher* level than the corresponding saturated hydrocarbons on the left. Except for the first pair, ethylene versus ethane, where the difference is nearly 33 Kcal, all the others show a difference of about 30 Kcal.

This observation, derived from energy measurements on these compounds, shows the reason why the unsaturated hydrocarbons, being more energetic than the saturated ones, are also more reactive chemically. They are, in fact, reactive in so many ways that, during the last eighty years of intensive investigations, chemists still have not learned all about their behavior. New reactions and products derived from the unsaturated hydrocarbons are discovered nearly every week. This is why we call them "lively."

This is why chemists are intrigued by them, and why the cat cracker, which produces ethylene, propylene, and butylenes in great quantity, is valued not only as a gasoline producer but as a generator of chemicals—a fertile engine that creates lively building blocks for the adventures of molecule building, or chemical synthesis. Many present-day syntheses of useful products were possible long ago—but only on a small scale in the laboratory, and at high cost. But the cat cracker, working day and night at high efficiency and using low-grade residues from petroleum, produces these unsaturated hydrocarbons at prices roughly five to ten cents per pound. At this low cost, manufacturers can afford to use them widely and turn out petrochemicals at a reasonable price.

One of the chemical reactions of unsaturated hydrocarbons is *hydrogen addition;* thus

$$H_2C = CH_2 + H_2 \text{ gas} \xrightarrow[\text{Pt catalyst}]{\text{Ni or}} H_3C - CH_3$$

ethylene   ethane

at 5–10 atmospheres pressure
and temperature at 50–100° C.

Hydrogen literally adds to the ethylene, and the double bond becomes a single bond in the formation of ethane. Ethane, as we have just seen, is at a *lower* energy level than ethylene; hence the question arises: is there a heat effect in the above reaction? The answer is clearly "yes." Although the temperature of the system must be raised above room temperature in order to induce the hydrogen addition, thereafter the mixture becomes hotter by itself due to the saturation of the double bond. Careful measurement of the heat effect gives the following result:

$$H_2C = CH_2 + H_2 = H_3C - CH_3; \qquad \triangle H = -32.8 \text{ Kcal}$$
$$(28 \text{ grams}) + (2.001 \text{ grams}) = (30.0001 \text{ grams})$$

Additional reactions of the same type gave the following results:

$$\begin{array}{c} H \\ H_3C - C = CH_2 + H_2 = H_3C - CH_2 - CH_2; \\ \triangle H = -30.1 \text{ Kcal} \end{array}$$
$$\begin{array}{c} H_3C - CH_2 - C = CH_2 + H_2 = H_3C - CH_2 - CH_2 - CH_3; \\ H \qquad\qquad\qquad \triangle H = -30.3 \text{ Kcal} \end{array}$$

Examination of Table V shows that the value for heat of hydrogen *addition* to an unsaturated compound is equal to the heat of formation of the olefin deducted from the heat of formation of the corresponding saturated hydrocarbon. Thus hydrogen addition to a double bond is an *exothermal* process; the addition process *lowers* the energy of the olefin to that of the corresponding saturated compound. Now, there is nothing very exciting about *lowering* the energy of a hydrocarbon—except when one wants something stable and resistant to change.

But the corollary of this energy-lowering process lies in the *reversal* of the hydrogen addition; if one wishes to change a saturated hydrocarbon to an unsaturated one, this can be done too. How? One has to pay the price, by putting *into* the system the energy demanded by the formation of a higher-energy compound. Thus,

$$H_3C - CH_3 \xrightarrow{\text{High temp.}} H_2C = CH_2 + H_2$$

ethane   ethylene

$$\triangle H = +32.8 \text{ Kcal}$$

dehydrogenation catalyst,

e.g. platinum, or chromium oxide

$\triangle H$ here is the same as that for hydrogen addition to ethylene, but with the opposite sign, that is, heat must be *added* during the process.

Reactions of this type, *dehydrogenations,* are in fact important commercial reactions for producing unsaturated hydrocarbons. The people who practice these reactions know full well, however, that they must supply the heat or energy required—in so doing, they re-energize the more stable saturated compounds and boost them to a more reactive level, with the formation of the olefins.

It is safe at this point to introduce a rather wide generalization, namely that reactions which use up double bonds are exothermal (liberate heat) while reactions that produce double bonds are endothermal (consume heat). One of the most intriguing reactions of double-bonded compounds is *polymerization,* whereby giant molecules with plastic or rubbery character are produced. For instance, ethylene itself can be made to polymerize by means of catalysts or under high pressure. The result (although not simple) can be expressed nearly as follows:

$$n \times H_2C = CH_2 \rightarrow$$
$$- CH_2 - CH_2 - CH_2 - CH_2 - CH_2 - CH_2 - CH_2 - CH_2 -$$

etc. and an extremely long chain of *single*-bonded carbon atoms, a thousand or more, is formed. The original double bonds of ethylene are used up in the process; accordingly the high-energy starting material *loses* energy in the form of heat. These polymerizations are, in fact, found to be highly exothermal; when they are produced on a large scale, special methods must be employed to remove this heat lest the reaction get out of control. One should never forget that it is the high energy of the starting material that is responsible for its reactivity, and for the variety of products that may be formed when the chemist exerts directive influences to shape the end result.

In the chapters that follow, much attention will be given to these addition reactions to the double bonds and their polymerizations. These are the keys to the petrochemical products formed from the olefins.

Chapter 7

PETROCHEMICALS FROM ETHYLENE

Ethylene, an old pro with a bright future, continues to astonish even those who know it best. Front-runner among the olefins, it exceeds all others in production and widespread use.* Early in the 1920s, ethylene was already in business in two leading roles enormously beneficial to the widening use of automobiles. Thermal cracking, developed about ten years earlier, as we have seen, by Burton and his Standard Oil associates, greatly increased the quantity of gasoline available to automobile users. Now ethylene was to put more sparkle into the gasoline in the form of the additive tetraethyl lead, introduced in 1923. This antiknock compound, as we have already discussed, permitted a great improvement in engine performance by suppressing the mysterious hammering action that occurred when designers increased the compression of engines in the effort to achieve higher fuel efficiency. In 1922 ethylene glycol was made available as a radiator antifreeze that gave reliable protection to engines operating increasingly over the continent in all seasons of the year.† This was a marked contrast to "wood alcohol" (methanol) and ethyl alcohol, which—although they have good antifreeze

* In 1962 the demand for ethylene reached 5.5 billion pounds per year, an amount so great that catalytic cracking alone (that used in gasoline production) did not meet the demand. Ethylene had to be produced for its own sake—that is, as a primary product, not merely as a by-product of some other process. The answer lay in cracking of naphthas (light gasolines) and in gas cracking, whereby propane was cracked to form ethylene plus propylene.

† Young readers will find it difficult to believe that before the mid-twenties it was common for people in the cold zones to "lay up" their cars for the winter. The hardships and hazards of win-

action—boil away too easily when engines are overworking. Ethylene glycol with its high-boiling point (197°C.) stays in the radiator. Following the early triumphs of tetraethyl lead and ethylene glycol, in rapid succession came a series of ethylene derivatives of great importance that included the following: ethyl alcohol, ethyl benzene, styrene and polystyrene, triethyl aluminum and triethyl boron, polyethylene—the miracle plastic of squeeze-bottle fame—and a remarkable series of solvents and water-soluble polymers. Of these, triethyl aluminum and triethyl boron are not very well known to the public; they are, however, remarkable incendiary compounds (self-igniters) and are useful in igniting jet fuels during high-altitude flights. Triethyl aluminum is valuable also in a totally different fashion, that of controlling polymerization processes whereby plastic products are "tailored" to conform to a prearranged plan. More about this special use of triethyl aluminum will be presented later in this chapter.

A. FROM ANTIFREEZE TO FILMS AND FIBERS*

The antifreeze fluid we speak of here is ethylene glycol, or 1, 2-dihydroxy ethane, a compound with the structural

---

ter driving included frequent tire blowouts due to brittleness of rubber at low temperature, radiator freeze-ups and cracking of engine blocks, and difficulty in starting engines due to poor ignition and the stiffening of lubricants in extreme cold. Not only these, but engines had to be cranked by *manpower* before electric starters operated reliably!

*This section is the first of several that present polymers in some detail. Others are in Chapters 8, 9, 10, and 11. An excellent general reference, written by persons outstanding in their fields, is found in *Scientific American,* September 1957, pp. 80–216. The first three articles are "Giant Molecules, Historical Survey," "How Giant Molecules Are Measured," and "How Giant Molecules Are Made." Others deal with synthetic as well as natural polymers,

H   H

formula $HO - C - C - OH$. The structural unit $C - OH$ is

H   H

the prime unit in alcohols, hence ethylene glycol is a member of the *alcohol* family; in fact, because it has two $C - OH$ groups, it is classed as a di-alcohol. There are three notable features about ethylene glycol:

(1) Its high ratio of OH groups to carbon atoms, one to one, makes this compound completely soluble in water, i.e. in all proportions it mixes completely with water.

(2) The fact of its having *two* OH groups makes this a high-boiling compound. Its boiling point is 197° C., in contrast to 100° C. for water. Accordingly in a hot water solution, as in automobile radiators, ethylene glycol will not boil away.*

(3) Solutions of ethylene glycol in water have very low freezing points, as shown by Table VI.

TABLE VI

Wt. Per Cent of Glycol in Water	Freezing Point °Centigrade	Freezing Point °Fahrenheit	Freezing Point Depression, °F
0	0	32	—
10	− 3.5	25.6	6.4
20	− 8	17	15
30	−15	5	27
40	−24	−11	43
50	−36	−32	64
58	−48	−54	86
80	−47	−52	84

Note that the mixture of glycol and water with the lowest freezing point is made up of 58 per cent glycol

including cellulose and proteins. These articles are highly recommended for anyone interested in these fascinating materials.

* Two other alcohols used widely as radiator antifreeze fluids are methanol (wood alcohol), with a boiling point 66° C., and

and 42 per cent water (by weight). Addition of more glycol up to 80 per cent produces no further benefit, and, in fact, solutions with *more* than 80 per cent glycol freeze at temperatures of -46 to $+9°$ F. Pure ethylene glycol, in fact, freezes at $+9°$ F. $(-13°$ C.), so that by itself it is not an effective radiator fluid—the addition of water improves it! In the event that liquid-cooled vehicles have to operate in the extreme cold of the arctic and antarctic (temperatures lower than $-54°$ F.), they must use other fluids as coolants, and here methanol and ethanol solutions (with some water present) are superior; that is, they do not freeze at temperatures as low as -90 to $-100°$ F.

It is clear, however, that in the workaday world away from areas of extreme cold, ethylene glycol is the choice antifreeze for protection down as far as $-50°$ F.—at which point sensible people will stay at home anyway!

The synthesis of ethylene glycol begins with the petro-chemical gas ethylene,

$$\underset{H}{\overset{H}{\diagdown}} C = C \underset{H}{\overset{H}{\diagup}}$$

and proceeds to the formation of ethylene oxide

$$\overset{H \quad H}{\underset{\diagdown \ O \ \diagup}{HC - CH}}$$

(also a gas) by either of two routes:

(1) Reaction of ethylene with a water solution satu-

---

ethanol (ethyl alcohol), boiling point 78° C. With boiling points below that of water, they tend to boil out of radiators when the engines become quite hot.

rated with chlorine. The principal compound formed is 2-chloroethanol:

$$Cl - \overset{\displaystyle H}{\underset{\displaystyle H}{C}} - \overset{\displaystyle H}{\underset{\displaystyle H}{C}} - OH$$

(commonly called ethylene chlorohydrin). The latter is treated with alkali, whereupon ethylene oxide is produced:

$$\underset{\displaystyle O}{H_2C - CH_2}$$

(2) Reaction of ethylene gas directly with oxygen from air in the presence of a silver catalyst at a temperature in the range of 200–300° C. Ethylene oxide is the main product, but the oxidation inevitably produces some CO_2 and H_2O, indicating that the process involves also some degradation of the ethylene molecule.

Following the production of ethylene oxide, the next step in manufacture is treatment of the oxide by steam at temperatures well above 100° C., or reaction with cooler water catalyzed by sulfuric acid:

ethylene
oxide

The acid-catalyzed route (b) produces a high yield of ethylene glycol, but the recovery of the glycol from the acidic solution presents difficulties. The route (a) is favored by several manufacturers because there is no acid separation problem involved. In the aqueous chlorination of ethylene there is a by-product, ethylene dichloride. This material, valuable in itself as a solvent for oils and fats, is a product of the reaction of free chlorine in the "chlorine water." The latter is actually a complex mixture, which attacks the ethylene as shown:

$$Cl_2 + HOH = HCl + HOCl$$
$$\text{hypochlorous acid}$$

ethylene dichloride   2–chloroethanol
(ethylene chlorohydrin)

Because the chlorine water contains mostly hypochlorous acid, its reaction with ethylene is predominant, and the chloroethanol is the main product.

In the second step, treatment of the chloroethanol by limewater in the "hydrolyzer" gives ethylene oxide.

ethylene oxide

Notice that the lime is consumed in the process, hence fresh limewater must be added continuously. Control of the degree of alkalinity (pH) is important in order to obtain a good conversion. Separation of the various products in the overall process is easy because of the wide spread in boiling points:

	Boiling point/760 mm
ethylene oxide	10.7° C.
ethylene dichloride	83.5
2-chloroethanol	128.7
ethylene glycol	197.0

Historically the chlorination process came first; it was the result of pioneering work done by Dr. George Curme, Jr., and his associates at the Mellon Institute in Pittsburgh in 1919 and 1920. Shortly thereafter, Carbide and Carbon Chemicals Corporation* began manufacturing ethylene glycol in a semi works plant in Clendenin, West Virginia, and in August 1922 announced its commercial availability. In 1925, the company put into operation a large-scale manufacturing process in South Charleston, West Virginia. Ethylene glycol was here to stay—and the motoring public loved it, for here was a superior antifreeze that would not boil away.

RECENT DEVELOPMENTS IN GLYCOL CHEMISTRY

Despite the ever increasing number of automobiles and trucks manufactured since the twenties, ethylene glycol manufacture has kept up with the demand quite well. The new cracking processes have produced huge quantities of ethylene at successively lower prices.† In fact, ethylene glycol capacity in the fifties began to exceed demand because the demand was almost entirely limited to the automotive industry. Ethylene oxide now is produced predominantly by the direct oxidation process. It is interesting to note that the silver catalyst, developed in the

* Now a division of Union Carbide Corporation.
† In January 1965, the price of ethylene, 99 per cent pure, fell below five cents per pound.

thirties for the process, was still the most effective catalyst for the purpose thirty years later.

In the fifties, the major companies, particularly Union Carbide Corporation, began developing a great variety of other products from ethylene oxide. In particular the reaction for hydrolysis (water addition) was manipulated in such a way as to produce a variety of higher-boiling solvents and polymer products. These were of the type:

$$\text{HO}-\overset{|}{\underset{|}{\text{C}}}-\overset{|}{\underset{|}{\text{C}}}-\text{O}-\overset{|}{\underset{|}{\text{C}}}-\overset{|}{\underset{|}{\text{C}}}-\text{OH}^{*} \qquad \text{diethylene glycol}$$

$$\text{HO}-\overset{|}{\underset{|}{\text{C}}}-\overset{|}{\underset{|}{\text{C}}}-\text{O}-\overset{|}{\underset{|}{\text{C}}}-\overset{|}{\underset{|}{\text{C}}}-\text{O}-\overset{|}{\underset{|}{\text{C}}}-\overset{|}{\underset{|}{\text{C}}}-\text{OH} \qquad \text{triethylene glycol}$$

$$\text{HO}-\overset{|}{\underset{|}{\text{C}}}-\overset{|}{\underset{|}{\text{C}}}-(\text{O}-\overset{|}{\underset{|}{\text{C}}}-\overset{|}{\underset{|}{\text{C}}}-)_{\underline{n}}-\text{OH} \qquad \text{polyethylene glycols}$$

where n becomes as large as 400 and the molecular weight nearly 20,000. All of these are water-soluble polymers, and for that reason enjoy special applications. Another product was the oxygen-carbon heterocyclic compound, dioxane, with the structure

$$
\begin{array}{c}
\text{H}_2 \ \ \text{H}_2 \\
\text{C}-\text{C} \\
\diagup \qquad \diagdown \\
\text{O} \qquad\qquad \text{O} \\
\diagdown \qquad \diagup \\
\text{C}-\text{C} \\
\text{H}_2 \ \ \text{H}_2
\end{array}
$$

Dioxane is a versatile solvent, entirely miscible with water, even though it is completely an ether.

* For simplicity's sake, only the carbon-oxygen skeleton is shown.

But the polymer that gave ethylene glycol an altogether new lift was one developed in the fifties. This material, a remarkable film- and fiber-forming polymer, was derived from an aromatic acid, terephthalic acid,

$$HOOC-\underset{\underset{H\ H}{|\ \ |}}{\overset{\overset{H\ H}{|\ \ |}}{\bigcirc}}-COOH$$

which was brought to react and to end with ethylene glycol, thus:

$$HO\overset{|}{\underset{|}{C}}-\overset{|}{\underset{|}{C}}-OH + HOOC\bigcirc COOH + HO\overset{|}{\underset{|}{C}}-\overset{|}{\underset{|}{C}}-OH + HOOC\bigcirc COOH$$

The removal of water produced a great linear structure. The successful fabrication of this polymer by the du Pont Company led to its commercial appearance under the names "Mylar" for the film, and "Dacron" as the fiber. The British product, developed independently during World War II, came to be known as "Terylene."

MYLAR FILMS AND DACRON FIBERS

The molecular structure of Mylar is the following:

$$HOC-\underset{\underset{H}{|}}{\overset{\overset{H}{|}}{C}}-O-\underset{\underset{O}{||}}{C}-\bigcirc-\underset{\underset{O}{||}}{C}-O-\underset{\underset{H}{|}}{\overset{\overset{H}{|}}{C}}-\underset{\underset{H}{|}}{\overset{\overset{H}{|}}{C}}-O$$

ethylene glycol unit

$$-\left(\underset{\underset{O}{||}}{C}-\bigcirc-\underset{\underset{O}{||}}{C}-O-\underset{\underset{H}{|}}{\overset{\overset{H}{|}}{C}}-\underset{\underset{H}{|}}{\overset{\overset{H}{|}}{C}}-O-\right)_n H$$

terephthalic acid unit
(n is a number over 100)

An ethylene glycol unit alternates with a terephthalic acid unit several hundred times to form a very long thread-like molecule. The binding structure that holds these component parts together is the grouping of atoms known as an *ester,* namely

$$
\begin{array}{ccc}
\text{H} & & \\
| & & \\
-\text{C}-\text{O}-\text{C}- \\
| & & \| \\
\text{H} & & \text{O}
\end{array}
$$

You will see that this occurs repeatedly in the chain; hence Mylar is known as a "polyester." This particular polyester, when it is rolled out in a thin film or spun into fibers, exhibits extraordinary structural strength. The films have great resistance to tearing or bursting under pressure; the fibers show remarkably high tensile strength, ranging from 23,000 to 40,000 pounds per square inch. The material also exhibits a melting point high enough (250–265° C.) to make it valuable in many high-temperature applications.

In recent years Mylar polyester has come into great prominence as a high-quality magnetic tape for sound, television, and data recording on account of its resistance to tearing, and the fact that its high tensile strength permits use of very thin films. In the form of fibers, the polyester is known as Dacron and finds extensive use in fabrics, men's shirts and the like, which retain their press even after washing. Mylar shows a high dielectric strength, 7000 volts per mil as a 1 mil film, and great electrical resistance—its volume resistivity is 10^{18} ohm-centimeters at room temperature. Hence it is valuable in electrical insulation, and as the dielectric layer between capacitor plates. It is certain that this tough durable material will work its way into numerous mechanical, electrical, and textile applications beyond those where it already enjoys high favor.

THE CHEMICAL BACKGROUND OF MYLAR

Terephthalic acid, I HOOC—⟨◯⟩—COOH , is a very high melting compound (m.p. more than 300° C.) and is slowly reactive to ethylene glycol even when hot. It is commonly converted to the methyl ester

II H_3C—O—C⟨◯⟩C—O—CH_3
                  ‖   ‖
                  O   O

which is then brought to react at elevated temperature with *excess* of ethylene glycol, thus:

$$HO—\overset{H}{\underset{H}{C}}—\overset{H}{\underset{H}{C}}—OH + H_3C—O—\underset{O}{\overset{\|}{C}}⟨◯⟩\underset{O}{\overset{\|}{C}}—O—CH_3 +$$

$$HO—\overset{H}{\underset{H}{C}}—\overset{H}{\underset{H}{C}}—OH \xrightarrow{\text{excess}}$$

$$HO—\overset{H}{\underset{H}{C}}—\overset{H}{\underset{H}{C}}—O—\underset{O}{\overset{\|}{C}}⟨◯⟩\underset{O}{\overset{\|}{C}}—O—\overset{H}{\underset{H}{C}}—\overset{H}{\underset{H}{C}}—OH + 2CH_3OH \uparrow$$

III   bishydroxyethyl terephthalate

The low-boiling methyl alcohol is boiled away in the process. Compound III is now heated above 100° C. under vacuum in order to induce the reaction of polyesterification, thus:

$$n \times HO-\underset{|}{\overset{|}{C}}-\underset{|}{\overset{|}{C}}-O-\underset{\overset{\|}{O}}{C}-\underset{}{\overset{}{\bigcirc}}-\underset{\overset{\|}{O}}{C}-O-\underset{|}{\overset{|}{C}}-\underset{|}{\overset{|}{C}}-OH \xrightarrow[\text{vacuum}]{\text{heat}}$$

$$HO-\underset{|}{\overset{|}{C}}-\underset{|}{\overset{|}{C}}-O-\left[\underset{\overset{\|}{O}}{C}-\bigcirc-\underset{\overset{\|}{O}}{C}-O-\underset{|}{\overset{|}{C}}-\underset{|}{\overset{|}{C}}-O\right]_n-H \ +$$

$$(n-1) \ HO-\underset{|}{\overset{|}{C}}-\underset{|}{\overset{|}{C}}-OH$$

(n is a large number)

IV

Notice in this case that it is the ethylene glycol, *in excess* in the beginning, which is now boiled away—then recovered, of course, for re-use. The process is one that is known technically as *ester interchange*.

Simple as it may seem on paper, this two-step process (formation first of III, and then conversion of III to IV by vacuum elimination of excess glycol) was the key to real success in forming the high polymer. Earlier efforts to produce the high polymer by direct combination of *one*-to-*one* amounts of terephthalic acid and ethylene glycol produced only a sticky low-melting material which had no fiber-forming character at all; its molecular weight was only a few thousand units—insufficient for the desired properties.

No sooner was success achieved by the modification described than the du Pont chemists, with customary thoroughness, began to alter the basic recipe to introduce small structural variations in the polymer. In place of terephthalic acid, they used phthalic and isophthalic acids (position isomers of terephthalic acid) and in place of ethylene glycol they used longer-chain alcohols, $HO-C-C-C-OH$, $HO-C-C-C-C-OH$, etc. The results agreed with their expectations; *all* of the new products were inferior in strength and melting point to the original product. These findings were very advantageous, as far as costs were involved. Old-style antifreeze, ethylene glycol, abundant and cheap, was by far the best alcohol for the purpose.*

There is, of course, a great variety of diacids and dialcohols to be explored in this respect, and it is likely that someone in time will come up with new polyesters of great utility. However, there is still the problem of the cost of raw materials. In this respect, ethylene glycol is hard to beat—so long as we have a petroleum industry producing ethylene from cracking processes.

B. ETHYL ALCOHOL, ETHYL CHLORIDE, AND TETRAETHYL LEAD

To say that ethyl alcohol has intrigued man and influenced his behavior through all of recorded history is to say the least about this unusual organic compound. It is true that people didn't know it as ethyl alcohol; they only knew it as a kind of demon or spirit that inhabited fruit juices—not when they were fresh, but after a mysterious effervescing "fermentation" had intervened —for reasons that nobody comprehended.

For a long time the idea of "spirits" pervaded the realm of the wine maker and the wine consumer, who obviously at times became high-spirited after using the wine. Finally in the middle 1200s an alchemist contrived to distill some wine, and then to sample the distillate. Yahoo! The sensation was overwhelming, and with wonderment and awe he labeled the distillate "ardent spirits."

* An excellent account of the early researches that led to success with Mylar is given by E. F. Izard of the du Pont Company in *Chemical and Engineering News*, 32 (1954), 3724.

Progress was rapid thereafter in this new era of "distilled spirits";* only five hundred years later alcohol was isolated as a pure substance and its chemical properties came under scrutiny.

STRUCTURE AND PROPERTIES

Ethyl alcohol has a simple structure compared, for instance, with sugar, starch, proteins, vitamins and the like; yet its physiological action inside the human or animal organism is profound.

Known also as "ethanol" or simply "alcohol," the substance has the molecular structure $H_3C - CH_2 - OH$. A catalog of its properties includes the following:

Boiling point/1.0 atmosphere, 78.3° C.

Freezing point, −126° C.

Critical boiling point, 263.7° C. at 50.1 atm.

Density, 0.8035 g/ml at 20° C.

Solubility in water, infinite (all combinations are miscible)

Solubility in benzene, xylene, cyclohexane, and similar hydrocarbons, infinite

Flammability, ignites easily at room temperature; flash point 9–11° C.

Heat of combustion, 328 Kcal per mole

The affinity of alcohol for water is high and, despite the fact that its boiling point is twenty-two degrees lower

---

* Much of the language that describes alcohol in beverages to this day smacks of alchemy, and it is fair to say that the hokum attending certain advertising of alcoholic beverages is matched only by the humbug of the tobacco auctioneer. For this reason, it is important, even imperative, that a person who wants to understand these subjects should read authentic accounts about alcohol and its uses. Excellent treatments of the subject are found in "ECT," the *Encyclopedia of Chemical Technology,* edited by Kirk and Othmer (New York: Interscience Publishers).

than that of water, the best fractionating columns will not separate the two completely. A distillate containing 95–96 per cent alcohol by volume is the best that can be obtained. An alcohol/water mixture of this composition distills unchanged at constant temperature, 78.1° C., and in distillation technology is known as an "azeotropic mixture."

Complete removal of water from alcohol to form so-called "absolute alcohol" (200 proof in the fermentation industry) is possible. For the purpose, chemical treatment with calcium or barium oxides, or with magnesium ethoxide or calcium hydride will eliminate the water; thereafter distillation of the fluid remaining yields anhydrous alcohol. Distillation of 95 per cent alcohol to which a third component, e.g. benzene, has been added will finally give anhydrous alcohol in a good fractionating column.

USES

The principal uses of alcohol lie in three areas:

(a) as a constituent of beer, wine, brandy, whiskey, and other alcoholic beverages;

(b) as an industrial and pharmaceutical solvent;

(c) as a chemical reagent for formation of ethyl esters, acetaldehyde, acetic acid, and other derivatives. Source for rubber during World War II.

The extraordinary solvent character of alcohol is one of its most notable features. This leads to its widespread use throughout the food, drug, and chemical world, for which purpose it is second only to water itself.

The very low freezing point of alcohol (−126° C.) makes it valuable as an antifreeze and refrigeration fluid for extremely low temperatures. Before the advent of ethylene glycol, alcohol was practically the only reliable antifreeze for automobile radiators. Furthermore, because the lowest freezing point attainable for ethylene glycol/water solutions is −56° F., alcohol still is the material of choice at lower temperatures.

For small-scale heating operations, alcohol has been used widely as a convenient fuel, as in alcohol lamps, and as canned heat, a gelatinized alcohol that can be ignited easily without spillage.

Alcohol is also entirely suitable as a component of gasoline for use in the internal combustion engine where it displays a beneficial antiknock action. Alcohol was, in fact, seriously proposed as a major component (10–25 per cent) of gasoline during the thirties when fermentation alcohol was very cheap. However, gasoline was even cheaper, and its forecasted shortage due to a prophesied exhaustion of petroleum fields never came true.

As a result of special needs during World War II, particularly to form butadiene for rubber synthesis, the production of ethyl alcohol in the United States rose to an all-time high of 600 million gallons in the year 1945. This was in contrast to the usual prewar production of about 100 million gallons per year, and production in the 1960s of 300–350 million gallons per year.

Because of its versatile character and low cost (less than one dollar per gallon in barrel lots), ethyl alcohol consumption for solvent and chemical purposes will probably increase steadily for years to come.

FORMATION OF ETHYL ALCOHOL

There are two primary processes for making ethyl alcohol: the first and oldest is the fermentation of sugars by yeast organisms, on which an elaborate technology has been built; the second is the employment of ethylene gas as the carbon source to which the elements of water, HOH, must be added.

I. *Alcohol via Fermentation.*

The fermentation of sugary materials—for instance, fruit juices, honey, molasses and the like—by action of yeast was a common but altogether mysterious process for hundreds of generations in the history of man. Only recently has the intricate chemistry of the process been worked out in detail. The overall process, without regard for the subtle intermediary stages, can be summarized, however, by a simple equation:

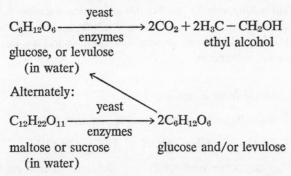

$$C_6H_{12}O_6 \xrightarrow[\text{enzymes}]{\text{yeast}} 2CO_2 + 2H_3C-CH_2OH$$

glucose, or levulose   ethyl alcohol
(in water)

Alternately:

$$C_{12}H_{22}O_{11} \xrightarrow[\text{enzymes}]{\text{yeast}} 2C_6H_{12}O_6$$

maltose or sucrose   glucose and/or levulose
(in water)

Starch may also be used as the sugar source, but in this event the yeast cannot attack starch directly; it is necessary first to convert starch to maltose or glucose by enzyme action or by acids. The enzyme process, using extracts from the sprouts of germinating seeds, e.g. barley, is common in the beverage industry and is called "malting" because the end product formed is maltose. The acid process produces mainly glucose ($C_6H_{12}O_6$), and the acid must be neutralized before the yeast can do its work.

The equation above tells us that in all cases the yield of alcohol *at best* is 92 grams from a basic sugar unit, $C_6H_{12}O_6$, of gram molecular weight 180. Hence the yield is about 50 per cent of the sugar present. The alcohol is formed in a water solution, and experimentally the highest concentrations of alcohol attainable are in the range of 12–15 per cent, and these only after five to ten days. The alcohol is, of course, an end product of yeast metabolism and, as it increases, it finally "intoxicates" the yeast, which therefore cannot go on and on producing alcohol indefinitely.

Thus by fermentation of sugars, one winds up with dilute aqueous solutions of alcohol, contaminated also by the leftover yeast plus various proteins, pigments, minerals, etc. The fluid product is not objectionable as a beverage, of course, after a few minor refinements! But if one is interested only in producing pure alcohol, there is still a long way to go. For these reasons chemists have been concerned about producing alcohol more quickly and easily. The best answer has been found to be in ethylene conversion.

II. Alcohol from Ethylene.

The fundamental transformation required is this:

$$H_2C = CH_2 + HOH = H_3C - CH_2OH$$

By one means or another one mole of water must be combined chemically with one mole of ethylene. The direct combination is in fact possible, but only at elevated temperature and pressure; the process is known as the "direct" hydration of ethylene. Another route is a two-step process in which the ethylene is first absorbed in concentrated sulfuric acid. The latter process, indirect hydration, was actually the first to be put into commercial production (1930, by Union Carbide Corporation). It is interesting to note that this "early" process followed by seventy-five years the first published *laboratory* method for converting ethylene to ethanol via sulfuric acid, carried out by M. Bertholet in 1855!*

---

* One should not assume that the lag was a result of inadequate technology. The reason was that pure ethylene began to be available in quantity from petroleum cracking only in the twenties.

These two methods for modern alcohol synthesis will be described briefly.

THE INDIRECT HYDRATION OF ETHYLENE VIA SULFURIC ACID

The reactions involved are the following:

(a) Ethylene gas flowing upward reacts with sulfuric acid flowing downward in tall towers at 50–80° C. under a gas pressure of 10–14 atmospheres.

$$H_2C = CH_2 + H_2SO_4 = H_3C - \overset{\displaystyle H}{\underset{\displaystyle H}{C}} - OSO_2OH$$

ethyl acid sulfate

$$2H_2C = CH_2 + H_2SO_4 = (H_3C - CH_2)_2SO_4$$

diethyl sulfate

(b) The mixture of sulfate products is diluted with approximately an equal volume of water, whereupon hydrolysis (splitting) of the sulfates is effected by heating at 100° C. or above.

$$H_3C - \overset{\displaystyle H}{\underset{\displaystyle H}{C}} - OSO_2OH + HOH = H_3C - CH_2OH + H_2SO_4$$

$$(H_3C - CH_2)_2SO_4 + 2HOH = 2H_3C - CH_2OH + H_2SO_4$$

$$(H_3C - CH_2)_2SO_4 + H_3C - CH_2OH =$$
$$H_3C - \overset{\displaystyle H}{\underset{\displaystyle H}{C}} - OSO_2OH$$
$$+ H_3C - CH_2 - O - CH_2 - CH_3$$

diethyl ether

How did Bertholet obtain his ethylene? From ethyl alcohol, the only known source at that time!

One should note that the primary reaction of ethylene always produces some diethyl sulfate (the greater the ratio of ethylene to H_2SO_4, the more disulfate is formed), and that the disulfate will form some diethyl ether. Consequently the latter is inevitably a by-product of the process. This, however, is not objectionable, because the ether itself is always in considerable demand.

The final reaction product is distilled, thereby removing water, ether, and ethyl alcohol; the residue is dilute sulfuric acid, which has to be concentrated by vacuum evaporation in order to re-form concentrated acid to be used over again. Redistillation of the alcohol product in a good fractionating column produces the azeotropic alcohol/water final product, which contains 95–96 per cent ethyl alcohol by volume.

THE DIRECT HYDRATION OF ETHYLENE

The addition of water to ethylene is thermodynamically favorable (exothermic) by 10.5 to 11 Kcal per mole at room temperature with an ultimate yield over 90 per cent in infinite time! But industrial success is not built on infinite time; therefore the solution to this problem is to raise the temperature and pressure in order to obtain a faster turnover. Variations in conditions produce the results shown in Table VII.

TABLE VII—ETHYLENE → ALCOHOL CONVERSION
BY CONTINUOUS FLOW THROUGH TUBULAR REACTORS

	Temp.	Ratio	Pressure	Equilib. Convers.	Rate
	°C.	$\dfrac{H_2O}{ethylene}$			
(a)	200	2/1	20 atm.	20%	Slow
(b)	300	0.6	66 atm.	5%	Fast

The conditions indicated by (b) in Table VII, approximate those described by the Shell Development Company for its commercial production of alcohol via ethylene, using a phosphoric acid catalyst. Many kinds of catalysts have been used and recommended, among which are aluminum oxide, aluminum silicate or silica gel, and oxides of tungsten and thorium. Phosphoric acid appears to be favored, but frequently it is dispersed over a variety of carriers.

Upon studying the table, one wonders how a process can achieve commercial success with only 5 per cent yield. The answer lies in the fact that unchanged ethylene is easily recovered after the first pass through the reactor, and recycled. Recycling is common in many petrochemical processes, and in this case the ultimate yield based on ethylene consumed is about 97 per cent.

Another feature of the process is that the conditions sustain the reactants in the vapor phase until they meet the catalyst. In both (a) and (b) above, the temperatures are above critical for ethylene, but below critical for water. However, the pressures are low enough to permit water to remain gaseous. Increase in pressure tends to favor the main reaction; but if it forces condensation of the water, a rapid decline in the rate of reaction occurs.

Although the process for direct hydration of ethylene had been known for some time, the first commercial production of alcohol by the process began only in 1949 on a very small scale. However, the process grew rapidly in favor, and in 1965 the production approximated sixty-two million gallons. Both products from ethylene (the direct plus that via sulfuric acid) have been able to compete successfully in price with fermentation alcohol. They have, in fact, had a stabilizing effect on the price, which in earlier times fluctuated greatly with sugar and grain prices. For instance, for industrial alcohol, regardless of origin, the price per gallon during 1959–1964 held steady at 52¢ (tank-car quantities). Previous to that, prices ranged widely from 20¢ to 95¢ per gallon.

SUMMARY

Ethyl alcohol, a material ancient in its origins, plays a prominent role in the modern world. It continues to be available by the yeast fermentation of sugar-containing solutions, and therefore may be regarded as an agricultural chemical. In recent years, however, the outpouring of ethylene from cracking of petroleum fractions has led to its use for numerous commercial syntheses on a large scale. Synthetic ethyl alcohol (accompanied by a small amount of ethyl ether) is now a major product from ethylene.

ETHYL CHLORIDE

Ethyl chloride, a gas at ordinary temperatures, has the molecular structure $H_3C - \overset{\displaystyle H}{\underset{\displaystyle H}{C}} - Cl$. It is easily liquefied under a few atmospheres pressure, for its normal boiling point is +13° C. It is one of a class known as halohydrocarbons, chloroform ($HCCl_3$) being another. Accordingly, ethyl chloride (also called chloroethane) can be made by chlorination of the hydrocarbon ethane; this is entirely feasible but the process is of minor importance commercially.

Liquefied ethyl chloride is stored under pressure in steel cylinders. Small cylinders of the liquid are used by physicians for anesthetic purposes. When the liquid is sprayed on the skin, rapid evaporation cools the surface sufficiently so that minor surgery can be done with little pain. Ethyl chloride also enjoys some use as a quick-acting general anesthetic by inhalation of the gas delivered from the self-same pressurized container.

The principal uses for ethyl chloride, however, lie in the preparation of various ethyl derivatives—compounds

$$H$$

that contain the H_3C-C- group. Of these, the most

$$H$$

important are (a) tetraethyl lead, (b) triethyl aluminum, and (c) ethyl cellulose.

Tetraethyl lead consumes the largest portion of the available ethyl chloride—approximately 400 million pounds in 1962. Triethyl aluminum production is increasing steadily because of the compound's fundamental role as a catalyst for stereo regular synthesis of high polymers from ethylene, propylene, and other olefins (Chapter 7, Section D, and Chapter 8, Section D). A notable property of triethyl aluminum is its spontaneous flammability in air. Because of this incendiary character it is employed by the armed forces, but it also has a more peaceful use as an igniter for the fuels of jet engines. When it is incorporated with the fuels, it helps to prevent flame-out of the engines.

The formation of triethyl aluminum directly from aluminum can be represented by the equation

$$2Al + 3C_2H_5Cl = Al(C_2H_5)_3 + AlCl_3.$$

The reaction is not this simple, however, because of formation also of $ClAl(C_2H_5)_2$ and $Cl_2AlC_2H_5$, and combination of the $AlCl_3$ with the other products. However, the volatility of triethyl aluminum permits its ultimate separation by fractional distillation.

Ethyl cellulose is made by the reaction of alkali cellulose (an intermediate for rayon production) with ethyl chloride under pressure at 125° C. If the cellulose is but lightly ethylated, the product is soluble in water—a nov-

elty for cellulose. A higher degree of ethylation (2.0 to
2.5 ethyl groups per six C atoms in cellulose) yields a
material soluble in hydrocarbons and alcohols, and also
compatible with many resins. These products are used as
tough coatings and films. Ethyl cellulose because of its
ether character is resistant to degradation by strong alkalis, a feature that is not enjoyed by such derivatives as
the acetate and nitrate esters.

FORMATION OF ETHYL CHLORIDE

The principal commercial method for production of
ethyl chloride involves the reaction of HCl with ethylene.
Numerous catalysts and solvents have been employed to
promote the reaction, which normally is quite slow. The
best combination seems to be aluminum chloride, $AlCl_3$,
dissolved in liquefied ethyl chloride held at 40° C. The
reactants are passed under pressure into this solution; the
overall reaction is represented by the addition process.

$$HCl + H_2C = CH_2 = H_3C - \overset{\displaystyle H}{\underset{\displaystyle H}{C}} - Cl$$

ethyl chloride

Ethyl chloride is also made by the direct reaction of
chlorine gas on ethane, light-catalyzed,

$$H_3C - CH_3 + Cl_2 \xrightarrow{\ h\gamma\ } H_3C - CH_2 - Cl + HCl$$

and by action of a solution of zinc chloride in concentrated hydrochloric acid on ethanol.

$$H_3C - \overset{\displaystyle H}{\underset{\displaystyle H}{C}} - OH + HCl(ZnCl_2) = H_3C - \overset{\displaystyle H}{\underset{\displaystyle H}{C}} - Cl$$

Ethanol $+ HOH(ZnCl_2)$

The last process is advantageous only if the ethanol is a fermentation product; it is rather pointless if the source was ethylene, in which case the direct reaction with HCl would be preferred.

TETRAETHYL LEAD (TEL)

Tetraethyl lead, a colorless oily liquid insoluble in water but soluble in hydrocarbons, is, as we have mentioned, widely used as a gasoline additive to prevent engine knock. It has a slightly sweet odor and is sufficiently volatile that its vapors are a real hazard because of high toxicity to humans and animals. Poisoning can occur by inhalation, by ingestion, and by absorption through the unbroken skin; therefore the handling of tetraethyl lead must be done with great caution against contact. However, these manipulative problems were overcome long ago, and presently tetraethyl lead in amounts exceeding 250,000 tons per year are handled in the petroleum industry without serious incident.

The common physical properties of TEL include: freezing point, $-135°$ C.; boiling point, $195°$ C. at atmospheric pressure with decomposition, but at $108.4°$ C. at 50 mm. pressure and at $82°$ C. at 13 mm. pressure; density 1.653 g/ml at $20°$ C. Because of its decomposition at elevated temperature, TEL is usually distilled with steam or at reduced pressure. When heated in the absence of air, TEL decomposes to form metallic lead and ethyl free

radicals, $H_3C - \overset{\displaystyle H}{\underset{\displaystyle H}{C}}\cdot$. In fact, some of the earliest work

on formation and reactions of free radicals was done on tetraethyl lead (Paneth and Lautsch), and it is probable that the easy formation of free radicals is the reason for the special value of the compound.

The great importance of tetraethyl lead dates back to the early twenties when Thomas Midgley, Thomas Boyd, and Charles Kettering discovered its extraordinary ability to suppress combustion knock in the automotive engine. Their search for a substance that would be effective against knock was an epic in the annals of American chemical research and deserves special study for its own merits.* To appreciate the story one has to be aware that in the 1910s and 1920s the American automobile industry and its close relative, the airplane industry, were bursting with expansive zeal and literally producing a revolution in the traveling habits of Western society. But the oppressive problem of engine knock bedeviled and plagued the industry, and many an engine, otherwise well built, was ruined before its time by engine knock. And nobody knew the cause!

Finally, after much study and experimentation, the investigators were forced to conclude that the cause was in the fuel and not in the engine itself. Gasoline hydrocarbons that had long straight chains† were found to cause engine knock even when the compression was quite low, e.g. 3/1 or 4/1, and the knock would worsen when the engine was laboring to climb a hill under slight acceleration. If the hydrocarbons were to be *branched,* or converted to cyclics and aromatics, their behavior was much improved during burning and the engine would not knock. But the matter of forming branched or cyclic hydrocarbons in the early twenties was not a simple one.

Then came the exciting discovery that non-fuel substances added to an ordinary knock-producing gasoline would stop the knocking. Iodine, aniline, arsenic derivatives, and a variety of odd substances were moderately effective, but tetraethyl lead by all odds was the best

* See S. P. Nickerson, "Tetraethyl Lead: Product of American Research," *Journal of Chemical Education,* 31 (1954), 560.
† See Chapter 3, *engine knock* and *octane number.*

knock suppressor of them all. This discovery in the Dayton, Ohio, Research Laboratory of General Motors, December 9, 1921, climaxed an arduous search that had lasted five years at a price exceeding three million dollars —a huge sum for research in those days. Fourteen months later, February 2, 1923, the first gallon of gasoline improved by addition of TEL was sold to a venturesome motorist in Dayton.

HOW TETRAETHYL LEAD IS MADE

In the laboratory the early methods for synthesis involved reactions of ethyl iodide or ethyl bromide with sodium lead alloys, or reaction of ethyl zinc or other ethyl-metal compounds with lead chloride. But on a massive scale ethyl zinc reactions were impractical because of high cost, and so were processes involving iodides or bromides. (In the twenties iodine and bromine were scarce and extremely costly.) Ethyl chloride was brought into the picture although it appeared to be insufficiently reactive so that product yields were very low. Nevertheless, two new workers in the enterprise, Professor Charles Kraus of Clark University and Dr. C. C. Callis, undertook extensive experiments with ethyl chloride and a series of sodium lead alloys. Finally success came with an alloy which was one to one atom-wise in metals, Na—Pb (sodium content 10 per cent, lead content 90 per cent). Reaction with ethyl chloride under pressure at a temperature high enough to melt the alloy and with good agitation produced tetraethyl lead in yields of 75 per cent and better. The process is summarized by the equation:

$$4H_3C - \overset{\displaystyle H}{\underset{\displaystyle H}{C}} - Cl + 4NaPb = Pb(C_2H_5)_4 + 4NaCl + 3Pb$$

The TEL was steam-distilled from the mixture, the sodium chloride was removed by water washing, and the lead was recovered for re-use.

Shortly after the laboratory process was proved out, the process was put into commercial production by the Standard Oil Company of New Jersey (1923). In 1924 Standard Oil and General Motors pooled their mutual interests in TEL and formed the Ethyl Corporation which then took over production and marketing of TEL. With various small refinements, the original Kraus-Callis method continued to be the best way of proceeding from ethyl chloride to tetraethyl lead.

Very recently, with the increased availability of the alkyl aluminums (see ethyl chloride reactions above), new syntheses of TEL and also of tetramethyl lead, $Pb(CH_3)_4$, by electrolysis with lead anodes have appeared. These involve alkyl aluminum complexes with chloro-aluminum compounds or organomagnesium chlorides. Tetramethyl lead is a newer product that has been found quite effective in raising the octane number of fuels that have a high content of aromatic hydrocarbons. For the latter, tetraethyl lead is rather ineffective.

TETRAETHYL LEAD IN GASOLINE

The use of TEL in gasoline was a victory for automotive improvement, but not without its complications. In addition to possible toxicity from excessive amounts, the accumulation of lead deposits in the engine presented a mean problem.

The problem was solved by adding ethylene bromide $(BrCH_2 - CH_2Br)$ and ethylene chloride $(ClCH_2 - CH_2Cl)$ to the TEL. In the presence of these halogen compounds, combustion converted TEL to lead bromide and lead chloride, compounds that are volatile enough at engine temperatures to escape completely from the cylinders with the exhaust gases. Both of these halogen compounds are made, of course, from ethylene, but the source of the bromine is a whole story by itself. Suffice it to say that the Ethyl Corporation and Dow Chemical Company obtained bromine from the sea. This extraction of bromine from sea water was an epic in itself and resulted not only in production of adequate bromine for all chemical needs, but also established a new magnesium industry, the magnesium likewise coming from the inexhaustible resources of the oceans. These two enterprises are described in the Nickerson article cited above.

Clearly the tetraethyl lead story is one that moved in many directions that no one could foresee in the beginning.

C. STYRENE AND POLYSTYRENE

1. STYRENE AND ITS ORIGINS

Styrene, or vinyl benzene,* is an intriguing and exciting substance. A bright clear fluid, it sparkles like a diamond when shaken in direct sunlight. This color effect is due to its high optical refraction and its light dispersing action. In other words, styrene bends a ray of light sharply and also causes a wide "dispersion" or separation of the

---

* Styrene is the first member of a class of hydrocarbons that has both a benzene ring and an ethylenic double bond. Its structure is:

benzene ring   vinyl group

red rays from the blue. For this reason, styrene stands out in the midst of various other hydrocarbons as a unique substance, and can be recognized on account of these optical qualities.

Furthermore, styrene reacts spontaneously with itself; upon standing for several months in a vessel containing a little air, the liquid thickens noticeably and finally turns into a solid block of transparent "plastic." When heated above room temperature, the liquid turns more quickly into the solid form. This behavior has been known for a long time; in fact, it is probable that styrene was the first hydrocarbon in which this spontaneous process, known as *resinification,* was observed by chemists.

Styrene was discovered in 1827 by Bonastre as a decomposition product from the distillation of liquid storax, a fragrant balsam. The actual progenitor of styrene from the storax was probably cinnamic acid, an acid that is now well known by chemical synthesis, and that readily yields styrene upon heating to its boiling point:

$$C_6H_5 - \overset{H}{C} = \overset{H}{C} - COOH \xrightarrow[\text{temp.} > 200° \text{ C.}]{} C_6H_5\overset{H}{C} = CH_2 + CO_2$$

cinnamic acid   styrene

The transformation of styrene into a solid polymer was reported by a Berlin pharmacist, E. Simon, in 1839. Despite this long history of styrene, the substance did not assume any technical importance until the 1920s when the famous German chemist Hermann Staudinger,* with his students, investigated the polymerization reaction in great detail; in fact, they established much of the modern theory of high polymers on the reactions of styrene.

* Professor Staudinger (Karlsruhe, Zurich, and Freiburg) was awarded the Nobel prize in chemistry (1953) "for his discoveries in the field of macromolecular chemistry."

In point of time, commercial polystyrene made its appearance on a small scale in Germany in the early thirties and in the United States in 1936 as a product of the Dow Chemical Company.

A meteoric rise in production and consumption of styrene in the United States occurred during World War II. The object during the war was to produce a synthetic rubber to replace the natural rubber supply that was cut off from America. For this purpose styrene was copolymerized with butadiene to produce the so-called GR-S rubber, which will be described in detail in Chapter 9. Following the war, styrene continued to grow in importance both for polystyrene plastics and for rubber formulations. The magnitude of production of polystyrene resins alone is revealed in the following figures for world production:

1959	520,000 tons of polymer
1960	700,000 tons
1963	750,000 tons

In 1963 the price of commercial lots of polystyrene had dropped to fourteen to sixteen cents per pound, figures low enough to make it useful in a great variety of structural forms.

The absence of technical employment of styrene for so long a time in its early history was due no doubt to the difficulty of preparing it on a large scale at low cost— and in sufficient *purity* so that its polymerization could be conducted reliably to a desired end result.

What made possible the great outpouring of styrene for plastics and rubber that began in the thirties and forties? Clearly, the main factor was the production of ethylene gas on a large scale as a result of catalytic cracking processes perfected at that time. The importance of ethylene lay in the fact that it was the key ingredient in the formation of ethyl benzene from which the styrene was derived by catalytic dehydrogenation, as shown below:

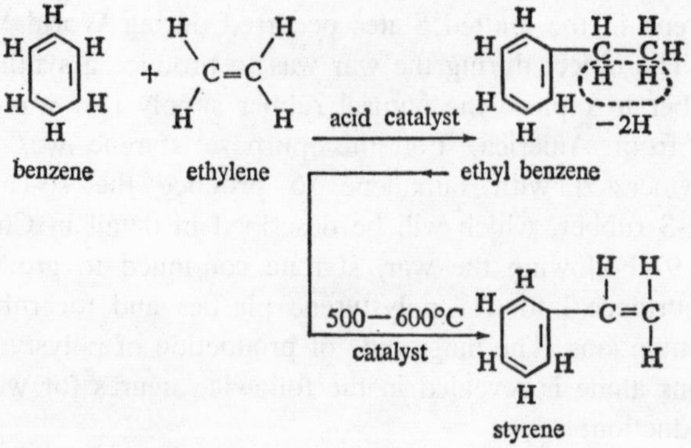

benzene   ethylene   acid catalyst   ethyl benzene

500—600°C
catalyst

styrene

However, the problems of converting ethyl benzene to styrene and recovering the styrene in a state of high purity (purity above 99 per cent) were not solved until the late thirties. Styrene of lesser purity contained sufficient amounts of divinyl benzene, aldehydes, peroxides, and even sulfur and chlorine compounds (derived from the commercial starting materials) so that the resulting polystyrene resins failed in various ways. A brief account of this story has been taken from the records of the Dow Company.

From a small beginning, polystyrene is now a well established giant in a gigantic industry, and a whole new technology has been built around it. Yet for more than a century the knotty problem of how to transpose a water white liquid—the form of styrene monomer—into a sparkling crystal clear solid and to keep it that way defied some of the most active brains in science. The promise of polystyrene had long been seen by many chemists; it could be made from a substance found in many naturally occurring materials, it could be made from relatively inexpensive raw materials and it was in that desirable category of products known as thermoplastics which could be remelted and reformed. But until the early thirties polystyrene's future was dimmed by what seemed an insurmountable flaw—even if it were made as sparkling as the liquid from whence it came, it still could not be kept for any length of time without *cracking* or *crazing* and *turning yellow*. Dow became interested in styrene chiefly because it could be made from ethylene, a petroleum product with which the company had much experience dating back to World War I. Research workers had succeeded in devising low-cost methods for production of ethylene products, and were now looking for new fields where they could be utilized. Styrene was a case in point. The problem was not to discover a new material, but—what is often much more difficult—to develop successful methods for the manufacture of a known one. The ultimate answer was the fashioning of a new type of distillation column for purification of liquid styrene, and the discovery of some efficient inhibitors to prevent losses of styrene monomer* during the distillation. Thus Dow became the first to purify styrene in large quantity. The new monomer was of such high purity that the polystyrene made from it was water white and crystal clear and retained these properties indefinitely. By 1934, semi-plant-scale work was foreshadowing the later commercial success.†

Here then was one example of a case in which an extremely pure monomer was required before a successful result could be gained for the polymer. Others that you will read about later involve ethylene and propylene in their polymerizations at low pressure, and also isoprene when used in rubber synthesis. Earlier it had seemed unbelievable that industrial chemicals could be made—and

---

* In the absence of inhibitors devised for the purpose, polymerization of the styrene occurred directly inside the still as a result of the heating.

† *Dow Diamond*, 19, 3 (1956), 6.

kept—at such high purity at such small cost. However, it was mass production of newly available olefins derived from petroleum cracking, coupled with ingenious purification methods, that forged the keys to success in the burgeoning new high polymer enterprises.

2. POLYSTYRENE

The early observation that the effort to purify styrene by distillation led to formation of polymer in the still was the key to a later commercial process for producing polystyrene. This heat-induced polymerization can be carried out in a continuous process in which styrene enters one end of a reaction train and polystyrene emerges at the other end. The mechanics of the process are shown in Figure 5.

In a pair of aluminum or stainless steel tanks, styrene is held at temperatures of 80–85° C. for two days, during which time 35 to 40 per cent of the styrene reacts to form polymer, and the mixture becomes quite viscous. At this stage, the mixture enters the long column; thin films of it flow downward through zones that become progressively hotter up to 200° C. The polymerization of remaining monomer is greatly accelerated by the rise in temperature; at the same time, passage of N_2 gas, countercurrent through the column, strips out practically all unreacted styrene in the hottest zone (180–200° C.). The product, which is thermoplastic and therefore fluid at this temperature, leaves the column, cools to the point of solidifying, then passes through an extruder and granulator that breaks up the polymers into fine beads.

In this kind of polymerization, it was thought that impurities present in the monomer in some way catalyzed the reaction. But recent studies appear to prove that the process involves altogether a thermal activation of the

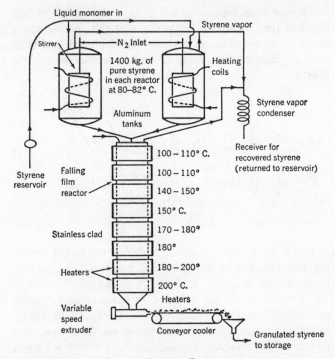

FIGURE 5

Reactor system for bulk polymerization of styrene by heat
(N_2 atmosphere maintained over reactant and product).

monomer double bonds, which then proceed to react by
addition of one to another to form the polymer, thus:

$$n \times \underset{H_5C_6}{\overset{H}{\underset{|}{C}}} = \underset{H}{\overset{H}{\underset{|}{C}}} = \begin{bmatrix} -\underset{C_6H_5}{\overset{H}{\underset{|}{C}}} - \underset{H}{\overset{H}{\underset{|}{C}}} - \underset{C_6H_5}{\overset{H}{\underset{|}{C}}} - \underset{H}{\overset{H}{\underset{|}{C}}} - \underset{C_6H_5}{\overset{H}{\underset{|}{C}}} - \underset{H}{\overset{H}{\underset{|}{C}}} - \underset{C_6H_5}{\overset{H}{\underset{|}{C}}} - \underset{H}{\overset{H}{\underset{|}{C}}} - \end{bmatrix}_n \quad \begin{matrix} A \\ \\ \text{etc.} \end{matrix}$$

(*n* is a large number, approximating 1000 or more)

In the above formulation of structure, the monomer units

are joined in a manner called *head to tail, head to tail,*
etc. But there is also a possibility that this homogeneous
process (all reactants in a single liquid phase) occurs in
random fashion, and some of the molecules are joined
thus:

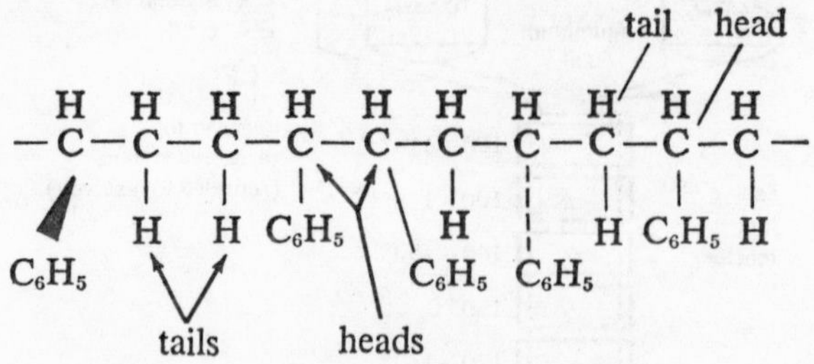

In other words, some head-to-head and tail-to-tail unions
are intermixed with head to tail, head to tail, head to
head, tail to tail, and so forth in a disorderly manner.
The final nature of the polymer, in terms of its hardness,
crystallinity, melting point, and susceptibility to attack
by solvents, is very much dependent on these structural
features. That structure represented by *A* above is known
as a stereo-regular polymer, and it has been found to be
harder, higher-melting, more crystalline, and less susceptible to solvent attack than the disorderly polymer structure represented by *B*. Unfortunately, the simple thermal
polymerization just described tends to produce a significant amount of *B*. More about these "stereo" characteristics of polymers will be described in Section D of
Chapter 8.

   Meanwhile, one problem remains regarding the termination of the chain growth process: how does this chain
lengthening process ever come to a stop when the ends
of the chains appear always to have unsatisfied bonds?
One possibility is simply that two chains meet, pair their
uncombined electrons, and form a longer chain, thus:

$$\begin{array}{cc} H & H \\ R-C\cdot+\cdot CR = R-CH_2-CH_2-R \\ H & H \end{array}$$

Another possibility is that the two reactive ends meet and interact by transfer of hydrogen from one to another, and then separate again.

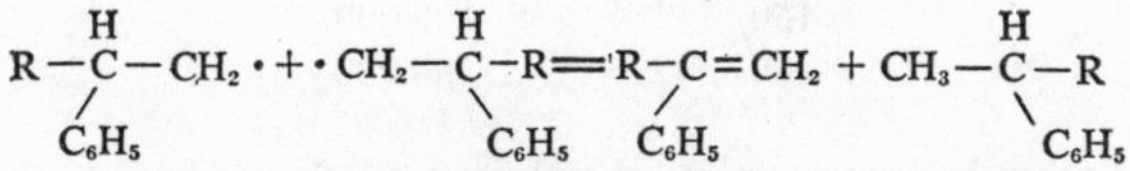

$$\begin{array}{ccc} H & H & H \\ R-C-CH_2\cdot+\cdot CH_2-C-R = R-C=CH_2 + CH_3-C-R \\ C_6H_5 & C_6H_5 \quad C_6H_5 & C_6H_5 \end{array}$$

One terminal bond becomes olefinic, or unsaturated, while the other becomes saturated. It turns out that this second kind of interaction is quite common for many of these olefin polymerizations.

Another prominent feature of olefin polymerizations is the amount of heat produced in the chain extension process. The reaction of styrene polymerization is exothermal to the extent of 17.5 Kcal per mole of styrene. Accordingly, in the reactor vessels shown in the figure, once the reaction rate becomes appreciable, only small amounts of heat need be added to bring the mixture to progressively higher temperatures. The mixture must not be allowed to overheat, and—for that reason—the coils in the reactor tanks are set up for cooling as well as heating.

Styrene polymerization according to the process described here forms a product whose average molecular weight is in the vicinity of 300,000. It is interesting to observe in this thermal polymerization that increasing temperature leads to a higher rate of conversion of monomer to polymer, but that a *fast* conversion produces polymers of *low* molecular weight. The table below shows the effect of temperature on the polymer molecular weight.

Variation of polystyrene molecular weight with increasing temperature:

Temp., °C.	Molecular weight
40	550,000
60	460,000
80	360,000
100	215,000
150	100,000
200	60,000

Mechanical properties of polystyrene depend very much on molecular weight, and structural regularity of the chain. In general, the lower-molecular-weight products will be lower melting, more readily soluble, and have lower tensile strength than the higher-molecular-weight polymers. Accordingly, the choice of temperature ranges for this reaction determines the kind of polymer to be made. Plastics intended for structural purposes should have the superior properties associated with high molecular weight, subject to this limitation—that the thermoplastics (heat-softening materials) can be molded at temperatures not inconveniently high (generally less than 250° C.) and still resist softening or deformation at boiling-water temperature. The commercial polystyrenes, for example, soften in the range 140–230° C. These so-called isotactic stereo-regular polymers are produced by metallic catalysts, to be described in Chapter 8.

3. POLYSTYRENE BY PROCESSES OTHER THAN THERMAL POLYMERIZATION

The thermal polymerization of styrene is one of several means for forming polystyrene. Its mechanism depends on the formation of free radicals, but these can be generated without high temperature, for instance, by the decomposition of peroxides. In addition, styrene can be caused to polymerize by action of proton acids, by Lewis acids, by basic anions, and by alkali metals. Such a diversity of initiators for polymerization may lead one to believe that there is no rational cause for styrene polymerization, and that anything goes. However, in each case it is possible to show that the agent "disturbs" the olefinic double bond, inducing it to react with other double bonds as a result of becoming polarized. These effects are described briefly in the parts that follow.

a. Free radical polymerization

Three effective generators of free radicals that activate styrene polymerization are shown below:

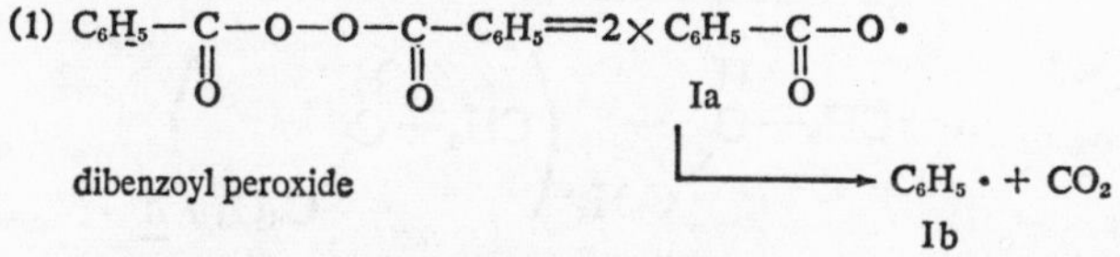

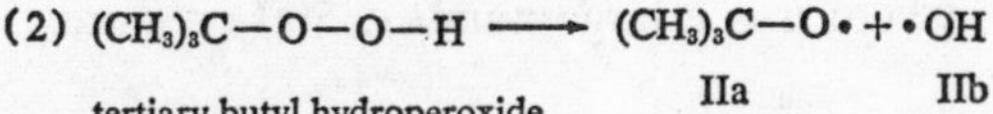

(1) $C_6H_5-\underset{\underset{O}{\|}}{C}-O-O-\underset{\underset{O}{\|}}{C}-C_6H_5 \Longrightarrow 2 \times C_6H_5-\underset{\underset{O}{\|}}{C}-O\cdot$

dibenzoyl peroxide   Ia

$\longrightarrow C_6H_5\cdot + CO_2$
Ib

(2) $(CH_3)_3C-O-O-H \longrightarrow (CH_3)_3C-O\cdot + \cdot OH$

tertiary butyl hydroperoxide   IIa   IIb

(3) $(CH_3)_2\underset{\underset{C\equiv N}{|}}{C}-N=N-\underset{\underset{N\equiv C}{|}}{C}(CH_3)_2 \longrightarrow N_2 + 2 \times (CH_3)\underset{\underset{C\equiv N}{|}}{\overset{\overset{CH_3}{|}}{C}}\cdot$

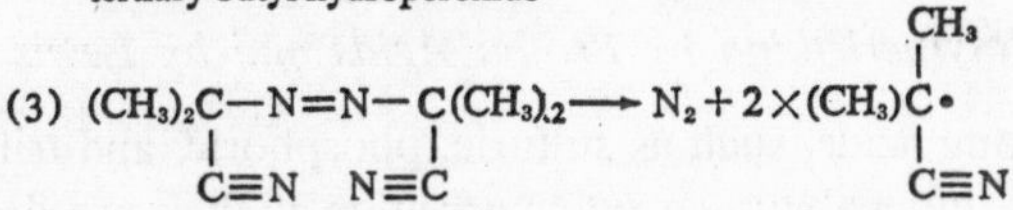

azo bisisobutyronitrile

Reaction (1) forms a primary free radical Ia, which decomposes to another free radical and gaseous carbon dioxide; reaction (2) forms two different kinds of free radicals, while reaction (3) produces two units of a single free radical.

Any one of the three compounds when mixed with styrene directly, or in a solution or emulsion, will induce styrene to polymerize. The process may be generalized in the following manner:

$$R\cdot + H_2C=C\underset{C_6H_5}{\overset{H}{\diagdown}} \longrightarrow R-CH_2-C\underset{C_6H_5}{\overset{H}{\diagdown}}\cdot \quad F_1$$

The free radical ($R\cdot$) attacks a styrene double bond to form a new free radical (F_1), which in turn attacks a second molecule of styrene, forming a new free radical.

$$F_1 + \underset{H}{\overset{H}{C}}=C\underset{C_6H_5}{\overset{H}{\diagdown}} \longrightarrow R-CH_2-C\underset{C_6H_5}{\overset{H}{\diagdown}}-CH_2-C\underset{C_6H_5}{\overset{H}{\diagdown}}\cdot$$

Continuation of the process leads to a high polymer:

$$R-CH_2-C\underset{C_6H_5}{\overset{H}{\diagdown}} - \left(CH_2-C\underset{C_6H_5}{\overset{H}{\diagdown}}\right)_{\underline{n}}$$

where n is a large number, 500 or more.

b. Polymerization by Proton Acids and by Lewis Acids

Strong acids, such as sulfuric, phosphoric, and trifluoro-acetic, induce styrene polymerization if they are first dissolved in appropriate polar solvents. Lewis acids, such as stannic chloride ($SnCl_4$), aluminum chloride, antimony pentachloride, ferric chloride, and boron trifluoride (all strictly anhydrous), are also very effective in these same polymerizations.

A notable feature here is that most of these materials induce polymerization at low temperatures; this situation was found to be particularly true in the case of the isobutylene polymerization that forms "Butyl" rubber. (See

Chapter 9, Section C.) Table VIII indicates the conditions of reaction and the results obtained. The extraordinary velocity of some of these reactions, particularly with aluminum chloride, is noteworthy.

TABLE VIII–STYRENE POLYMERIZATION WITH
PROTON AND LEWIS ACIDS

ACID SYSTEM	TEMPERATURE AND TIME		YIELD	MOLECULAR WEIGHT
	°C.	Hours	%	
H_2SO_4 in methylene chloride	−21	2	97	4,400
H_2SO_4 in liq. SO_2	−78	2	69	85,000
Chlorosulfonic acid in liq. SO_2	0	3	96	10,000
P_2O_5 in liq. SO_2	0	48	97	33,000
$SnCl_4$ in benzene	−5	−	−	7,000–20,000
$SbCl_5$ in nitrobenzene	25	−	−	12,000
$AlCl_3$ in methyl chloride (CH_3Cl)	−100	3−5 min.	98	50,000

c. *Polymerization by Basic Anions, Metal-organic compounds, and Alkali Metals.*

Styrene is polymerized not only by action of strong acids, but also by very strong bases, specifically basic anions; the more basic the ion, the more effective it is in promoting the reaction. Significantly, hydroxyl ions are ineffective and amide ions (NH_2^{-1}) are weakly effective, whereas the benzyl anion ($C_6H_5CH_2^-$) is quite active. Among the most active reagents are the organo-alkali compounds of the type R–Li and R–Na, one of which is amyl sodium, $C_5H_{11}Na$. This substance at low temperature (−20 to −40° C.) yields isotactic or stereo-regular polymers. These results are akin to those obtained by the

Ziegler catalysis of ethylene and propylene polymerization by reagents of the type, triethyl aluminum coupled
with titanium trichloride. The nature of the anion-induced
reaction is shown by the example:

$$B^- + \underset{H}{\overset{H \quad H}{C = C}}_{C_6H_5} \longrightarrow B - CH_2 - \underset{C_6H_5}{\overset{H}{C}} : ^- \qquad (B^- \text{ is a strongly basic anion})$$

$$B - CH_2 - \underset{C_6H_5}{\overset{H}{C}}{}^- + \underset{H}{\overset{H \quad H}{C = C}}_{C_6H_5} \longrightarrow B - CH_2 \underset{C_6H_5}{\overset{H}{C}} - CH_2 - \underset{C_6H_5}{\overset{H}{C}}{}^-$$

and so forth, until a polymer $\quad B - CH_2 CH - CH_2 - \underset{C_6H_5}{\overset{H}{C}}{}^-_{\quad C_6H_5} \quad$ is formed .

The negative ion B^- has a specific affinity for the CH_2
group: hence a strictly "head to tail" polymerization occurs. Furthermore, metal alkyl catalysts permit control of
molecular weight—the more metal compound, the lower
the molecular weight.

The fact that catalytic activity of this type depends on
extraordinary base strength imposes a stern practical limitation of the experimental conditions—anything reactive to
very strong bases must be excluded, such as water, acids,
alcohols, mercaptans, amines, carbon dioxide, alkyl halides, ketones and aldehydes, and, indeed, even acetylene.
Naturally, this requirement is not easy to meet; hence,
there is an inclination to avoid alkali-induced polymerizations, if something simpler can be found.

The alkali metals also induce the polymerization of
monomeric styrene. In 1914, H. Schlenk observed that
addition of metallic sodium to styrene produced colora-
tions, and finally the production of a polymer, which was,
however, of relatively low molecular weight. The same

polymerization can be induced also in liquid ammonia (at $-33°$ C.) by addition of sodium; in this case, it is probably the amide ion (NH_2^-), formed by the Na–NH_3 reaction, that induces the chain growth process. Again, the molecular weight is low, on the order of 5000.

The above examples show the extraordinary inclination of styrene toward formation of polymeric structures. The variety of conditions that will initiate polymerization naturally leads to a variety of final products. Accordingly, polystyrene is poorly defined unless one has additional information on molecular weight, chain branching, and stereo-regularity. Commercial products will vary considerably depending on their mode of formation.

d.   The Change from Thermoplastic Soluble Polymers to Unmeltable, Insoluble Polymers.

Ordinary polystyrene, formed as it is by a *linear* extension of the growing chain, is a material that can be melted at temperatures ranging from 140 to 230° C. Furthermore, this "meltable" polymer will dissolve in a variety of solvents, including benzene, toluene, ethers, cyclohexane, and monomeric styrene. Such solutions are quite viscous; as the solvent evaporates, the solution thickens still more, and finally the "plastic" polymer is recovered.

However, these plastic properties can be drastically altered if one copolymerizes styrene with a trace of divinylbenzene

$$H-C=CH_2$$

$$H-C=CH_2$$

This compound polymerizes in the same fashion as styrene, but—because of its two vinyl groups—it can form a double chain, thus:

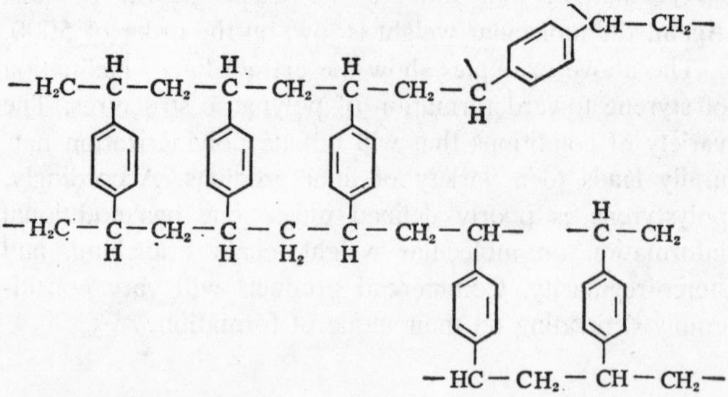

Here one sees that aromatic rings form cross-links between individual chains. As these chains extend in various directions—not only in the linear fashion—the result of the cross-linking is to tie together a great many single chains. This molecular cross-linking can be likened to having a collection of strings in a pile, and then knotting each of them to another, one or more times. It is apparent then that to disentangle any one string from the pile becomes impossible. Cross-linked polymers of this type likewise cannot be disentangled from each other, for they are indeed a single gigantic molecule with unique properties. These properties include *infusibility*—the structure is unmeltable below its thermal cracking point; and *insolubility* —no solvent will dissolve such a molecule. At best, a solvent may cause some swelling* of the polymer by entering into the spaces between the individual strings, but no real solution of separate particles occurs.

---

* The swelling sometimes forms a gelatinous mass; hence the process is referred to as "gelation," particularly if it involves particles originally in solution becoming insoluble by the cross-linking reaction.

It is interesting to see that a very small amount of cross-linking of ordinary styrene chains by divinylbenzene is sufficient to cause a pronounced change in thermal behavior and solubility of polystyrene. As little as .1 per cent divinylbenzene in the styrene produces a cross-linked copolymer that resists melting and is almost impervious to the action of the ordinary solvents that dissolve polystyrene easily. The material is now *non-thermoplastic—* whatever shape it has, it keeps.

There are useful practical consequences to this cross-linking. If one polymerizes styrene *in bulk* with .5 per cent to 1 per cent of divinylbenzene, the solid tough polymer that forms is forever set in its shape and size. Here now is a material of great durability that is well constituted to resist the ravages of time and decay. In fact, divinylbenzene, which produces this notable change in styrene, can do the same for a great many other olefin polymers, transforming ordinarily meltable and soluble products into new ones that cannot be melted or dissolved by any ordinary solvents. There is a price to pay, of course, in dealing with such materials—whatever shape they have they will keep, and therefore one must *preform* them exactly to one's needs. *Thermoplastic* materials, on the other hand, can be reformed repeatedly until the desired shape is achieved. However, they lack the durability of the other type.

e. Foamed Plastics

Any account of polystyrene would be incomplete without speaking of "foamed plastics," of which polystyrene was one of the first successful examples. During the late forties the Dow Chemical Company produced insulating board of very light weight for home and building use. The material was gas-expanded polystyrene of a density about half that of cork. It was immediately recognized as a superior material for building insulation and, despite a cost higher than that for conventional materials, its use increased steadily. Recently, foamed polystyrene—known commercially as "Styrofoam"—has appeared everywhere in the form of pails, buckets, boxes, etc., with walls about one inch thick that are intended as coolers for beverages and other materials to be preserved at low temperature. One might imagine that the Styrofoam has been blown up with air bubbles: this is possible, but is rarely the case. It is more common to generate carbon dioxide (CO_2) *inside* the softened polymer mass. The result is a material uniformly expanded by millions of tiny gas bubbles. One technique of foaming styrene is the following:

Preformed polystyrene is dissolved in about twice its weight of styrene monomer, and dibenzoyl peroxide is added as the initiator. At room temperature a slow polymerization occurs, with the peroxide meanwhile liberating CO_2 as shown in reaction Ia on p. 121. Later the polymerization is finished off by raising the temperature to about 100° C., whereupon the CO_2 expands greatly and foams out the plastic.

A considerable variety of CO_2-generating materials can be used with the same ultimate result, namely, that a thermoplastic material at elevated temperature is foamed out by expansion of internally generated carbon dioxide—much as bakers have done for a thousand years in producing cakes and bread that "rise" because of the yeast-generated carbon dioxide gas inside.

SUMMARY

In styrene and its companion, divinylbenzene, chemists have found building blocks to produce an extraordinary array of intriguing and useful structural materials. Styrene can be made to polymerize under a variety of conditions, and the molecular size and arrangement can be varied to suit almost any need. The normal styrene polymer can also be modified in the direction of cross-linking so that what was at first thermoplastic and soluble in common solvents can be converted to a non-fusible material with great resistance to attack by all solvents. The result is that polystyrene in its various forms, including foamed polystyrene, is a material of enormous practical importance in the world today. The success of polystyrene depends equally on the fact that monomeric styrene can be produced ever more cheaply from benzene and ethylene—materials now available in abundance from petroleum.

D. POLYETHYLENE—SUCCESS STORY OF A CHEMICAL SQUEEZE PLAY

Some readers will find it hard to believe that there was a time when every bottle was a *glass* bottle—rigid and hard, as a bottle was supposed to be. One might squeeze it, but there it stood, solid and unyielding.

All of that has been changed. Squeeze a modern plastic bottle, and out pours an amazing variety of things—mustard, ketchup, soaps or shampoos, lotions, perfumes, or deodorants. How did this come about? From some improved form of glass?

The answer depended on the formation of giant molecules that are essentially great chains of carbon atoms, each carbon bearing two hydrogen atoms and in turn being linked to two other carbon atoms:

Here x and y are large numbers, 1000 or more. In order to form these very long molecules, it was necessary to begin with short molecules having a special kind of chemical reactivity—the reactivity that would string together a succession of carbon atoms end to end in order to form the long chain. This might seem like stringing beads on a long thread in order finally to form a necklace with hundreds of beads in place. But on the molecular scale, this is easier said than done. Chemists had tried on many occasions to build long carbon chains but failed to go beyond fifty or sixty carbon atoms in length. The products were ordinary soft waxes, easily dissolved by a variety of solvents like benzene, ether, gasoline and the like, and lacking the structural strength needed in a good building material.

Finally, on a small scale, from the laboratories of Imperial Chemical Industries, London, England, came the answer to the mystery of long chain building. The starting material was ethylene gas $(H_2C = CH_2)$; the time was the late thirties, and European nations were on the brink of war. None could foretell then that here was a triumph of synthetic chemistry that would soon excite world attention, and lead to production of the first plastic material in the billion-pound-per-year class.* Why?

Too many struggles with ethylene polymerization had produced only disappointments and greasy products that fell far short of the high hopes of the investigators. To make ethylene polymerize at all, chemists had already gone to pressures that seemed at the limit of commercial practicability for the period, namely to about 3000 pounds per square inch (psi), or 200 atmospheres. Still, nothing of value had appeared. (For comparison, one should be

* Billion-pound-per-year production of polyethylene was achieved in 1959, and the rate of increase in production is still high.

aware that "super pressure" steam boilers were operating at pressures of only 1200–1300 psi.)

Then came the English workers Fawcett, Gibson, and Perrine,* putting on the squeeze at a pressure of 35,000 psi (2400 atmospheres!) at temperatures of 140–250° C. These almost insufferable conditions finally turned the trick and produced from ethylene gas a waxy high-melting material that was virtually insoluble in all common solvents at room temperatures.

How could such an extraordinary process ever succeed on a large commercial scale when the machinery for handling these great pressures outside the laboratory simply did not exist?

Two answers were forthcoming to this hard question:

1. The special virtues of the new product as a superior electric insulator and its applicability in the war efforts of Britain and America led to the perfection of the needed high-pressure machinery during World War II to meet military needs; after the war the process was further extended to large-scale civilian use. Nevertheless, about ten years' time was required for this development.

2. The extraordinary high pressure was ultimately found to be unnecessary when catalysts were developed to induce the polymerization at very moderate pressure. This second achievement was no less revolutionary than the first, and it contributed greatly to the production of polyethylene on a fantastic scale hitherto undreamed of— two billion pounds per year by 1965.

Let us take up the events, however, in their historical order, considering that the high-pressure process was in

* U. S. Patent No. 2,153,553 was granted to E. W. Fawcett, R. D. Gibson, and M. W. Perrine on April 11, 1939. They and other colleagues had already acquired British and French patents on their high-pressure processes for ethylene polymerization.

use for more than ten years, and that polyethylene from this process was able to assert itself as a leading commercial polymer before the low-pressure operation was established.

High-Pressure Polyethylene

The conditions required to induce ethylene to form very long polymer molecules involved extraordinarily high pressures, along with elevated temperature. In addition it was found that the ethylene had to be of very high purity, and a small amount of oxygen or peroxide had to be present to catalyze the reaction. (A trace of oxygen was good—too much stopped the reaction altogether!) Once started, the polymerization was exothermic,* double bonds being used up, and the heat produced had to be removed at a proper rate to prevent the process from going out of control. Small variations in the reaction conditions had a way of producing a low-value wax instead of the desired resin. The know-how for this vital process control was developed by the chemists and engineers of Imperial Chemical Industries and was an essential part of the information supplied by Imperial to its licensees.†

As production became more widespread, investigators discovered that properties of the polymer were varying

---

* The heat of reaction was 800 calories per gram of ethylene reacting, or 24.4 Kcal per mole.

† The first of these was du Pont, which used the Imperial process in a new plant which began wartime production of polyethylene in 1943. Union Carbide, although developing a process of their own, also used the Imperial process in a plant that went into production in the spring of 1943. Du Pont, through the pioneering efforts of Dr. Martin Brubaker, made a real advance by developing a technique for the polymerization of ethylene in an aqueous emulsion. This permitted better control of the heat evolution attending the reaction.

somewhat from one process to another. Hardness, or crystallinity, density, melting point, and tensile strength were the centers of concern. Downward variations in these properties meant that the product would not meet commercial specifications for structural strength and stability at elevated temperature. The cause of this trouble was mysterious and elusive. The first explanation—a logical one—suggested that variation in molecular weight was responsible. This explanation, however, did not hold true—polymers (from different batches) that had much the same molecular weights did not have the same properties. (Molecular weights of these polymers were in the range of 200,000 to 500,000.)

How else could one explain the dilemma?

The answer lay in the mechanism of the polymerization reaction and, in particular, the role of free radicals in it. At a temperature high enough to energize the process, a peroxide decomposes to form a free radical $R - O$, which attacks ethylene,

$$\begin{array}{c} H H \\ \diagdown \diagup \\ C = C \\ \diagup \diagdown \\ H H \end{array}$$

$$\text{to form } ROC - C \cdot \text{ I.} \\ \begin{array}{cc} H & H \\ & \\ H & H \end{array}$$

This second free radical collides with another ethylene molecule, reacts and forms

$$\begin{array}{cccc} H & H & H & H \\ ROC - C - C - C \cdot \\ H & H & H & H \end{array}$$

The latter reacts again with more ethylene to form a longer chain that still has an unpaired electron, and the final result is formation of a very long structure:

$$RO \left(\begin{matrix} H & H \\ -C-C \\ H & H \end{matrix} \right)_n \begin{matrix} H & H \\ -C-C\cdot \\ H & H \end{matrix} \quad \text{II,}$$

where n is 1000 or more.

How does the chain stop growing?

Obviously, one answer is that two similar chains, each with unpaired electrons, may collide and unite to form

$$RO \left(\begin{matrix} H & H \\ C-C \\ H & H \end{matrix} \right)_n \begin{matrix} H & H & H & H \\ -C-C-C-C- \\ H & H & H & H \end{matrix} \left(\begin{matrix} H & H \\ C-C \\ H & H \end{matrix} \right)_k OR, \quad \text{III.}$$

This fairly simple polymerization mechanism therefore predicts the formation of very long *linear* (unbranched) molecules. The physics of such bodies predicts that they should have high melting points (certainly well above the boiling point of water), have high tensile strengths, and be quite hard—certainly harder than ordinary paraffin waxes. In other words, they should be thoroughly "crystalline" in character. Paul Flory, then of the Standard Oil Company of New Jersey, reasoned that if *large* polyethylene molecules failed to have the desired properties, they simply could not have a *linear* structure, that is, they must have *branches*, as shown:

$$RO - \begin{matrix} H & H & H & H & H & H \\ C-C-C-C-C-C- \\ H & H & | & H & H & | \end{matrix} \left(\begin{matrix} H & H \\ C-C \\ H & H \end{matrix} \right)_n \quad \text{IV}$$

$$\begin{matrix} HCH & & HC-CH_3 \\ | \quad H & & H \\ HC-C-CH_3 \\ H \quad H \end{matrix}$$

These branches interfered with crystallization of the large molecules, and therefore lowered the melting points, hardness, and tensile strength.

His prediction has been abundantly confirmed by careful infrared and X-ray study of the ethylene polymers—some of them, indeed, have considerable branching. The following mechanisms have been advanced to explain branching:

1. The long free radical, II, coils back upon itself and "bites itself in the back":

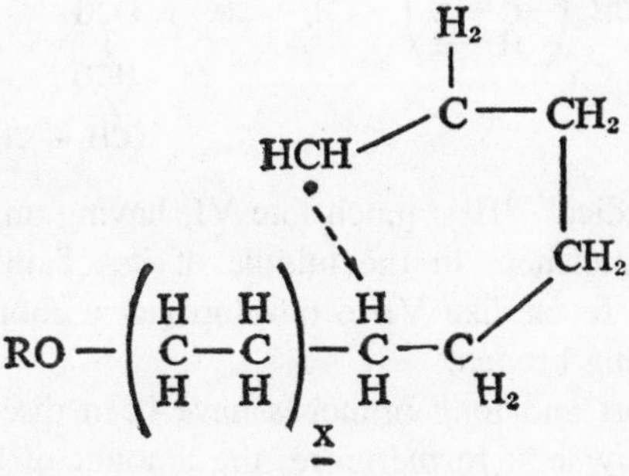

An H atom is pulled away from an already satisfied carbon atom, and a new free radical is formed:

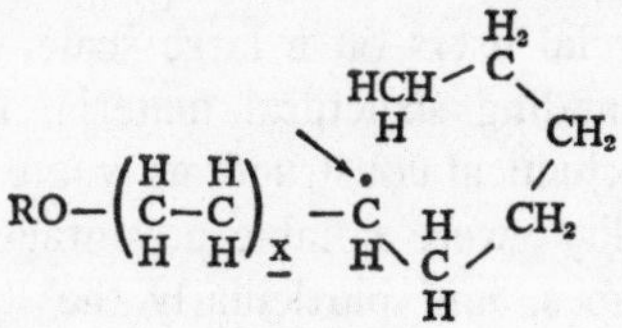

The unpaired electron (indicated by arrow) is then free to react with whatever comes along, e.g. (a) a short radical like I, which will then form a short branch, or (b) a long radical like II, which will then form a long branch.

2. The long free radical II collides with a long *molecule* of polymer (a "dead" one that is not growing any more) and performs a similar pulling away of an H atom:

$$ROCH_2-CH_2 \left(\begin{matrix} H & H \\ C-C \\ H & H \end{matrix} \right)_{\underline{n}} -C-C \cdot + HCH \begin{matrix} R \\ | \\ HCH \\ / \\ (CH_2-CH_2)_{\underline{n}} -R \end{matrix}$$

II

will produce a "satisfied" molecule:

$$ROCH_2-CH_2 \left(\begin{matrix} H & H \\ -C-C- \\ H & H \end{matrix} \right) -CH_2-CH_3 + \begin{matrix} R \\ | \\ \cdot CH \\ | \\ HCH \\ / \\ (CH_2-CH_2)_n -R \end{matrix}$$

The new radical VII is much like VI, having an unpaired electron somewhere in the middle of its chain, and accordingly it reacts like VI to develop (a) a short branch, or (b) a long branch.

Both short and long branches have been discovered in ethylene polymers; furthermore, the amount of branching is influenced by temperature and time.

In summary, the high-pressure (25,000–35,000 lb/in^2) process for ethylene polymerization succeeded in producing very large molecules and a plastic material that attracted commercial users on a large scale. Polyethylene became an outstanding structural material for all kinds of lightweight mechanical constructions where its flexibility and "unbreakability" were notable advantages. Bottles of all sizes and shapes, and particularly the "squeeze bottle" for lotions and sprays, came into general use. The low price of the ethylene monomer permitted a difficult process to become a commercial reality because the final product was still salable at a reasonable price.

What shortcomings are there in high-pressure polyethylene? *One:* its structure is not ideal, that is, the hoped-for long molecules were not attained, because of a side reaction that produced considerable chain branching. *Two:* the extreme high pressures required to effect the polymerization are a constant hazard. The reactors, known as "cannons" among the workers, were far from the kind of machinery that is desirable in modern mass production. A Union Carbide engineer connected with the early commercial operations wryly remarked that "equipment failures and explosions due to high pressures produced a ton of scrap metal for every ton of polyethylene we turned out!"

Clearly, some improvements were in the works if inventors were still alive to the challenge. The answer came from Germany in a remarkable reaction discovered by Professor Karl Ziegler.

Low-Pressure Polyethylene

During World War II and the late forties, many unusual metal hydrides (metal-hydrogen compounds) were either made for the first time or produced in commercial quantities unknown before. One of these was the extremely reactive material, lithium aluminum hydride ($LiAlH_4$),* a substance that reacts explosively with water. In 1949 Professor Karl Ziegler† discovered that $LiAlH_4$ and also aluminum hydride (AlH_3) react readily with ethylene gas, as follows:

$$LiAlH_4 + 4C_2H_4 = LiAl(C_2H_5)_4 \qquad I$$
$$AlH_3 + 3C_2H_4 = Al(C_2H_5)_3 \qquad II$$

* The preparation of $LiAlH_4$ was announced for the first time by the American scientists Finholt, Bond, and Schlesinger in 1947.

† The outstanding work of Dr. Ziegler in high polymers, as well as in numerous other aspects of synthetic chemistry, was recognized by award to him of the Nobel prize in chemistry in 1963, the award being shared with Giulio Natta, whose name is also famous in polymer chemistry.

Compound II, triethyl aluminum, was known from the thirties, but this was a new synthesis for it.* By increasing the pressure of ethylene on these hydrides (or on triethyl aluminum), Ziegler made the strange discovery that *more* ethylene was being absorbed than could be accounted for by the formation of the ethyl compounds I and II.

Where was the ethylene going? What now was being formed?

His further research showed that ethylene molecules were *adding* to the ethyl groups to make longer carbon chains, as shown below:

$$Al(C_2H_5)_3 + \underline{x}\ CH_2{=}CH_2 \xrightarrow[100°C]{100\ \text{atmos.}} Al \underset{\diagdown}{\overset{\diagup}{-}} \begin{matrix} (CH_2{-}CH_2)\,\underline{m}\ {-}\,C_2H_5 \\ (CH_2{-}CH_2)\,\underline{n}\ {-}\,C_2H_5 \\ (CH_2{-}CH_2)\,\underline{o}\ {-}\,C_2H_5 \end{matrix}$$

$$\text{III}$$

$(m + n + o = x)$　　　　　　　　　　time, 1 hr. or more

Compound III was somewhat unstable, particularly at higher temperatures; in the presence of the excess ethylene it decomposed to give *long-chain* hydrocarbons and aluminum hydride, or triethyl aluminum:

$$\text{III} + \underline{x}CH_2 = CH_2 \xrightarrow{\text{heat}} AlH_3 + Al(C_2H_5)_3$$
$$+ CH_2 = CH(CH_2 - CH_2)_{\underline{m}-1} - C_2H_5$$
$$\text{IV}$$
$$+ CH_2 = CH(CH_2 - CH_2)_{\underline{n}-1} - C_2H_5$$
$$\text{V}$$

etc.

---

* Triethyl aluminum is no ordinary substance, for it catches fire spontaneously in air, and reacts explosively with water! Compound I is like it. Clearly Ziegler was playing with fire, and he knew it. But he was hunting for bigger game than mere incendiary chemicals, although in wartime these materials had an obvious purpose. His object was the creation of giant molecules by use of novel catalysts, for which purpose the aluminum alkyls were under investigation despite their dangerous character.

Here then was a truly catalytic polymerization of ethylene, with either aluminum hydride or triethyl aluminum doing the work, instead of the enormous pressures required in the earlier high-pressure process. However, the compounds IV and V were not really "high" polymers; they were soft and low-melting and their molecular weights were only in the range of 1000–5000. Clearly, the goal had not yet been achieved and more chemical labor was needed.

Reaction of ethylene with triethyl aluminum at higher temperatures, namely 200° C., gave an unexpected result —the formation of ethylene "dimer," $CH_2=CH-CH_2-CH_3$, in nearly quantitative yield (i.e., most of the ethylene turned into dimer). The dimer, which is 1-butene, is interesting by itself, but seemed to represent only a backward step in the effort to reach high polymers. An accidental contamination of the reacting mixture by a trace of nickel was found to be a factor in this result. Later this butene synthesis from ethylene was perfected by the deliberate introduction of nickel metal, whereupon the process worked very satisfactorily at low temperature (110° C.) and a pressure of only 40 atmospheres.

Now Ziegler began to investigate the effect of various transition metals on the ethylene "growth" reaction, by adding compounds of zirconium, titanium, cobalt, and platinum. The polymerization of ethylene with triethyl aluminum alone, even at several thousand pounds pressure, failed to go beyond products with molecular weights of about 5000. By adding traces of these transition compounds to the polymer recipe, Ziegler observed the profound effect that they exerted in extending the growth reaction, and this led to his process for preparing commercial-plastic-grade polyethylene at low pressures. Ziegler discovered that a catalyst composed of an aluminum alkyl and small amounts of transition metal salt, for instance titanium tetrachloride, was capable of polymerizing ethylene at low pressure and at 50 to 100° C. to a substance of very high molecular weight:

$$x(CH_2 = CH_2) \xrightarrow[\text{1\% (AlR}_3 + TiCl_4)]{} (- CH_2 - CH_2)_x$$

where x varies from 1000 to 40,000

For success in this growth reaction, the ethylene must be thoroughly purged of active impurities, particularly *oxygen, sulfur, water,* and *acetylene,* although the presence of inert materials like saturated hydrocarbons and nitrogen does no harm. Accordingly, the reaction could be carried out in an inert hydrocarbon solvent, for example, diesel oil. A wide variety of organometallic compounds, such as aluminum dialkyl chlorides, zinc alkyls, and sodium aluminum alkyls, served as effective catalysts in place of triethyl aluminum. Apparently any of the transition metal salts could be used in place of titanium tetrachloride. Ziegler's work and patents covered the use of salts of zirconium, hafnium, vanadium, tantalum, and chromium. He found, furthermore, that the molecular weight of the product could be varied at will, controlled by the ratio of aluminum alkyl to transition metal salt. This relationship is illustrated in the table below.

Effect of Catalyst Composition on Molecular Weight of Ethylene Polymers

	Molar ratio $AlR_3/TiCl_4$	4 hr. yield, grams	Average molecular weight
A	12	440	272,000
	6	430	292,000
	3	460	298,000
	1	440	284,000
	0.63	480	160,000
B	0.53	460	40,000
	0.50	300	21,000
	0.20	10	31,000

Clearly the conditions indicated by A gave both good yields and high-molecular-weight products; those indicated by B were unsatisfactory. We can see also that TiCl$_4$ alone would be no catalyst at all for the polymerization.

A detailed description of one of the operations (1955) reported that highly purified titanium tetrachloride was added to a thoroughly anhydrous solution of diethyl aluminum chloride in xylene or diesel oil, whereupon a brown precipitate was produced.*

Ethylene was bubbled into the mixture for thirty minutes and the polymer precipitated from the solution as a white powder, which was easily removed by filtration. Molecular weights of some of the products were as high as 3,000,000.

This process, exceedingly simple in many respects, represented the end of a long arduous journey that had begun twenty years earlier. Furthermore, the catalyst system, which came to be known as "Ziegler catalyst," was effective in forming high polymers of regular structure from many other olefins, including particularly propylene and styrene, of which we will hear more later.

The new polyethylene, called "low-pressure polyethylene" for obvious reasons, was a material of *higher density* than the earlier "high-pressure" polyethylene.† It was also higher melting, harder, and more crystalline. The fundamental reason for this change in properties is that low-pressure Ziegler polyethylene is almost completely linear,

* One of the most complex features of the titanium catalyst system is the nature of the titanium compound that follows the introduction of the TiCl$_4$. A titanium trichloride is produced, which may exist in at least four different forms, designated alpha, beta, gamma, and delta; their colors vary from violet to brown. Furthermore, they are not alike in their catalytic action.

† High-pressure polyethylene has a density of 0.92, whereas Ziegler polyethylene shows a density of 0.95. A still higher density product is that from the Phillips Petroleum Company process ("Marlex"), which has a density of 0.96.

and lacks the crystal-inhibiting effect of the numerous "branches" found in the high-pressure product.

The English chemist R. Robinson has formulated the polymerization mechanism with triethyl aluminum as follows:

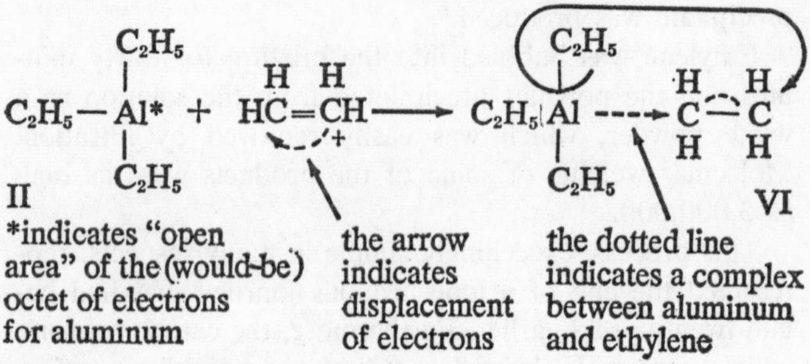

$$
\begin{array}{cccc}
& C_2H_5 & & C_2H_5 \\
& | & H\ \ H & | \qquad\qquad\ \ \cdot H\ \ \ H \\
C_2H_5-Al^* & + & HC=CH & \longrightarrow & C_2H_5\ Al \ ----\ C = C \\
& | & & | \qquad\qquad\qquad\ H\ \ \ H \\
& C_2H_5 & & C_2H_5 \\
\mathrm{II} & & & \qquad\qquad\qquad\qquad \mathrm{VI}
\end{array}
$$

*indicates "open area" of the (would-be) octet of electrons for aluminum	the arrow indicates displacement of electrons	the dotted line indicates a complex between aluminum and ethylene

$$
\begin{array}{c}
\qquad\qquad H\ \ H\ \ H \\
= C_2H_5\ Al^*-C-C-C-CH_3 \\
\qquad\qquad | \ \ \ H\ \ H\ \ H \\
\qquad\quad C_2H_5 \\
\qquad\qquad\qquad\qquad \mathrm{VII}
\end{array}
$$

Repetition of addition of ethylene to VII produces

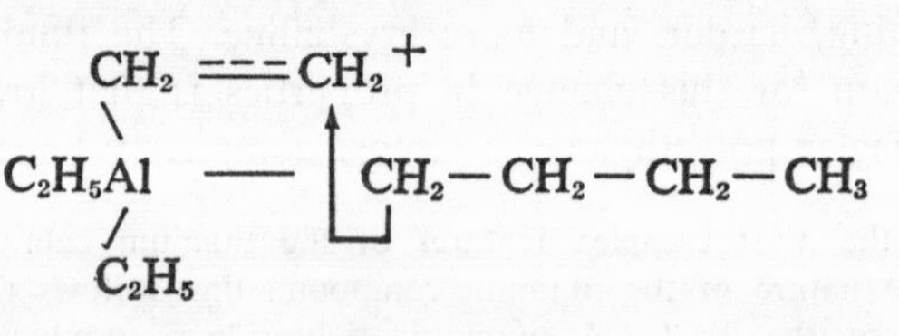

$$
\begin{array}{c}
CH_2 ===CH_2{}^+ \\
\ \backslash \\
C_2H_5Al \ \longrightarrow\ \ CH_2-CH_2-CH_2-CH_3 \qquad \mathrm{VIII} \\
\ / \\
C_2H_5
\end{array}
$$

which then rearranges to

$$
\begin{array}{c}
C_2H_5Al^*-(CH_2)_5CH_3 \qquad \mathrm{IX} \\
\ / \\
C_2H_5
\end{array}
$$

Thus the long branch grows by two carbons at a time, and always in a *linear* manner.

This mechanism explains the formation of compounds like III described before. How then does one avoid the next reaction where III was breaking down too soon to give the low-molecular-weight products IV and V? It is precisely here that the action of the titanium chloride, or similar transition metal, occurs. The mechanism is not known clearly but it appears that the geometry of a new complex between titanium and aluminum permits chain growth to continue, before *displacement* of the long branch by an incoming olefin molecule stops the growth. More of this will appear in the chapter on polypropylene. In any event, the role of the co-catalyst, titanium or otherwise, is a vital one in producing the very large molecules with molecular weights well over 100,000.

Other Processes for Ethylene Polymerization.

The Ziegler developments spurred other investigators to develop additional polymerization processes, especially among the major American oil companies, which had so much ethylene gas at their disposal. Two processes that are commercially successful are those of the Phillips Petroleum Company and Standard Oil of Indiana.

In the Phillips "Marlex" process, a fixed bed of catalyst is set up to operate at temperatures of 130–190° C., the catalyst being chromium oxide on a silica-alumina support. Ethylene under pressure in a xylene solvent flows down through the catalyst bed, the pressure being 500–600 psi.

In the Standard Oil process the catalyst bed is made up of nickel and molybdenum reduced from their oxides by hydrogen, the catalyst again being supported on silica-alumina granules. The ethylene in toluene, xylene, or other hydrocarbon flows through the catalyst bed, the pressure ranging from 1000–8000 psi at temperatures 100–150° C.

In both the Phillips and Standard processes, many operating details are of great importance in determining yield, molecular weight, and character of the polymer product. Most important is the exact nature of the catalysts, particularly manner of formation and particle size.

The Ziegler process, also widely used in the United States, has the advantage of operating at atmospheric pressure, but overall it appears to be slightly more expensive because of the unusual catalysts required.

This description of ethylene polymerization is more detailed than other processes to be discussed in this book. The reasons are: first, the ethylene polymerization appeared on the surface to be a simple straightforward process, but in reality turned out to be a most subtle and difficult undertaking, enlisting the prolonged labors of many distinguished chemists before success was achieved; second, the efforts to achieve ethylene polymerization bore additional fruit very promptly, because a fundamental advance had been scored. The new catalytic process was extended to propylene polymerization with great success in the creation of precisely constructed structures that had unique value, both as plastics and as fibers.

Thus an advance in one area led almost simultaneously to advance in another—a situation that represents the best in scientific progress, for it demonstrates that truth and knowledge are not confined to specifics. A good principle has many applications and it remains only for the ingenious worker to put it into action.

Chapter 8

PETROCHEMICALS FROM PROPYLENE

A. ALLYL CHLORIDE—FORERUNNER OF EPICHLOROHYDRIN AND GLYCEROL

Until the twentieth century the only practical source of glycerol ("glycerin") lay in the ancient practice of soap-making from animal and vegetable fats. Soap was the main objective of the process, but in time glycerol was discovered and isolated from the "sweet water" remaining after the soap was removed. Its isolation in pure form was not simple; nevertheless, this was the only way to get it.

Finally, like hundreds of other complex compounds of biological origin, glycerol too took its place among the growing number of full-fledged "synthetics." In 1939 six Shell Oil chemists* reported a series of chlorination reactions that soon led to synthetic glycerol in great abundance, and formation of a glycerol derivative called "epichlorohydrin." The latter became a key compound in production of the remarkable new series of "epoxy" resins. These men put a new twist in a familiar reaction, the addition of chlorine to olefins. The well-known result was this:

$$
\begin{matrix}
& H & H \\
H_3C - & C = C \\
& & H
\end{matrix}
\quad + \quad Cl_2 \longrightarrow
\begin{matrix}
& H & H \\
H_3C - & C - CH \\
& Cl & Cl
\end{matrix}
$$

propylene, condensed
or dissolved in a <u>solvent</u>   dichloropropane

This chlorine addition in a liquid phase is extremely rapid, even at ordinary temperatures.

* J. Burgin, W. Engs, H. P. Groll, G. Hearne, F. F. Rust, and W. E. Vaughn, Shell Development Company, Emeryville, Calif. They reported their findings in *Industrial and Engineering Chemistry* for October, November, and December 1939.

But the Shell workers discovered a strange deviation from the normal reactivity—in the *gas* phase (no liquid present), chlorine and the olefin failed to react by addition at temperatures as high as 150° C. They went on to report that "the reaction of halogen with olefins containing a double bond in an unbranched chain, as in propylene, is changed from *addition* to *substitution* by operating at elevated temperatures. This substitution occurs in the olefin with formation of allyl-type unsaturated halides. The optimum temperature ranges from 300 to 600° C., depending on the particular olefin and halogen employed." Thus:

$$\underset{\substack{|\\H}}{\overset{\substack{H\\|}}{HC}} - \underset{\substack{|\\H}}{\overset{\substack{H\\|}}{C}} = \underset{}{\overset{\substack{H\\|}}{C}} + Cl_2 = \underset{\substack{|\\H}}{\overset{\substack{H\\|}}{ClC}} - \underset{\substack{|\\H}}{\overset{\substack{H\\|}}{C}} = \underset{}{\overset{\substack{H\\|}}{C}} + HCl$$

allyl chloride
b.p. = 45°C.

Note that the chlorine now has attacked the CH_3 group adjacent to the double bond, and not the double bond itself. Conditions were: *Two* moles of propylene and *one* mole of chlorine premixed at room temperature, then led rapidly through a Pyrex tube reactor at 600° C. The excess of propylene favored complete consumption of chlorine in the reaction zone to prevent access of chlorine to the allyl chloride product. Excess propylene was recovered and recirculated with more chlorine. Yield of allyl chloride based on chlorine consumed was 66 to 67 per cent.* Further modification of reaction conditions led to somewhat higher yields of allyl chloride; also, the technique was worked out for preheating the chlorine and propylene separately, then mixing them in the reactor with a minimum of "flaming" and violence.

* The remainder of the chlorine was accounted for in the fact that some addition of chlorine to the double bond occurred, along with a little polychlorination. Such products were easily separated from the desired allyl chloride because of their higher boiling points.

Here then was the experimental groundwork for an expanded industrial process leading to useful products.

Allyl chloride is a highly reactive material that enters readily into formation of alcohols and halides. Here are some of its reactions:

$$H_2C = \underset{\underset{\displaystyle |}{|}}{\overset{\overset{\displaystyle H}{|}}{C}} - CH_2Cl + \text{aq. NaOH} \longrightarrow H_2C = \underset{\underset{\displaystyle H}{|}}{\overset{\overset{\displaystyle H}{|}}{C}} - \overset{\overset{\displaystyle H}{|}}{\underset{\underset{\displaystyle H}{|}}{C}} - OH$$

allyl alcohol

$$\xrightarrow[\text{(HOCl)}]{Cl_2 + HOH} \quad Cl - \underset{H}{\overset{H}{C}} - \underset{O}{\overset{H}{C}} - \underset{H}{\overset{H}{C}} - Cl$$

glycerol dichlorohydrin

glycerol dichlorohydrin $\xrightarrow[\text{Ca(OH)}_2]{\text{lime}}$ $H_2C - \overset{H}{\underset{O}{C}} - CH_2 - Cl$

epichlorohydrin

$$\xrightarrow{\text{NaOH}} HOC - \underset{H}{\overset{H}{C}} - COH$$ glycerol
$$\underset{OH}{\overset{H \;\; |\;\; H}{}}$$

$$H_2C = \overset{H}{C} - CH_2OH + HOCl = Cl - \underset{H}{\overset{H}{C}} - \underset{|}{\overset{H}{C}} - COH$$
$$\underset{OH}{}$$

glycerol monochlorohydrin

$$\underset{H \;\; O \;\; H}{HOC - \overset{H}{C} - COH} \xleftarrow{\text{NaOH}}$$

glycerol

by-product

$\xleftarrow{\text{water} + \text{heat}}$

glycidol $= HC - \overset{H}{\underset{O}{C}} - COH$

These numerous transformations are summarized in *Figure 6.*

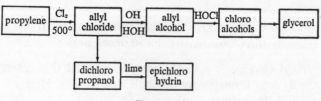

FIGURE 6
Commercial preparation of glycerol.

As the diagram shows, the primary allyl chloride may be converted to glycerol chlorohydrins in two ways. The first involves the hydrolysis to allyl alcohol and subsequent treatment with chlorine and water (HOCl) to give principally glycerol monochlorohydrin. The second method involves the direct addition of HOCl to allyl chloride to give glycerol dichlorohydrins. The chlorohydrins obtained from allyl alcohol may be converted to glycerol in 94 per cent yield by treatment with aqueous sodium carbonate under pressure at 150° C.

The glycerol dichlorohydrins obtained by the direct addition of HOCl to allyl chloride may be converted to epichlorohydrin, which may add a molecule of water to form glycerol monochlorohydrin, which may in turn lose a mole of HCl to form glycidol. Glycerol dichlorohydrin, epichlorohydrin, and glycerol monochlorohydrin may be converted to glycerol in excellent yield by hydrolysis with dilute aqueous sodium hydroxide. Glycidol is converted to glycerol by the addition of water.

COMMERCIAL PRODUCTION

In 1947 Shell Chemical Company began the commercial production of glycerol, based on these laboratory methods. In the mid-fifties the company built extra plants to double their glycerol capacity. Dow Chemical Company also began glycerol production in the fifties by processes similar to those of Shell.

In 1955, Shell Chemical Company announced plans to build a new plant to make glycerol by a different process and suggested that the old plant might be used almost entirely for the production of *epichlorohydrin,* which had found a very large market as an ingredient in the manufacture of epoxy resins.

This new process, according to Shell, involves the addition of hydrogen peroxide to acrolein in the presence of *osmium tetroxide* to give glyceraldehyde, which is subsequently hydrogenated to glycerol.

The acrolein is obtained by the oxidation of propylene, or of allyl alcohol. Hydrogen peroxide came from the liquid-phase oxidation of isopropyl alcohol at temperatures of 90–140° C.

Hydrogen peroxide normally reacts with unsaturated aldehydes to form acids, but in the presence of osmium oxides the reaction can be controlled to give excellent yields of dihydroxy aldehydes. The net result is $CH_2=CH-CHO + OsO_4 + HOH = HOCH_2-CHOH-CHO + OsO_3$. The osmium trioxide is unstable and changes to osmium tetroxide and osmium dioxide:

$$2OsO_3 \rightarrow OsO_4 + OsO_2.$$

Osmium dioxide is oxidized back to the osmium tetroxide with hydrogen peroxide,

$$OsO_2 + 2H_2O_2 \rightarrow OsO_4 + 2H_2O,$$

and the process repeats itself by the continued addition of the peroxide.

Temperatures of 20–50° C., an excess of aldehyde, and a concentration of osmium tetroxide of 0.4–2.0 per cent (based on the acrolein) are preferred. The reaction is complete in twenty minutes to two hours. After filtering out the catalyst, one may isolate the dihydroxy aldehyde by distillation, but if it is to be used as an intermediate, e.g., for conversion to a trihydroxy compound, no separation is necessary. The osmium tetroxide may be left in the reaction mixture and Raney nickel* added as the hydrogenation catalyst. During hydrogenation the osmium tetroxide is reduced to metallic osmium and recovered as such.

The following example illustrates the process of obtaining glycerol from acrolein: To a solution containing about five moles of acrolein per liter of water, at room temperature, was added osmium tetroxide (0.45 per cent by weight of the acrolein) as a 2 per cent water solution. The solution turned black very quickly. An aqueous 34 per cent solution of hydrogen peroxide was added drop by drop with stirring at temperatures of 25–30° C. over a period of two hours at such a rate that the black color of the solution was not destroyed. The total hydrogen peroxide added was equal to 0.88 mole for each mole of acrolein present. The yield of glyceraldehyde was 78 per cent; but in the preparation of glycerol, the aldehyde was not isolated.

The crude glyceraldehyde was hydrogenated to glycerol without isolating it from the reaction mixture. About 3.0 grams of Raney nickel was added per mole of glyceraldehyde present in the reaction product. Hydrogenation was accomplished at about 120° C. under a hydrogen pressure of 1000 psi. The yield of glycerol was 78 per cent based on the starting acrolein.

In a further development of this process a recent patent issued to Shell Chemical Company describes the direct hydroxylation of allyl alcohol to give glycerol. Thus, glycerol may be made by the following steps: (1) Propyl-

* Raney nickel is an activated metallic nickel catalyst developed by Murray Raney for use in hydrogen reactions.

ene is oxidized to acrolein. (2) Acrolein is hydrogenated to allyl alcohol. This may be accomplished in the vapor phase by passing acrolein and isopropyl alcohol vapors at 390–400° C. over a catalyst consisting of four parts magnesium oxide and one part of zinc oxide whereby allyl alcohol is obtained in 80 per cent yield and the alcohol is converted to acetone. (3) The allyl alcohol is hydroxylated to glycerol with hydrogen peroxide in the presence of a suitable catalyst.

PROPERTIES AND USES OF GLYCEROL

Glycerol is a colorless, viscous, hygroscopic liquid that boils at 280° C. with some decomposition. Glycerol has a sweet taste, is nontoxic and finds wide application as a humectant (moistening agent) in foods, confections, cosmetics, pharmaceuticals, etc.

Glycerol reacts with a mixture of nitric and sulfuric acids to form glyceryl trinitrate, which is the principal ingredient in dynamite.

Monoesters or diesters of glycerol and fatty acids react with acid anhydrides such as adipic acid or phthalic anhydride to give polyesters used as alkyd resins, which are prime ingredients in high-grade varnishes. These resins differ from those made from ethylene glycol in that esterification of the three hydroxyl groups of glycerol gives rise to three-dimensional "intertwined" resins that are insoluble and infusible. The melting points of glycol-based alkyd resins may be materially increased by adding small amounts of glycerol to the ethylene glycol before esterification with the dibasic acid.

EPICHLOROHYDRIN

Epichlorohydrin, aside from possible conversion to glycerol, finds its widest application in the formation of the popular epoxy resins, which in turn are used extensively in fiber glass coatings. These materials are discussed in detail in Section C of this chapter.

B. ISOPROPYL BENZENE; AVIATION GASOLINE WITH CHEMICAL VIRTUES

At the onset of World War II it became apparent that air power and the ability to attack an opponent at his home bases would be decisive factors in winning the war. This is easily said, but the problems of carrying heavy loads, including vehicle, men, fuel, and bombs by air across the oceans and deep into a hostile area were among the hardest ever faced by scientists. Everything depended on the great engines as they strained to lift enormous loads off the ground; take-off was (and is!) critical, for at this point the fuel load is greatest. Those engines must not knock! If they do,* power goes down, and the plane likewise.

Special technical requirements dictated that the fuel be low in olefins, and low also in tetraethyl lead—furthermore, that its octane rating be over a hundred, if possible. The higher the better! A certain amount of the newly available gasoline from catalytic cracking was acceptable, but this had to be supplemented by "alkylate" fuel (Chapter 9). Benzene and the alkyl benzenes are notably high in octane rating, but benzene itself is beneficial in gasoline only up to a point. Toluene (methyl benzene) is a good fuel, but in wartime its greatest use lay in the area of explosives as the prime ingredient for TNT (trinitrotoluene).

* One must remember that the engines of the forties were piston engines which, like your automobile engine, depend on a high-octane fuel to avoid "knocking."

For some time organic chemists knew that ethylene and propylene could be combined easily with benzene to produce ethylbenzene,

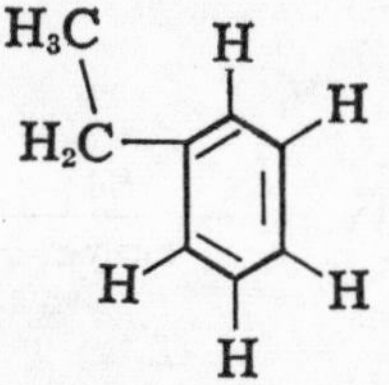

$$H_3C$$
$$H_2C$$

and isopropyl benzene (also called "cumene")

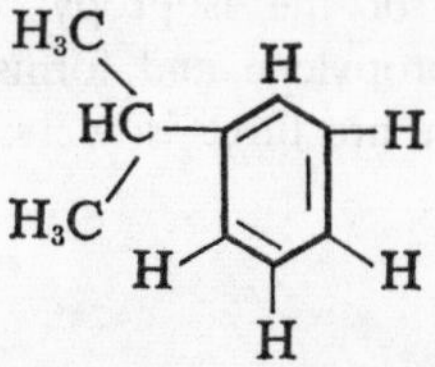

$$H_3C$$
$$HC$$
$$H_3C$$

Both of these are excellent fuels. Large-scale *economic* production of these compounds, however, was still a problem; furthermore, ethylbenzene suddenly assumed importance in a totally different area, that of rubber synthesis via production of styrene (Chapter 7, Section C). Only one choice remained: make isopropyl benzene and put it into aviation fuel. The source of propylene? Catalytic cracking, of course! The benzene was derived mostly from the coking of coal* used in steel mill operations, which were running also at high speed. Accordingly, the petroleum companies rapidly set up huge plants to produce isopropyl benzene in quantity.

The process for the reaction that forms isopropyl benzene is fairly simple. A mixture of benzene and propylene

* Large-scale production of benzene from petroleum was successful at a later date. At present, more benzene is made from petroleum than from coal.

gas under pressure is fed into a reactor that contains an acid catalyst. The catalyst can be sulfuric acid or aluminum chloride, but phosphoric acid on an inert solid is most common.

benzene   propylene   isopropyl benzene,* b.p., 152° C.

A certain amount of the isopropyl benzene inevitably reacts with more propylene and forms di-isopropyl benzene, of which there are three isomers.

b.p., 211° C.
para, or 1, 4-di-isopropyl benzene

(The 1, 2- and 1, 3-di-isopropyls are also formed.)

* It is interesting to see that the product always has the branching structure, and *not* the linear alternate

which some might expect. However, the fundamental chemistry of the acid-catalyzed olefin reaction requires that a *branched*

Because of their higher boiling points these hydrocarbons are easily separated from the isopropyl benzene by distillation. They are a little too high-boiling to be suitable for aviation fuel. Experimental conditions are arranged, of course, to minimize their formation and to produce cumene in maximum yield. Accordingly, the ratio of propylene to benzene in the charge is kept low, in which case unreacted benzene is recovered and recycled into the reactor with fresh propylene. Excess of propylene on the other hand leads to the formation of propylene *polymers,* a situation not wanted here.*

By this deliberate synthesis of a pure hydrocarbon from a refinery gas, the American petroleum industry created a new fuel that helped turn the tide of air war to victory for the Allies.†

In practice it turned out that the propylene used for this *fuel* synthesis did not need to be of top purity; a small amount of lower-boiling ethylene and higher-boiling butylenes did no harm. They in turn led to the formation of some ethylbenzene and butyl benzenes, which were acceptable in the fuel. However, when it came to the synthesis of ethylbenzene for styrene production, this was a different matter—the ethylbenzene formed had to be of top purity.

---

compound should be formed. It turns out that this is a great advantage, as will be seen later.

* Certain propylene polymers, however, have been in great demand for the production of detergents (hard-water soaps). One of these is the so-called tetramer $C_{12}H_{24}$. For its production much the same process can be used, but in this case, propylene alone is used in the charge stock and the benzene is left out.

† "The Allies were washed to victory on a flood tide of high-octane aviation gasoline!" exclaimed a prominent petroleum chemist who participated in these developments.

In the next section we shall see where high-purity isopropyl benzene becomes important.

ISOPROPYL BENZENE BOWS OUT OF FUELS AND INTO PLASTICS

Some of you have probably wondered what happened to all this wonderful high-octane aviation fuel when the air age shifted from pistons to jets. What do the jets burn? Kerosene,* the earliest and simplest of the petroleum fuels! Consequently, after the war when conventional polymer and cracked gasolines, along with alkylate gasolines, became abundantly available for automobile engines at a modest price, demand for isopropyl benzene fell to a low level. However, isopropyl benzene production revived again when it took a new turn by entering directly into petrochemical production of *phenol* and *acetone*. These two are necessary ingredients for preparation of the fascinating epoxy resins that burst upon the plastics scene in the fifties. (See Section C below.)

HOW CAN ISOPROPYL BENZENE BE CONVERTED TO PHENOL AND ACETONE?

It had been known for some time that isopropyl benzene takes up oxygen slowly from the air, but it does so much more quickly if pure oxygen is bubbled into it, at elevated temperature. Investigations of the product showed that it was a *hydroperoxide;* its formation is by the reaction:

---

* The quality of jet fuel is not to be minimized. In addition to the requirement of a very low sulfur content, the kerosene must also have a very low freezing point in order to remain fluid in the frigid upper atmosphere.

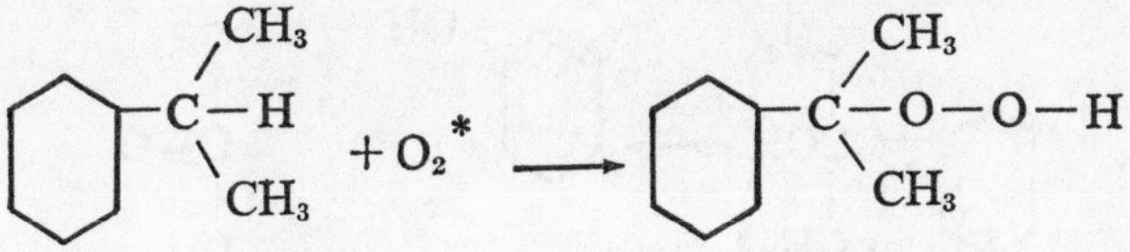

I + heat   II cumene hydroperoxide

As a typical hydroperoxide, this one had definite value in connection with the polymerization of olefins. That is, it functioned as a generator of free radicals that were effective in initiating the polymerization process.

However, in time, the Hercules Powder Company developed a new reaction that first produced cumene hydroperoxide in high yield and then converted it smoothly to phenol and acetone. Sulfuric acid was used as a catalyst. The reaction appeared to follow the course:

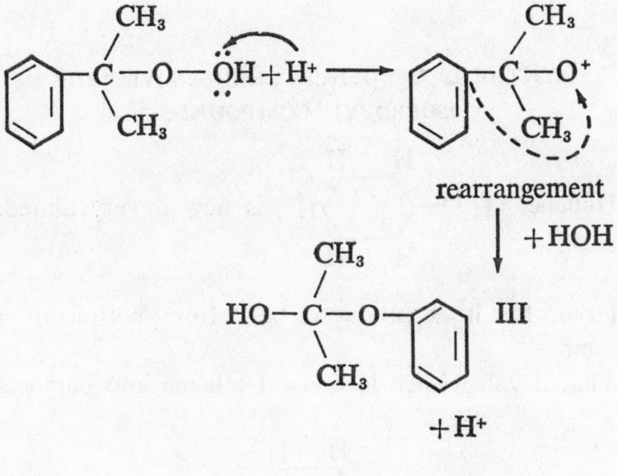

rearrangement

$+ HOH$

III

$+ H^+$

The kind of alcohol-ether represented by III usually falls apart with formation of a phenol, while the three-carbon unit becomes a ketone, thus:

* This reaction is catalyzed by the presence of peroxides, as are many other oxidations.

unstable   phenol   acetone

Acetone is valued by itself as an excellent solvent, as well as a reactant for a great many syntheses; phenol has great uses in medicinals and dyes, as well as in the Bakelite or "phenolic" plastics. Accordingly, this new synthesis, based on cheap, readily available cumene, was a startling development. Before long, great quantities of phenol and acetone were being produced in new plants using this process, and the phenol production equaled that by any other method.

SYNTHESIS OF OTHER PHENOLS VIA THE ISOPROPYL COMPOUNDS

Toluene is now a very abundant

material, for it is produced both from petroleum and coal tar.

What if you wished to convert toluene into paracresol,

a material needed for production of an important antioxidant? If the reaction for formation of phenol is well understood, then you will see that the isopropyl derivative of toluene, namely, para-isopropyltoluene,

$$H_3C-\!\!\!\bigcirc\!\!\!-C\!\!<\!\!\begin{array}{c}CH_3\\H\\CH_3\end{array}\qquad\text{(also called para-cymene),}$$

could be formed from toluene and propylene, then be converted to paracresol by the following process:

$$H_3C-\!\!\!\bigcirc\!\!\!-CH\!\!<\!\!\begin{array}{c}CH_3\\CH_3\end{array}\ \xrightarrow[\text{heat}]{O_2}\ H_3C-\!\!\!\bigcirc\!\!\!-C\!\!<\!\!\begin{array}{c}CH_3\\O\!-\!O\!-\!H\\CH_3\end{array}$$

para-cymene hydroperoxide

paracresol $H_3C-\!\!\!\bigcirc\!\!\!-OH$ $\begin{array}{c}\text{acid}^+\\\text{heat}\end{array}\Big|\begin{array}{l}\text{same result as}\\\text{with cumene}\\\text{hydroperoxide}\end{array}$

acetone $H_3C-\underset{\underset{O}{\|}}{C}-CH_3$

Note again that acetone is a by-product of the process, being derived, of course, from the isopropyl group.

The Hercules Powder Company now produces paracresol by this process, but it obtains the necessary para-cymene from a different source (wood turpentine).

Therefore, we see in propylene gas a convenient lever by which chemists can pry an −OH group into benzene rings, thereby producing *phenolic* compounds. Acetone is always a by-product, but as long as acetone demand continues as high as for the epoxy resins, there is no harm in this. Alkylated phenols are useful in so many ways that their production via the isopropylation reaction is greatly favored.

C. BISPHENOL-A AND THE
EPOXY RESINS

Imagine pouring together in a glass jar two honey-colored liquids; mix them thoroughly, then wait a few minutes. Before long the mixture warms up spontaneously, suddenly becoming too hot to hold in your hands. Soon, what was fluid becomes a transparent solid, extremely hard and durable.

Set the material aside to cool while you do other things, but come back about an hour later for a second look. Another surprise will be in store for you; very probably, the glass vessel will be shattered—not by explosion or expansion, but by contraction of the solid within as it cools. How could this occur?

You will see that the original sticky liquid, as it became solid, fastened itself so firmly to the glass by its great adhesive power that, in cooling, it pulled the glass to pieces inwardly. The result was like the implosion of an evacuated glass bulb.

The transformation that you have witnessed is the final and permanent "setting" of an epoxy resin—another of the miracle plastics built on petroleum. Here you have not only a new structural solid formed by interaction of two liquids, but an adhesive in the bargain that can bond to glass, wood, metal, or other plastics to form a joint of unbelievable strength.

Turn back and repeat your experiment, but this time lay out a sheet of clean metal—steel, aluminum, or brass —and place on top of it a mat of fiber glass. Again mix the honey-colored liquids, one marked "Resin," the other marked "Curing Agent," and paint this over the glass mat, pressing it firmly down on the metal surface. Before long the fluid will harden, encasing the glass fibers and binding everything together on the metal sheet. Now the glass fibers will impart to the plastic additional strength and resistance to cracking, while the metal, of course, is protected forever from rusting or corrosion. Here you have the makings of a metal boat hull coated with glass-reinforced epoxy resin—known commonly by the simple term "fiber glass." Thousands of boat hulls have been manufactured with this superb protection, so that the owner need have no concern for rusting or leakage.

Likewise, these epoxy resins have been compounded with numerous other fibrous materials to produce structural "epoxies" useful for everything from laboratory table tops to automobile fenders. The common fibrous materials used are cotton waste, wood flour, asbestos and the like. These fibers contribute great impact strength to the plastic, and guard against brittleness and cracking as well.

The epoxies have had a meteoric rise during the fifties and sixties. They had a small beginning in a U. S. Patent No. 2,324,483 issued to Pierre Casan in 1943. Casan described the reaction of bisphenol-A in alkaline solution with epichlorohydrin, a compound already described in Section A above. Let us see what is involved in these reactions.

CHEMICAL MAKE-UP OF EPOXY RESINS

The chemical processes revealed by Casan involve formation of a long polymer molecule by interaction of bisphenol-A* with epichlorohydrin:

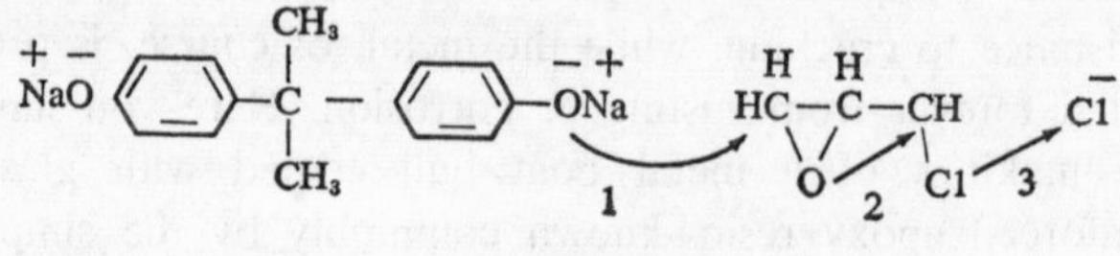

I
bisphenol-A sodium salt
in alkaline water solution

epichlorohydrin, II

$-C-C-$
The $\diagdown\diagup$ group is known as the "epoxy."
$\quad\quad O$

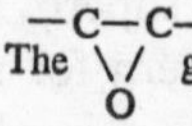

Arrow 1 indicates attack of phenol oxygen on the epoxy.
Arrow 2 indicates that epoxy oxygen attacks the C—Cl bond.
Arrow 3 indicates that a chloride ion leaves the carbon, while a new epoxy ring is formed.

---

* Bisphenol-A is a diphenol derived from acetone and phenol in the presence of a strong acid, as follows:

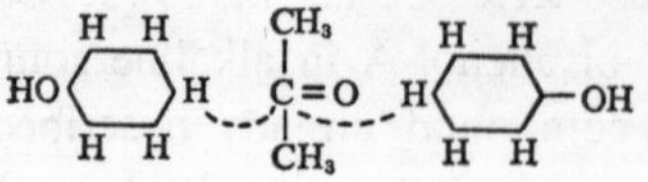

Phenol (a benzene compound with an *OH* group)

$\begin{bmatrix} \text{The dotted lines indicate the} \\ \text{points of reaction.} \end{bmatrix}$

Product is

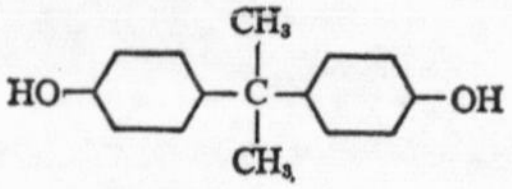

"Bisphenol-A"

The OH groups are slightly acidic and will react with sodium hydroxide.

The reaction occurs on *both* ends of the bisphenol-A, and the result is:

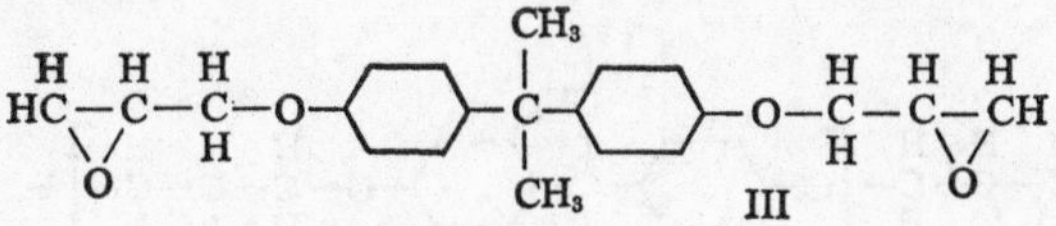

$$
\underset{O}{\overset{H\ H\ H}{HC-C-C}}-O-\!\!\bigcirc\!\!-\underset{CH_3}{\overset{CH_3}{C}}-\!\!\bigcirc\!\!-O-\underset{H}{\overset{H\ H\ H}{C-C-CH}}\underset{O}{}
$$

III

Notice that—after reacting with the −ONa group of the bisphenol-A—the epichlorohydrin regenerated the epoxy ring. As such it is ready to react with more bisphenol-A, thus:

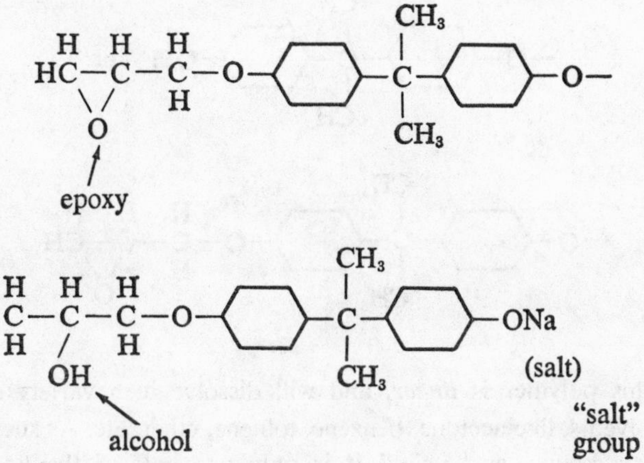

$$
\underset{O}{\overset{H\ H\ H}{HC-C-C}}-O-\!\!\bigcirc\!\!-\underset{CH_3}{\overset{CH_3}{C}}-\!\!\bigcirc\!\!-O-
$$

↑
epoxy

$$
\underset{OH}{\overset{H\ H\ H}{C-C-C}}-O-\!\!\bigcirc\!\!-\underset{CH_3}{\overset{CH_3}{C}}-\!\!\bigcirc\!\!-ONa
$$

alcohol   (salt)

"salt"
group

Note now that an epoxy group remains that can react with more bisphenol-A, while the "salt" group on the other end can react with more epichlorohydrin. The original epichlorohydrin appearing in the middle now contains a free alcohol group, −OH.

After the reaction between bisphenol-A sodium salt and epichlorohydrin has proceeded in the alkaline solution for fifteen to twenty minutes at 80–90° C., a taffylike product begins to precipitate from solution. This polymer material has the general structure

$$HC-\underset{\underset{O}{\diagdown\diagup}}{\overset{H}{\underset{|}{C}}}-\overset{H}{\underset{H}{\underset{|}{C}}}-\overset{H}{\underset{|}{C}}-\Bigg[O-\bigcirc-\overset{CH_3}{\underset{CH_3}{\underset{|}{C}}}-\bigcirc-O-\overset{H}{\underset{H}{\underset{|}{C}}}-\overset{H}{\underset{OH}{\underset{\diagup}{C}}}-\overset{H}{\underset{H}{\underset{|}{C}}}-\Bigg]_{\underline{n}} - \quad IV$$

where n is a number from 3 to 10; to the right of n is the group

$$-O-\bigcirc-\overset{CH_3}{\underset{CH_3}{\underset{|}{C}}}-\bigcirc-O.H \quad or$$

$$-O-\bigcirc-\overset{CH_3}{\underset{CH_3}{\underset{|}{C}}}-\bigcirc-O-\overset{H}{\underset{H}{\underset{|}{C}}}-\overset{H}{\underset{\underset{O}{\diagdown\diagup}}{\underset{|}{C}}}-\overset{H}{CH}$$

This polymer is *linear,* and will dissolve in a variety of solvents, like acetone, benzene, toluene, ether, etc. As such, it is known as "resin." It is only one half of the final "cured" epoxy product described at the beginning. The other half is the "curing agent," which is a compound that will react with IV to cross-link it with other IV molecules and produce a network of interlinked three-dimensional structures of great molecular size. This final great molecule (molecular weight in the hundred thousands) will be insoluble in all common solvents and will be permanently hard, or infusible.

A considerable variety of "cross-linking" or curing agents can be used because the structure IV has in it *two* kinds of reactive groups, the "epoxy"

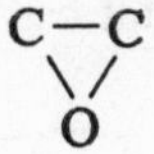

$$C - C$$
$$\diagdown \diagup$$
$$O$$

and the alcohol C—OH groups. Casan in his original work prescribed phthalic anhydride as the curing agent that linked the molecules of type IV via their —OH and epoxy groups (Steps I and II).

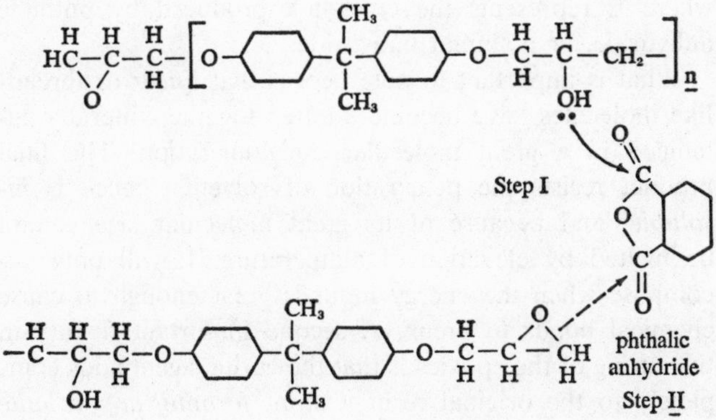

The result is

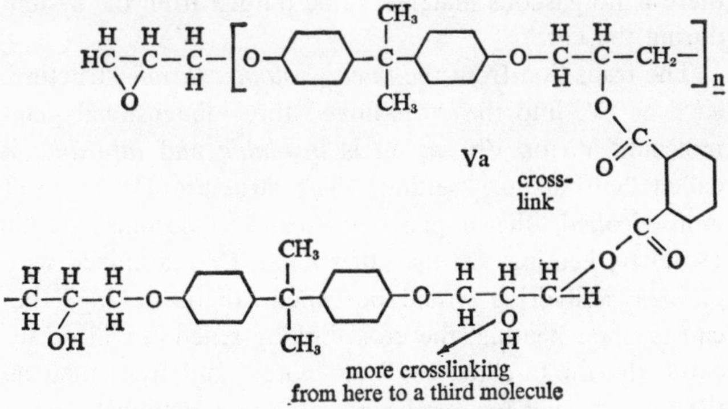

Va

cross-link

more crosslinking
from here to a third molecule

The reaction of cross-linking has now generated a new alcohol group (−OH); this in turn can react with more phthalic anhydride to become linked to a third molecule of IV, and so on. The result can be symbolized as follows,

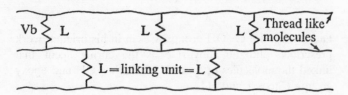

where L represents the cross-link produced by phthalic anhydride, or a similar anhydride.

What is important to note here is that *linear* or thread-like molecules have become knotted together—literally entangled in a great molecular conglomeration. The final product resists the penetration of solvents, hence is *insoluble,* and because of its great molecular size cannot be melted by elevation of temperature. It will only decompose when the energy input is great enough to cause chemical bonds to break. A second important feature in the curing of the epoxies is that the curing agent adds completely to the original resin *without forming any volatile by-products* such as water, alcohol, or ammonia. Thus there is no gaseous material to be purged from the system during the cure.

The transition from the *linear, soluble, fusible* structure, such as IV, into the cross-linked three-dimensional giant molecule Va or Vb, which is *insoluble* and *infusible,* is called "curing" or "setting." The structure IV by itself is also called "thermoplastic," because it becomes plastic (soft) on heating. On the other hand, IV intermixed with phthalic anhydride would be called "thermosetting," because, upon heating, the cross-linking reaction will occur, cause the mixture to "set," or "cure," and from then on the product will forever be infusible and insoluble.

Other curing agents for the epoxy resins are ammonia-like compounds called "amines," which have structures like the following:

$H_2N - CH_2 - CH_2 - NH_2$ and

$$H_2N - \overline{CH_2} - CH_2 - N - CH_2 - CH_2 - \overline{NH_2}$$
$$H$$

(the underlined groups are amino groups)

Note here that these compounds each have *two* amino groups, or more. These amine curing agents can react with epoxy resins in the following way:

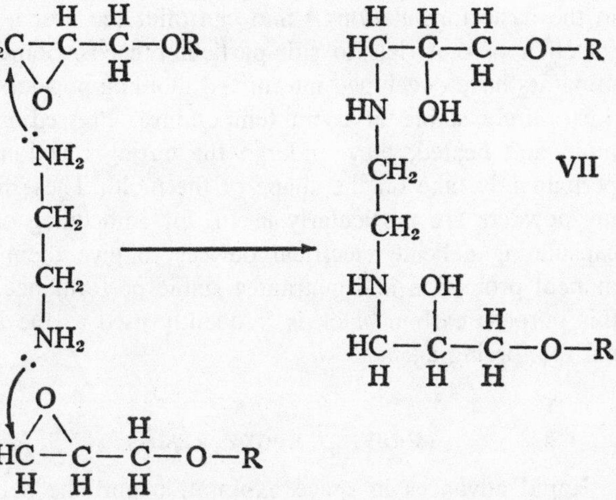

Again, a threadlike molecule VI has been joined to another by the cross-linking, or curing, agent. It should be clear, too, that the amount of cross-linking in the final product will depend on the amount of curing agent used, the temperature of the mixture during cure, and the duration of the process.

The particular choice of cross-linking agent depends on those characteristics that the user desires in his product. For instance, some applications call for a very rapid hard-

ening of the "mix," that is, a fast cure; the aliphatic
amines are good for this purpose. These mixtures heat up
rapidly too. In other cases, one wants a slow cure, i.e., a
long "pot life" so that the fabricator has time to spread
out a coating or work it into desired form. In this case
the anhydrides are more suitable. Perhaps a person wants
no cure at all at low temperature, and wants to induce curing only by heating the product. In general, these behavior characteristics cannot be foretold accurately by
theory—they must be determined by experiment with different mixtures. The commercial producers of these materials have developed and tested a great many variations
in the basic formulations,* and can offer the user a wide
selection of materials to suit particular needs. Some for-
mulators have developed intermixed molding powders that
are entirely stable at room temperature. Pressed into a
mold and heated, they undergo the curing reaction and
permanently take on the shape of the mold. These molding powders are particularly useful for embedding or en-
capsulating delicate electrical devices to give them permanent protection and guarantee stable performance. For
this purpose carbon black is frequently used as the internal reinforcing agent.

MODIFIED EPOXY RESINS

Rapid advances in space exploration and the demand
for materials of extraordinary stability have created a
need for thermosetting plastics with high strength and
resistance to extremes of temperature. Until a few years
ago these needs were satisfied by the Bakelite-type resins
(phenol-formaldehyde polymers) and epoxy resins based
on bisphenol-A. Phenol-formaldehyde polymers have excellent high-temperature stability. However, the reaction

---

* Two of the major producers of epoxy resins in the United
States are Shell Development Company and Dow Chemical Company. Their technical bulletins are readily available upon request.

required to convert the primary fusible Bakelite (commonly called a "novolac") into the infusible high-temperature material requires heat and pressure, and the cross-linking reaction generates by-product water. The latter creates problems of voids in the polymers, shrinkage, and corrosion. The epoxy resins, as we have seen, can be cured without external application of heat, do not require pressure, and generate no by-products that have to be removed before high-temperature usage. However, the epoxies based on bisphenol-A are less thermostable than the Bakelite phenolics.

To solve this problem the Dow Chemical Company introduced, in 1959, an ingenious variation of the epoxy polymer. The Dow chemists saw in bisphenol-A simply a phenol with *two* reactive –OH groups. Now, the novolac resin is likewise a phenol but it has a great many reactive OH groups, thus:

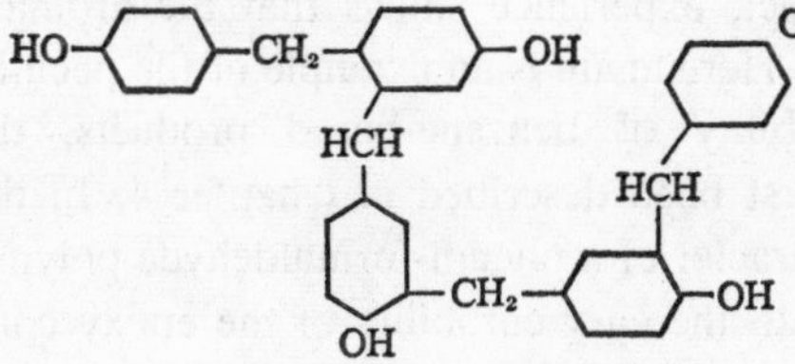

(novolac polymer)

Accordingly, it will react with epichlorohydrin in the same manner as bisphenol-A, and the product (in the presence of alkali) will be:

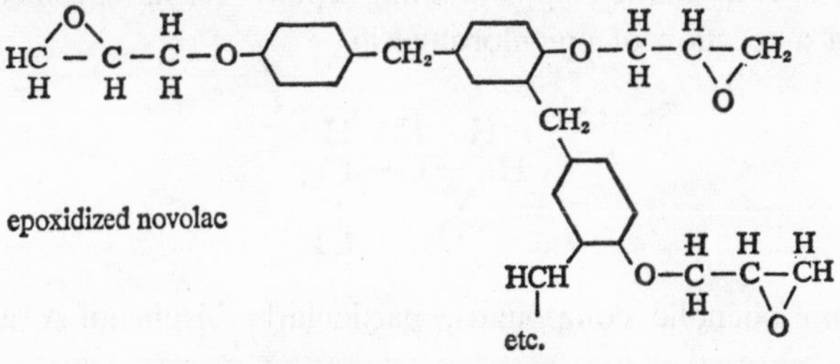

epoxidized novolac

Note that the phenolic −OH groups have been converted
to new units each of which contains the reactive epoxy
structure

$$-\overset{|}{C}-\overset{|}{\underset{\diagdown\diagup}{C}}-$$
$$O$$

This structure is still essentially
threadlike (a thread, however, with side branches), but
it is not cross-linked as is the structure Vb above. Hence
it is soluble and can be softened by heating (fusible). The
one thing remaining to convert it to the insoluble, infusible, tough solid state is to "give it the cure," that is, make
it react with a cross-linking agent through its lively epoxy
groups. This is easy, for the same curing agents used for
the bisphenol-A resins are effective with these novolac
epoxies. To achieve the desired high-temperature stability
in the final product, experience shows that the aromatic
diamines are best. Here again is an example of the peculiar
and unusual stability of benzene-based products, this
stability having first been described in Chapter 4. In this
way, the good character of a phenol-formaldehyde polymer
has been wedded to the easy curability of the epoxy compounds in the creation of a new product of unique value.

SUMMARY

The aromatic-ring-containing epoxy resins are based
on a reaction of epichlorohydrin

$$\overset{H}{HC}-\overset{H}{\underset{\diagdown\diagup}{C}}-\overset{H}{\underset{|}{CH}}$$
$$O \qquad Cl$$

with phenolic compounds, particularly bisphenol-A and

novolacs of the Bakelite series. The primary *linear* polymers still contain reactive epoxy

$$-\overset{|}{C}-\overset{|}{\underset{\diagup\diagdown}{C}}-$$
$$O$$

groups, and will react further with di-functional compounds like acid anhydrides and diamines. The result is an intricately crosslinked giant molecule in which threadlike components have been tied together, thus

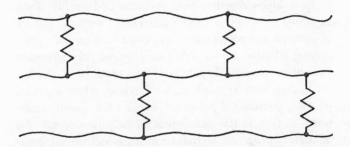

to form a rigid material of high stability. The essential starting materials are the following:

1. *propylene,* which is a source of acetone and epichlorohydrin;
2. *benzene,* which is a source of phenol;
3. bisphenol-A, formed by the phenol and acetone;
4. novolac resin, formed by phenol and formaldehyde.

The variety of combinations of these materials is very large, so that epoxy resins can be tailored to fit almost any need in the way of thermosetting plastics that have great structural durability.

D. POLYPROPYLENE, CHEMICAL COUSIN OF THE POLYETHYLENES—ITS CHARACTER AND PROPERTIES*

The successful polymerization of propylene,

$$\begin{array}{c} H \\ \diagdown \\ \diagup \\ H \end{array} C = C - CH_3 ,\ \begin{array}{c} \\ H \end{array}$$

to form high-strength plastic products and quality fibers as strong as nylon, is closely intertwined with the history of low-pressure polyethylene. Professor Karl Ziegler's great accomplishment in simplifying the ethylene polymerization (use of organometallic catalysts) was matched by Professor Giulio Natta's† work with propylene, which led to a precisely constructed polypropylene in 1954. Shortly afterward—in fact, in the record time of only three years—the laboratory processes of Natta and his principal collaborators, G. Mazzanti, P. Corradini, and G. Dall'Astra, had been put into industrial practice by the Montecatini Company of Italy; the result was a variety of films, fibers, and molded products of great beauty and utility. In 1961, American companies which had acquired licenses for use of the Natta patents were likewise turning out polypropylene products for commercial use in the United States.

---

* A proper understanding of polypropylene is best gained by first reading about polyethylene in Section D of Chapter 7.

† Dr. Giulio Natta, director of the Institute of Industrial Chemistry at the Politecnico di Milano, Italy. Recognized for his contributions by award of the Nobel prize in 1963, which he shared with Dr. Ziegler.

Because propylene, along with ethylene, is one of the most abundant gaseous products derived from petroleum cracking, it is only natural to be highly enthusiastic about its employment as a source of polymers. One might even think offhand that there would be great similarities in the two polyproducts. But here it is necessary to be cautious —certainly in light of the knowledge that ethylene itself may lead to several kinds of polymers, depending on the molecular building process employed. Comparison of polypropylene in its well-ordered crystalline form with high-density linear polyethylene shows certain similarities, but also some sizable differences, as seen in Table IX.

TABLE IX—PROPERTIES OF OLEFIN POLYMERS

	Polypropylene	High-Density Polyethylene
Density, g/ml.	0.901	0.95–.96
Crystalline melting point, °C.	160–167	132–137
Hardness, Rockwell R	95	38–58
Tensile strength, lb/in^2	5000	2500–5000
Molecular weight	100,000	100,000–800,000
Deformation under load; % change at 2000 lb/in^2 at 50° C. for 6 hrs.	2	10–20

Action of ether and hydrocarbon solvents—very slight at room temperature

Polypropylene is less dense than the polyethylenes; in fact, it is the lightest of all commercial plastics. Its melting point is considerably higher, which leads to its use in high-temperature processes where polyethylene is unsuitable. Its tensile strength is generally higher, and its deformation under load much smaller. Like polyethylene, polypropylene is an excellent electrical insulator, and displays even higher ohmic resistance than the former.

Polypropylene has greater stiffness, greater optical clarity, and a higher surface luster than products from polyethylene. Its resistance to swelling or permeation by organic solvents *at room temperature or below* is great, and generally higher than that of polyethylene. Both polymers, however, at elevated temperatures (60° C. or more) suffer on contact with benzene and other aromatics, carbon tetrachloride, carbon disulfide and the like, and ultimately will dissolve.*

Polypropylene, despite its very low content of carbon-carbon double bonds, is more susceptible to deterioration by oxygen and oxidizing agents than is polyethylene. The reason lies in polypropylene's polymer chain construction, which contains so-called "tertiary hydrogen atoms" as a result of the presence of the branching methyl groups shown in the formula:

Polypropylene chain: *indicates tertiary hydrogen

$$-\underset{\underset{CH_3}{|}}{\overset{\overset{H^*}{|}}{C}}-CH_2-\underset{\underset{CH_3}{|}}{\overset{\overset{H^*}{|}}{C}}-CH_2-\underset{\underset{CH_3}{|}}{\overset{\overset{H^*}{|}}{C}}-CH_2-\underset{\underset{CH_3}{|}}{\overset{\overset{H^*}{|}}{C}}-CH_2-$$

monomer units

---

* Recently, plastics fabricators have placed on the market a variety of plastic containers intended for storage of gasoline, fuel oils, solvents and the like. Most of these containers are presumed to be polyethylene because of their low cost. The use of these containers is *very hazardous,* unless there is total assurance that the storage temperatures will be low. Such containers stored in automobile trunks and sheds exposed to direct sunlight will become hot enough to disintegrate due to solvent action, thereby spilling combustible liquids in places where fire may easily break out.

Organic chemists have known for a long time that hydrogen of this type (an H atom connected to carbon which itself is connected to *three* other carbon atoms) is quite different from CH_2 or CH_3 hydrogen, and, in fact, is usually susceptible to oxidation.* Accordingly, polypropylene (in contrast to linear polyethylene, which should have none of these tertiary H atoms) is attacked by oxygen, nitric acid, chlorine, and bromine. The attack is very slight at room temperature, but increasingly destructive as the temperature rises. Oxygen forms "hydroperoxides," having structures like these:

$$-\overset{\displaystyle \underset{\displaystyle CH_3}{|}}{\underset{\displaystyle |}{\overset{\displaystyle |}{C}}}-CH_2-\cdots$$

The C—O—O—H unit breaks down to form free radical groups like CO⋅ and ⋅OH; these in turn attack other parts of the polymer molecule. Increase in oxygen content leads to discoloration, odor, reduced molecular weight, and brittleness. The oxidation is accelerated by exposure to ultraviolet light and summer sunshine (photo-oxidation). Polypropylene therefore must be more thoroughly protected against oxidation than polyethylene. Protection against non-radiant oxidation is accomplished by use of ordinary antioxidants; where outdoor exposure is involved, protection is increased by use of carbon black or other opaque pigments.

* This we have already seen in the case of the oxidation of isopropyl benzene and subsequent formation of phenol and acetone (Section B, this chapter).

PREPARATION OF POLYPROPYLENE BY USE OF
ZIEGLER CATALYSTS

The synthesis of high-molecular-weight polypropylene that at the same time exhibited high crystallinity and high melting point was accomplished by employment of the same catalysts used earlier by Ziegler for polymerization of ethylene, namely triethyl aluminum and titanium tetrachloride.* The latter must be reduced first to titanium trichloride in the proper form and then complexed with the aluminum compound. The polymerization of the propylene gas, as with ethylene, proceeds at moderate pressure of 1–40 atmospheres in the presence of a hydrocarbon diluent in which the catalyst is well *dispersed,* not dissolved. The temperatures likewise are moderate, 20–120° C.

The polymerization process can be carried out batchwise or in continuous fashion, the fluid medium being usually n-heptane with *thorough* exclusion of moisture. The prepared catalyst is added as a slurry, and propylene is fed in at a controlled rate. The desired crystalline polymer is insoluble in the heptane and precipitates upon formation as a finely divided granular solid that envelopes the catalyst particles, hence removing them from the field of reaction. Propylene addition is continued until the slurry becomes very heavy with 30 to 40 per cent suspended solids. Recovery of the polymer from the hydrocarbon slurry involves water washing and acid treatment to remove the catalyst from the polymer.

The purity requirements for the monomer and diluents are strict because of the extraordinary reactivity of the

* Natta was apparently the first to succeed in producing the polymer, but both Ziegler and Natta hold extensive patents on the processes.

catalysts. Oxygen, carbon dioxide, and any other acidic material must be rigorously excluded, and olefins other than propylene must be eliminated because they slow down the reaction rate and interfere with the desired crystallinity of the polymer. Low-molecular-weight saturated hydrocarbons are entirely suitable as solvents and diluents.

Polymer products remaining dissolved in the hydrocarbon solvent are of the amorphous disordered type, and their melting points are much lower than those of the insoluble crystalline products. The exact mode of preparation of the Ziegler-type catalyst and its *state of dispersion* in the solvent system are major factors in determining crystallinity (or lack of it) in the polymer product. For best crystallinity the catalyst must present an oriented surface to the reacting monomer, thus function in a *heterogeneous* system. *Dissolved* catalysts produce disordered polymers that remain in solution in the solvent.

Control over molecular weight is accomplished by temperature variation, the highest molecular weights being obtained at low temperature. A crystalline polypropylene with molecular weight under 20,000 can be obtained by operation at temperatures of 120–220° C., whereas at temperatures of 50–100° C. (all other catalyst and reaction conditions being the same) molecular weight of the product will be 100,000 or more.

POLYPROPYLENE BY USE OF OXIDES (NON-ZIEGLER CATALYSTS)

As with ethylene polymerization, the polymerization of propylene—because of its great practical importance—has been attempted by a variety of catalysts. One object of these attempts has been to avoid difficulties encountered in formulation of the subtle titanium chloride catalysts*

---

* See footnote on the effect of catalyst composition on yield and molecular weights of ethylene polymers, p. 141.

as well as to find substitutes for the alkyl aluminums, which are incendiary chemicals of the first order. Another good reason is the natural human inclination to avoid the compulsions of operating under somebody else's license derived from prior patent rights. Even though one is guaranteed a sure thing, the price is high, and in a competitive free-enterprise system one is tempted to strike out in a new direction for himself.

Two positive results in this direction are found in the processes worked out by Standard Oil Company of Indiana and the Phillips Petroleum Company. Their earlier methods for polymerizing ethylene were likewise effective for propylene. Thus, the Phillips process for "Marlex" polyethylene was successfully extended to propylene. The same catalyst, chromium oxide on silica-alumina powder, was satisfactory. The Standard Oil process involves use of their earlier molybdenum oxide (or metal molybdates) on aluminum oxide of high surface area, with extra activity supplied by promoters such as calcium or sodium hydrides, lithium aluminum hydride, or alkyl aluminums. The nature of the polymers formed was much the same as in the Ziegler-Natta processes.

New developments in these areas of catalyst activity and specificity are almost continuous, and we can be certain that the last word on olefin polymerization has not been written.

STRUCTURE OF POLYPROPYLENE

The molecular structure of polypropylene hinges on an interesting proposition in geometry. Let us view several molecules of propylene as though they were lying *flat* on this page:*

---

* Laying out an olefin molecule on a plane is perfectly valid for the carbon chain, as well as for the H atoms attached to the doubly-linked carbons. *Two* of the H atoms attached to the CH_3 group will lie outside the plane, one above, one below.

$$\underset{\text{tail}}{\overset{H}{\diagdown}}\underset{1}{\overset{}{\underset{}{C}}}=\underset{2}{\overset{}{\underset{}{C}}}\underset{\text{head}}{\overset{CH_3}{\diagup}}\quad\underset{\text{tail}}{\overset{H}{\diagdown}}\underset{1}{\overset{}{\underset{}{C}}}=\underset{2}{\overset{}{\underset{}{C}}}\underset{\text{head}}{\overset{CH_3}{\diagup}}\quad\underset{\text{tail}}{\overset{H}{\diagdown}}\underset{1}{\overset{}{\underset{}{C}}}=\underset{2}{\overset{}{\underset{}{C}}}\underset{\text{head}}{\overset{CH_3}{\diagup}}\quad\underset{\text{tail}}{\overset{H}{\diagdown}}\underset{}{\overset{}{\underset{}{C}}}=\underset{}{\overset{}{\underset{}{C}}}\underset{\text{head}}{\overset{CH_3}{\diagup}}$$

The double-linked carbon atoms *1* and *2* are labeled "tail" and "head," the head carbon being attached to the CH_3 group. The double link between carbon atoms *1* and *2* will necessarily lie in a different plane at right angles to the page.

Assume now that polymerization joins these molecules head to tail, head to tail repeatedly, but bear in mind that the proper angle for carbon atoms linked singly in a long chain will be $109°$. The result will be:

$$\text{Isotactic}$$
$$A$$

with carbons *1* and *2* still lying flat on the page. However, the CH_3 group connected to carbon 2 will be found standing *above* the plane of the paper and the H atom next to it will be *below*. (Remember that the wedge symbol indicates a bond *above* the plane of the paper; and a dotted line, a bond lying *below* the plane.) Likewise the H atoms joined to carbon *1* will lie either above or below the page.

Let us go back to the propylene molecules again and line them up differently for the polymerization, with CH_3 groups alternately up and down.

$$\overset{H}{\diagdown}C=C\overset{CH_3}{\diagup}\qquad\overset{H}{\diagdown}C=C\overset{H}{\diagup}_{CH_3}\qquad\overset{H}{\diagdown}C=C\overset{CH_3}{\diagup}\qquad\overset{H}{\diagdown}C=C\overset{H}{\diagup}_{CH_3}$$

Head-to-tail polymerization now gives what is known as the "syndiotactic" form:

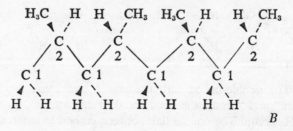

B

Note now that the CH_3 groups alternate *above* and *below* the plane of the paper. This structure, despite its similarity with (*A*), is not, of course, identical to it.

One more mode of polymerization of the propylene molecules is possible. This would be a random distribution of CH_3 and H atoms on the Number 2 carbon atoms of the chain.

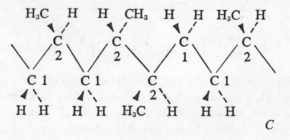

C

This random arrangement leads to a disordered structure, where, in a sense, "anything goes." Natta has named the completely uniform structure (*A*) "isotactic," meaning constant order; (*B*) he calls "syndiotactic," implying an alternation; (*C*), the one that is disordered, is simply called "atactic." Furthermore, these are not figments of the imagination—they are real situations, and Natta has been able to isolate materials like these from his polymerizations of propylene. The well-ordered polymers are crystalline, hard, high-melting, and insoluble in ordinary solvents, in contrast to the disordered "atactic" polymers, which are noncrystalline, rather soft, low-melting, and soluble in ordinary solvents. By careful X-ray analysis, Natta has been able to confirm the identity of these several structures, and thus establish the validity of this molecular geometry.

As we have written formula (A), there is still a flaw in it due to the fact that this formula calls for the CH_3 groups to be only about 2.2 A. units apart.* Natta's X-ray studies showed, on the contrary, that in reality they are much farther apart than this, namely 6.5 A. How can this be?

The answer lies simply in seizing the long carbon chain of formula (A) and twisting the carbons around the long axis. When the twisting is done to such a degree as to form a corkscrew with every fourth methyl group returning to its starting position, then amazingly it will be found (on the atomic scale, of course) that the distance between methyls is 6.5 A.! Furthermore, when such corkscrew, or helix, models are made, one finds that they are able to pack together very closely. Contrariwise, the models corresponding to the disordered (C) molecules cannot be packed together tightly; the methyls interfere with each other in a standoffish manner.

Clearly one can see then that the isotactic structure in its compactness lends itself to crystallinity, which explains also a high melting point, hardness, and resistance to penetration by solvents. The "atactic" molecules corresponding to (C) are "amorphous" or formless; in their disorder they are attacked readily by solvents, and are soft and low-melting. Solvent fractionations are therefore possible to separate isotactic from atactic structures, and this was done successfully by Natta—not only in the case

* One A. (Angstrom) unit is 10^{-8} centimeters, a unit of length commonly applied to light waves and atomic distances. In long carbon-carbon chains, the average distance between the singly linked C atoms is 1.54 A.

of polypropylene but also for other polymers derived from
alpha olefins of the type

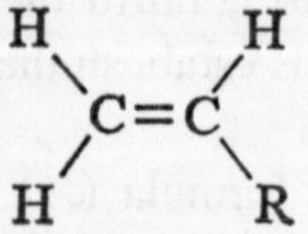

$$H \underset{H}{\overset{}{\diagup}} C = C \underset{R}{\overset{H}{\diagdown}}$$

for instance styrene

$$H \underset{H}{\overset{}{\diagup}} C = C \overset{H}{\underset{\underset{H}{\overset{H}{\bigcirc}}H}{\diagdown}}$$

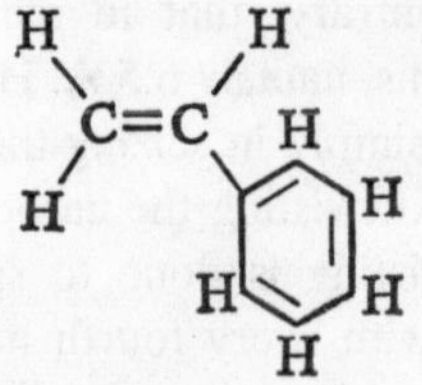

SUMMARY

Polypropylene and other polymers derived from olefins
of the type

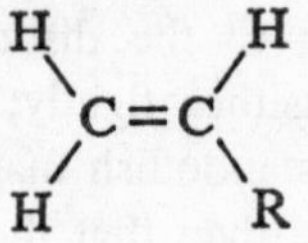

$$H \underset{H}{\overset{}{\diagup}} C = C \underset{R}{\overset{H}{\diagdown}}$$

may exist in three different arrangements* as shown in
Figure 7.

In Figure 7, the carbon backbone lies flat on the plane
represented by the rectangular figures. (In polystyrene, R
is a benzene ring—C_6H_5). The tetrahedral configuration of
C atoms requires that the groups *attached to* the carbon
backbone must be *above* and *below* the plane of the backbone, not in it. Accordingly, stereo variations are possible,
and these variations influence the physical character of the

* The R group may be methyl (CH_3), ethyl (C_2H_5), phenyl
(C_6H_5), chlorine, or any atom grouping *different* from H.

final polymer. One should note too that head-to-tail, head-to-tail linking of the monomer units predominates; this is a characteristic of free radical polymerization, and head-to-head, tail-to-tail is only a remote possibility.

Polymers of the isotactic or syndiotactic type (crystalline high-density polymers) were produced selectively by Natta and his colleagues by stereospecific catalysts, which exerted a special control on the synthesis reaction. This was an altogether new accomplishment in the fabrication of precisely-constructed giant molecules.

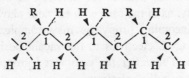

ISOTACTIC

All of the R groups are on one side of the plane. The wedge means group is *above,* dotted line means group is *below* the plane.

SYNDIOTACTIC

R groups *alternate* above and below the plane.

ATACTIC

R groups are above and below the plane in random fashion (no regular order).

FIGURE 7

The arrangements of polymers derived from the olefins.

MECHANISM OF FORMATION OF ISOTACTIC POLYMERS

The process for forming orderly polymers of the (A) type appears to involve a reaction like this:

$$
\begin{array}{c}
R' \\
| \\
C-H \quad \delta^- \\
\diagdown C_* \diagdown \cdots \diagdown CH_2-CH_2R \\
H \diagup | \diagup \quad \delta^{+} Al \\
H \qquad \diagup \diagdown \\
R \quad R
\end{array}
\quad = \quad
\begin{array}{c}
R' \\
\diagdown \\
H \quad C-CH_2-CH_2-R \\
\dagger C \quad H \\
Al \quad H \\
\diagup \diagdown \\
R \quad R
\end{array}
$$

In other words, the C=C unit intrudes between the $\delta+$ and $\delta-$ portions of the organoaluminum compound, thus adding two carbons to the chain. This occurs repeatedly at a fast rate, always in the manner indicated. The result is a uniform head-to-tail union of monomers.

Alternately, as in the case with ethylene shown in Chapter 7, the incoming propylene may complex briefly by donating its C=C electrons to the vacant position around the Al atom. Thereafter the complexed group shifts over to the position indicated above.

However, the above mechanism is obviously oversimplified because it fails to account for the role of titanium trichloride, which is an intimate part of the catalyst. It appears that the titanium-aluminum complex is one that provides an oriented surface on which the growth reaction continues unhindered to form a very large molecule. Without the titanium, the growth terminates too soon.

* The arrow indicates displacement of electrons from the double bond toward the end carbon, making it negatively charged, as indicated by the symbol−δ.

† The bond between Al and CH_2 is one in which the Al bears a slight positive charge; and C, a slight negative charge.

Chapter 9

PETROCHEMICALS FROM THE BUTYLENES AND BUTADIENE

We have seen in Chapter 5 that considerable gas is produced by cracking of liquid petroleum fractions. For the purpose of producing gaseous hydrocarbons, one may rely either on thermal or catalytic cracking.* The composition of the gas that is formed varies, depending on the starting material and the cracking conditions. In general, the following differences are found in the two kinds of cracking:

(a) Catalytic cracking produces gases richer in olefins than thermal cracking. Isobutane is abundant, and methane and ethane are minor products. C_3 and C_4 olefins are high.

(b) Thermal cracking produces gases less rich in olefins than catalytic cracking; methane and ethane are relatively abundant, but isobutane is not. However, in thermal cracking the olefin content of the gases increases notably as the temperature is increased. For instance, in one operation the olefin content of the gas increased from 15 per cent to 50 per cent when the temperature was raised from 450° C. to 510° C., while at the same time the yield of gas itself was doubled. Yield of ethylene is higher than yield of C_4 olefins.

Because of the enormous demand for ethylene products

* For production primarily of high-octane gasoline the great volume of oil that goes through catalytic crackers these days means that a huge supply of gas from this source is constantly available. However, the demand for gaseous olefins is so great that their production outside of gasoline sources is done independently, and much of this is via thermal cracking.

(see Chapter 7), a large amount of ethylene is produced by thermal cracking—so-called steam cracking—outside of catalytic operations. Meanwhile the C_4 hydrocarbons are derived mainly from the cat crackers.

Whatever the source, the gas derived from cracking must first be separated into fractions containing *one, two, three,* and *four* carbon atoms, and this is done by a combination of liquefaction and distillation. The C_4 fraction, about which we are concerned here, is a complex mixture with possibly six compounds present.

Compounds in C_4 Gas Fraction		B.P., °C.
n-butane	$H_3C-CH_2-CH_2-CH_3$	-0.5
isobutane	$H_3C-\overset{\overset{H}{\mid}}{\underset{\underset{CH_3}{\mid}}{C}}-CH_3$	-10
1-butene	$H_2C=\underset{\underset{H}{\mid}}{C}-CH_2-CH_3$	-5
2-butene	$H_3C-\underset{\underset{H}{\mid}}{C}=\underset{\underset{H}{\mid}}{C}-CH_3$	$+2$
isobutene (isobutylene)	$H_2C=C(CH_3)_2$	-6
butadiene	$H_2C=\underset{\underset{H}{\mid}}{C}-\underset{\underset{H}{\mid}}{C}=CH_2$	-3

If butadiene is appreciable and must be removed, special extraction or extractive distillation will separate it from the others. Thereafter the separation processes and chemical treatments will be determined by the ultimate products that are to be made from the C_4 compounds. Presently the most desired end products are evident from transformations shown in *Figure 8.*

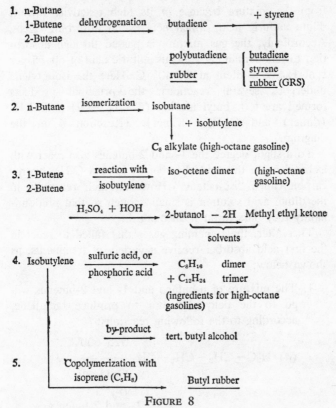

FIGURE 8

Formation of commercial products from the C_4 hydrocarbons.

From the diagram one can see that some of the processes call for a single starting material, e.g. No. 4, which requires isobutylene to which is added isoprene to make Butyl rubber; in other cases, a mixture of starting materials is acceptable, as in No. 1. Obviously then, in the handling of the original C_4 gas mixture, one does not need to separate all components as pure compounds.

The separation processes will not be given here except for the first step. Isobutylene is most readily separated from the mixture because of its high reactivity toward dilute sulfuric acid, which acts as an absorbing agent. Accordingly, the gas mixture is passed through absorption towers containing aqueous sulfuric acid of 60–65 per cent H_2SO_4 content at 30–40° C. Here the isobutylene undergoes several reactions; the principal products formed are tert. butyl alcohol $(CH_3)_3C-OH$ and C_8H_6 (dimer) and $C_{12}H_{24}$ (trimer). (Reaction 4 in the diagram.)

To a slight degree the 1- and 2-butenes also react with isobutylene in the acid absorber to form a C_8H_{16} hydrocarbon called "iso-octene." However, their reactivity in the dilute acid solution is small enough so that predominantly they pass through unchanged.

Thereafter, the remaining gases that failed to react in the first acid absorber receive a variety of treatments, as shown below:

1. The mixture of n-butane and 1- and 2-butenes will go to the dehydrogenator to produce butadiene, according to the following reactions:

$$\text{(a) } H_3C - CH_2 - CH_2 - CH_3 \xrightarrow[\substack{Cr_2O_3 \text{on} \\ Al_2O_3}]{525\text{--}600° C.} \begin{array}{l} \text{1- and 2-butenes} \\ \text{+ some butadiene} \end{array} + H_2$$

$$\text{(b) } \begin{array}{l} \text{1- and 2-butenes} \\ \text{mixed with steam} \end{array} \xrightarrow[\text{very short contact}]{700\text{--}1300° C.}$$

$$\overset{\text{H}}{H_2C} = \overset{}{C} - \overset{\text{H}}{C} = CH_2 \quad \text{(Butadiene)}$$
$$+ H_2$$

Usually the hot product from reaction (a) will be mixed with steam (as a diluent to prevent side reactions) and then passed directly into the second reactor at higher temperature. In reaction (b) contact time with the catalyst must be decreased to avoid excessive carbon deposition; e.g. at 1300° C. contact time is less than 0.1 second. The butadiene (30–50 per cent per pass) is further refined by extractive processes (furfural or cuprous ammonium acetate extraction). The unconverted butenes plus residual butane are separated and recycled to produce additional butadiene.

2. Butane may be reserved for use in the alkylation process, wherein isobutane and isobutylene react together to form so-called "alkylate" fuel. The principal component of the alkylate is the C_8-saturated hydrocarbon 2, 2, 4-trimethyl pentane

$$\begin{array}{ccc} & CH_3 & H \ \ H \\ H_3C - C & - & C - C - CH_3, \\ & CH_3 & H \ \ CH_3 \end{array}$$ which is highly valued as

an engine fuel because of its 100 octane rating. To this end, n-butane must be isomerized by treatment with a strong Lewis acid to form isobutane:

$$H_3C - CH_2 - CH_2 - CH_3 \xrightarrow[\text{acid catalyst}]{\text{isomerization}} H_3C - \overset{\displaystyle H}{\underset{\displaystyle CH_3}{C}} - CH_3$$

n-butane   isobutane

With this introduction to the formation and reactions of C_4 hydrocarbons, we will now examine a few products derived from them.

A. LOW POLYMERS AND ISO-OCTANE FROM THE BUTENES

It has been known for a long time that strong acids induce a variety of reactions in olefins, among which is *addition polymerization*. The latter has already been described in the case of polystyrene in Chapter 7. Isobutylene undergoes addition polymerization readily when treated with strong acid, but—at room temperature and above—the reaction does not go far, that is, only two or three isobutylene molecules manage to combine with each other. At very low temperatures, isobutylene, surprisingly enough, forms high polymers in the presence of strong Lewis acids. In fact, by this means, Butyl rubber is formed, as will be described in Section C below.

A governing feature in the reactions of olefins is the following: When a molecular group like $-CH_3$ (methyl) or $-CH_2-CH_3$ (ethyl) is attached to a doubly-bonded carbon atom as in $H_2C=C-CH_3$ (propene) or in
$$H$$
$H_2C=C-CH_2-CH_3$ (1-butene), there is a displacement of
$$H$$
the double-bond electrons *away* from the attached group.

We picture the effect thus,

$$\overset{1}{H_2C} = \overset{2}{\underset{\underset{-\delta}{\smile}{\overset{|}{\underset{H}{}}}}{C}} - CH_3 \ , \quad \text{and} \quad \overset{1}{H_2C} = \overset{2}{\underset{\underset{-\delta}{\smile}{\overset{|}{\underset{H}{}}}}{C}} - CH_2 - CH_3$$

indicating that electrons are pushed toward the number 1 C atom. Accordingly, it takes on a slight negative charge, indicated by the symbol $-\delta$. This is all that is necessary to set the stage for reaction with a strong acid, which, of course, furnishes a proton, H^+. The proton is electrophilic (electron-loving); when it meets an olefin molecule like one of the above, it seizes upon the displaced electrons and forms a stable covalent bond with them.

$$H^+ + \overset{1}{H_2}\overset{H}{\underset{2}{\underset{\smile}{C}}} = \overset{3}{\underset{}{C}} - CH_3 \longrightarrow \overset{\overset{1}{H}}{\underset{H}{HC}} - \overset{\overset{2}{H}}{\underset{+}{C}} - \overset{3}{CH_3}$$

$$\text{I} \qquad\qquad\qquad\qquad \text{Ia}$$

$$H^+ + \overset{1}{H_2}\overset{H}{\underset{2}{\underset{\smile}{C}}} = \overset{3}{\underset{}{C}} - CH_3 - CH_3 \longrightarrow \overset{\overset{1}{H}}{\underset{H}{HC}} - \overset{\overset{2}{H}}{\underset{+}{C}} - \overset{3}{CH_2} - \overset{4}{CH_3}$$

$$\text{II} \qquad\qquad\qquad\qquad \text{IIa}$$

Because I and II had no overall charge to begin with, their combination with a *plus* particle (H^+) must produce charged bodies Ia and IIa in which the number 2 C atoms carry a + charge. (Obviously the reaction pulls electrons *away* from the second carbon, which by consequence must then manifest a *positive* charge.) Such bodies are called "carbonium" ions, because the electric charge is attached to a C atom.

The attachment of *two* methyl groups to one vinyl group produces a large displacement of electrons, which leads to high reactivity with protons. This is precisely the case with isobutylene, which we now write

$$H_2C = C \begin{array}{c} CH_3 \\ \\ CH_3 \end{array}$$

III

Its reactivity toward acid is greater than propene or the other two butenes, and its polymerization is rapid. The proton reaction

$$H^+ + H_2C = C \begin{array}{c} CH_3 \\ \\ CH_3 \end{array} \longrightarrow H_3C - \overset{+}{\underset{\underset{CH_3}{|}}{C}} - CH_3$$

III   IIIa

generates the tertiary carbonium ion IIIa.

Because of the high reactivity of III this molecule is now attacked by IIIa which, in fact, acts as an electron-seeking agent just like a proton.

$$H_3C - \overset{\overset{\displaystyle CH_3}{|}}{\underset{\underset{\displaystyle CH_3}{|}}{C}}{}^{+} \quad + \quad \overset{H}{HC} = \overset{\overset{\displaystyle CH_3}{\diagup}}{\underset{\diagdown CH_3}{C}} \quad \longrightarrow$$

IIIa

$$H_3C - \overset{\overset{\displaystyle CH_3}{|}}{\underset{\underset{\displaystyle CH_3}{|}}{C}} - CH_2 - \overset{\overset{\displaystyle CH_3}{|}}{\underset{+}{C}} - CH_3$$

IVa

IVa is now a new carbonium ion, and in principle it might go on to react with another molecule of III;

$$H_3C - \overset{\overset{\displaystyle CH_3}{|}}{\underset{\underset{\displaystyle CH_3}{|}}{C}} - CH_2 - \overset{\overset{\displaystyle CH_3}{|}}{\underset{+}{C}} - CH_3 \quad + \quad H_2C = \overset{\overset{\displaystyle CH_3}{\diagup}}{\underset{\diagdown CH_3}{C}}$$

$$\longrightarrow \quad (CH_3)_3\, C - CH_2 - \overset{\overset{\displaystyle CH_3}{|}}{\underset{\underset{\displaystyle CH_3}{|}}{C}} - CH_2 - \overset{\overset{\displaystyle CH_3}{\diagup}}{\underset{+\diagdown CH_3}{C}}$$

Va

Each time a new carbon + ion is formed, it in time finds the olefin monomer, attacks it, and adds another group of four carbon atoms. This, in fact, does happen at low temperature (below −80° C.) in the formation of Butyl rubber. But at higher temperatures, something else happens—the carbonium ions to a considerable degree decompose by losing a proton, or they rearrange in various ways. The ion IVa loses a proton two ways:

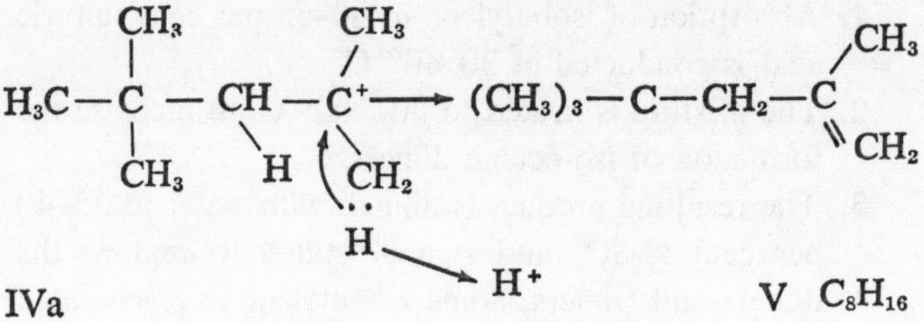

$$\begin{array}{ccc}
& CH_3 & CH_3 \\
& | & | \\
H_3C-\overset{|}{\underset{|}{C}}-CH-\overset{|}{C^+} & \longrightarrow & (CH_3)_3-C-CH_2-C\overset{\diagup CH_3}{\underset{\diagdown CH_2}{}} \\
& CH_3 \quad H \quad CH_2 & \\
& \ddot{} & \\
& H & \\
& \searrow H^+ & \\
IVa & & V \quad C_8H_{16}
\end{array}$$

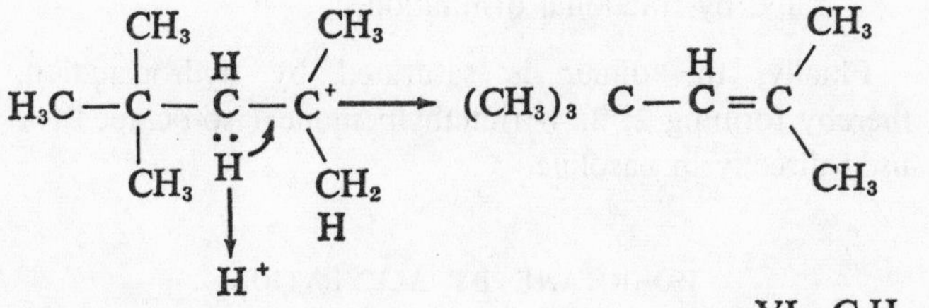

$$\begin{array}{ccc}
CH_3 \quad H \quad CH_3 & & CH_3 \\
| \quad | \quad | & & H \quad \diagup \\
H_3C-C-C-C^+ & \longrightarrow & (CH_3)_3 \quad C-C=C \\
| \quad \ddot{H} \quad | & & \diagdown \\
CH_3 \quad \downarrow \quad CH_2 & & CH_3 \\
\quad H^+ \quad H & & \\
& & VI \quad C_8H_{16}
\end{array}$$

and olefins V and VI are formed. These compounds have actually been separated and identified from the butylene reaction. Because they are the same algebraically as $2 \times C_4H_8$, they are known as butylene "dimers." Compound Va in losing a proton would form $C_{12}H_{24}$ and, since this is $3 \times C_4H_8$, it would be called a "trimer."

Actually, in the acid-catalyzed polymerization of isobutylene by warm sulfuric or phosphoric acid, the dimer is the chief product in an amount three times that of the trimer. Tetramer and higher polymers are practically absent.

In practice, the overall process is carried out in four stages:

1. Absorption of isobutylene in 60–65 per cent sulfuric acid is conducted at 30–40° C.
2. The mixture is heated to 80–100° C. to increase the formation of iso-octene dimers.*
3. The resulting product is diluted with water to 35–40 per cent H_2SO_4 and steam-distilled to remove the dimers and trimers. Some isobutylene is regenerated in the process and some tertiary butyl alcohol also distills across.
4. The dimer, trimer, and tertiary butanol are separated by fractional distillation.

Finally, the dimer is saturated by hydrogenation, thereby forming 2, 2, 4-trimethylpentane (iso-octane), or used directly in gasoline.

ISO-OCTANE BY ALKYLATION

The 100 octane hydrocarbon, 2, 2, 4-trimethylpentane, may be made directly from isobutylene and isobutane. An excess of isobutane is used; the catalyst is sulfuric or hydrofluoric acid and the temperature is kept low. The reaction again proceeds through carbonium ions:

(a.) $(CH_3)_2 - C = CH_2 + H^+ \longrightarrow (CH_3)_3 \ C^+$ II
       I

(b.) $(CH_3)_2 - C = CH_2 + \overset{+}{C}(CH_3)_3 \longrightarrow (CH_3)_2 \ \overset{+}{C} - CH_2C(CH_3)$
                                           III

At this stage a remarkable thing happens: the isobutane reacts with the carbonium ion III by virtue of the fact

* If this mixture is not heated, but diluted with water and steam-distilled, most of the original isobutylene can be recovered in high purity.

that III captures a *hydrogen negative ion* from the isobutane, IV

$$(CH_3)_2 - \overset{+}{C} - CH_2C(CH_3)_3 \; + \; HC(CH_3)_3 =$$

This breaks away as a hydride ion, H—

III   IV

$$(CH_3)_2 \; \underset{H}{C} - CH_2 - C(CH_3)_3 \; + \; \overset{+}{C}(CH_3) \quad \text{II}$$

V

Note now that the isobutane has been converted to the original tertiary butyl cation II, while III is transformed to the saturated compound iso-octane, V.

The ion II now goes back and attacks more of I, the isobutylene, thereby forming III, which then captures a H⁻ ion from IV, and so forth, and the end result is a high yield of V.

An excess of isobutane is required for the purpose; otherwise the competing reaction of isobutylene combining with itself would form considerable amounts of the iso-octene dimer.

This ingenious process is practiced on a large scale, not only with isobutylene and isobutane, but with other combinations, e.g. propylene and isopentane $H_3C - \underset{CH_3}{\overset{H}{C}} - CH_2 - CH_3$. The end products are *branched* saturated hydrocarbons of high octane rating, and therefore very desirable for production of quality gasoline.

B. ALCOHOLS FROM THE BUTENES

Two alcohols are derived from the C_4 olefins, tertiary butanol and secondary butanol, also called 2-butanol.

In addition to these there are two other possible alcohols with four C atoms and one OH group. These four alcohols show some remarkable differences in properties, which are listed in the table below with structures of the compounds.

STRUCTURES AND PROPERTIES OF BUTYL ALCOHOLS

Compound	B.P., °C.	Solubility; g/100g of water
(a) 1-butanol (n-butyl alcohol) $HOCH_2 - CH_2 - CH_2 - CH_3$	118	8
(b) 2-butanol (sec. butyl alcohol) $\begin{matrix} H \\ \| \\ H_3C - C - CH_2 - CH_3 \\ \| \\ OH \end{matrix}$	99.5	22
(c) tert. butyl alcohol $(H_3C)_3\ C - OH$	82.5	miscible
(d) isobutyl alcohol $(H_3C)_2\ CH - CH_2OH$	108	9

The freezing point of tertiary butanol is +25° C., but the other compounds freeze at very low temperatures, −90 to −114° C. Tertiary butanol is also soluble in water in all proportions, while the others show low solubility. 2-butanol has an asymmetric C atom, that is, one to which four different groups are attached; therefore 2-butanol exhibits *stereo-isomerism*. There are two forms, and one is the mirror image of the other. Preparations of these alcohols are given briefly below:

(1)   Tertiary Butanol.

This alcohol is a by-product of operations involving purification of isobutylene, or its conversion to the gasoline components, C_8H_{16} and $C_{12}H_{24}$, which were described in Section A. The alcohol is of small importance commercially; but because of the large amount of isobutylene that is made for rubber synthesis or for fuel purposes, the quantity of tertiary butanol formed is considerable.

The formation of tertiary butanol follows the absorption of isobutylene in diluted sulfuric acid.

(a) $(CH_2)C = CH_2 + H^+ \rightleftharpoons (CH_3)_3C^+$

50-65% aqueous H_2SO_4, 30°C.

Much of the cation (CH_3) C^+ reacts further with isobutylene to give dimer, but some of it reacts with the water present to give alcohol.

(b) $(CH_3)_3C^+ + HOH \rightleftharpoons (CH_3)_3COH + H^+$, and the alcohol is recovered by steam distillation.

Reactions (b) and (a) are reversible; hence to a large degree when the butanol in acid is distilled, it reverts back to isobutylene. Accordingly, the process is a good one for storing and then regenerating pure isobutylene. However, the distillates do contain the tertiary butanol, which is further purified for commercial use.

It is interesting to note that if the commercial demand for isobutylene is much greater than for tertiary butanol, the latter is simply cycled back into the sulfuric acid reactors. Reactions (b) and (a) in reverse then generate the desired isobutylene.

(2)   *Secondary Butanol* (*2-Butanol*)

This alcohol has considerable uses by itself, but its main employment lies in conversion to methyl ethyl ketone, a valuable solvent related to acetone.

$$H_3C - \underset{\underset{OH}{|}}{\overset{\overset{H}{|}}{C}} - CH_2 - CH_3 \quad \xrightarrow[\substack{dehydrogenation \\ 400°C.}]{catalytic} \quad H_3C - \underset{\overset{||}{O}}{C} - CH_2 - CH_3 + H_2$$

methyl ethyl ketone, soluble in water, but not totally miscible. b.p., 80°C.

1- and 2-butenes are the source of the 2-butanol. Because they are much less reactive to dilute sulfuric acid than isobutylene, they escape largely from the acid absorber that removes the latter. They are absorbed readily by passage now through absorbers containing acid of 75 to 95 per cent content of H_2SO_4 to form sulfate esters.

(a) $H_2C = \overset{\overset{H}{|}}{C} - CH_2 - CH_3 + \overset{+}{H} \mid \overline{O}SO_3H \longrightarrow H_3C - \underset{\underset{OSO_3H}{|}}{\overset{\overset{H}{|}}{C}} - CH_2 - CH_3$

(b) $H_3C - \overset{\overset{H}{|}}{C} = \overset{\overset{H}{|}}{C} - CH_3 + \overset{+}{H} \mid \overline{O}SO_3H \longrightarrow H_3C - \underset{\underset{OSO_3H}{|}}{\overset{\overset{H}{|}}{C}} - CH_2 - CH_3$

alkyl sulfate ester

Note in this case that both 1- and 2-butenes form the same final product, a sulfate ester where the sulfuric acid radical has joined to the No. 2 C atom.

The desired 2-butanol is generated by diluting the acid extract to about 45 per cent H_2SO_4, heating the mixture, and distilling out the alcohol. In this process the sulfate ester undergoes a reaction called "hydrolysis," that is, splitting with water:

$$H_3C - \underset{\underset{+H \mid OH}{\overset{\mid}{O \mid SO_3H}}}{\overset{\overset{H}{\mid}}{C}} - CH_2 - CH_3 \longrightarrow H_3C - \underset{\overset{\mid}{OH}}{\overset{\overset{H}{\mid}}{C}} - CH_2 - CH_3 + H_2SO_4$$

Thus the sulfuric acid is regenerated too, but in a dilute solution. For re-use as an absorber, it must be concentrated by distilling out water under reduced pressure.

(3)   Normal Butyl Alcohol (1-Butanol)

This compound cannot be made from the petroleum butenes, because the acid reactions described above in (1) and (2) put the alcohol group, −OH, on carbon atoms away from the end of the chain. However, 1-butanol can be derived from petroleum, although not from C_4 compounds, but from ethylene via ethyl alcohol. The following transformations are involved in its preparation:

$$\text{Ethylene} \longrightarrow \text{ethyl alcohol} \xrightarrow{\text{oxidation}} \text{acetaldehyde}$$

$$\text{Alkali} \longrightarrow H_3C - \underset{H}{C} = \underset{H}{C} - \underset{H}{C} = O \xrightarrow[+2H_2]{\text{hydrogenation}}$$

$$\text{crotonaldehyde}$$

$$H_3C - CH_2 - CH_2 - \underset{OH}{\overset{H}{C}H}$$

$$\text{1-butanol}$$

1-butanol has value in itself as a solvent, but a large amount of it is converted to butyl acetate, an ester derived from acetic acid. Butyl acetate is the best solvent for nitrocellulose spray lacquers, and is widely used for this purpose. 1-butanol is also made from starch via an ingenious fermentation process whereby acetone is also formed (the Weiszmann method, developed in World War I). Hence, like ethyl alcohol, 1-butanol is an agricultural chemical. (In analogy to petrochemicals these are sometimes called "agrichemicals.")

During World War II the above series of reactions were modified ingeniously to produce butadiene from the acetaldehyde, which in turn came from fermentation alcohol. The butadiene went into rubber synthesis. In the course of time, a variety of jokes sprang up around the question, "How many cocktails went into the rubber vats today?" No one knew the answer for sure, but it was indeed a very large number!

SUMMARY

The C_4 fraction of gases from hydrocarbon cracking is a source of 1- and 2-butenes, isobutylene, isobutane, and butadiene. From these lively gases, one can produce three kinds of rubber, as well as high-octane gasoline and a variety of valuable solvents.

C. BUTYL RUBBER—A GAS BARRIER OF UNIQUE QUALITY

The name "Butyl" refers to a synthetic rubbery material used to make tire inner tubes and other products that must be chemically stable and resistant to gas penetration. Butyl is composed of very large hydrocarbon molecules that have a small but essential content of double bonds (C=C groups) that are disposed to react with sulfur in the process known as "vulcanization."* Commercial

* Vulcanization is a reaction discovered by the American chemist Charles Goodyear, by which crude natural rubber, which is

grades of Butyl rubber* are produced by the copolymerization of isobutylene (Chapter 6) with small amounts of isoprene at a very low temperature (-140 to $-150°$ F.). Anhydrous aluminum chloride is the catalyst, which, for the purpose, is dissolved in methyl chloride, a material normally a gas but that is liquid at the low-reaction temperatures.

Butyl was first prepared in 1937 as an outgrowth of research on the polymerization of isobutylene to high-molecular-weight products; boron trifluoride (BF_3) was used as a catalyst. These polymers were found to be rubberlike although nonvulcanizable in the ordinary sense, because they lacked any residual double bonds. Attempts to produce a vulcanizable material by copolymerizing various diolefins with isobutylene were not at first successful because the products then formed were of a molecular weight too low to be valuable as plastics or rubber. It was found that one of the causes of trouble was the presence of impurities in the starting materials, these impurities acting as "poisons" in preventing molecular growth up to a sufficient level. Various modifications of the polymerization recipe led finally to the replacement of the boron trifluoride (BF_3) by anhydrous aluminum chloride. Of the various solvents tried, methyl chloride was found to be most stable in the presence of aluminum chloride, and at the same time a good solvent for it and the reactants.

Even at the very low temperature used for the polymerization process, the reaction was vigorous and difficult to control because of its great rapidity and heat evolution. For a time, even liquid ethylene was used as a diluent

---

notably sticky and normally stretchy, but with little "snap," is converted by heating with sulfur into the product that we usually think of as rubber—that which is snappy but not sticky.

* Product of Enjay Chemical Company, subdivision of Standard Oil Company (New Jersey).

for the reaction mixture to moderate the reaction and secure a product more uniform in terms of molecular weight. An additional complicating factor was that the polymer product precipitated from solution promptly upon formation, sometimes in the form of great chunks.

Ultimately the desired control was obtained by the right combination of three factors:

(a) The purified reactants, isobutylene and isoprene, were mixed with methyl chloride (of high purity and free of water) and chilled to −140° F.

(b) The aluminum chloride was also predissolved in methyl chloride.

(c) The reactants and catalyst solution were fed into a chilled reactor (−130 to −140° F.) in which vigorous agitation was maintained in order to break up the polymer particles as they precipitated from solution and to keep them in a finely divided condition. The proper temperature for the process was secured by encasing the reactor in a tank of liquid ethylene (b.p., −103° C.) or through the use of cooling coils with liquid ethylene as cooling fluid.

The flow plan for the process is shown in *Figure 9.*

Inspection of the figure shows that the product, as a thin soup or "slurry," overflows from the reactor into a flash tank that contains hot water under vigorous agitation. Here an antioxidant is added to prevent breakdown of the polymer during later processing; a trace of zinc stearate is also added to coat the polymer "crumbs" and prevent them from sticking together during the filtration that follows. The wet crumbs pass over a screen and filter, then through a tunnel drier, and finally through an extruder and a hot mill. These operations drive out any residual water from the polymer. The mill produces sheets of polymer (at elevated temperature). The sheets pass

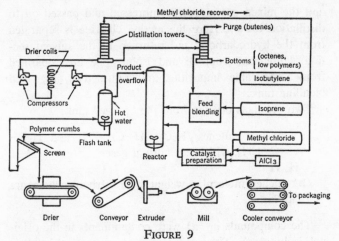

FIGURE 9

Isobutylene-isoprene copolymerization manufacture of Butyl rubber.

along a cooling conveyor to the packaging section, and then to the ultimate consumer.

So much for the product of the main reaction. What now about the methyl chloride solvent and *unreacted* starting materials? It is here that the wizardry of "recycle economics" comes into play. This process begins at the flash tank (see *Figure 9*), where recovery is started.

PRODUCTS FROM THE FLASH TANK

The flash tank contains water hot enough to vaporize any unreacted starting materials, methyl chloride solvent, and some liquid by-products derived from the starting materials. Vapors arising from the tank undergo compression, which liquefies them again along with water condensate. Water is separated as a lower layer, and the organic materials pass through drier coils that contain aluminum oxide. This takes out the last traces of water, and the mixed gases are recompressed and passed on to distillation towers. Here the methyl chloride is separated from the hydrocarbons and returned to the solvent section. Unreacted isoprene and isobutylene are separated from undesirable impurities and returned to the feed blending tank.

Two products emerge from the "purge" tank:

(a) normal butenes, $H_2C=CH-CH_2CH_3$ and H_3C-
  $C=C-CH_3$, which are normal gases,
  H H

(b) higher molecular weight hydrocarbons which are liquids.

The compounds in (a) were contaminants in the original isobutylene. They are less reactive than the latter, hence they tend to accumulate. They are purged from the system because they tend to inhibit the desired polymer growth process. However, they are perfectly acceptable as materials for other syntheses as shown in Section A above.

The materials in (b) resemble low-boiling components of gasoline and may be used for that purpose. They must be removed from the recycle compounds because of their inhibiting effect on the polymerization reaction.

The use of these recovery processes assures that nothing is wasted; furthermore, the recovery assures that the atmosphere around such a plant is not contaminated by solvent vapors and materials that could be harmful or dangerous.

SOURCES OF RAW MATERIALS FOR BUTYL SYNTHESIS

The primary raw materials required for Butyl rubber, namely isobutylene and isoprene, are derived from catalytic cracking of gas oils and other petroleum residues not suitable for fuels. Here again we see the "Golden Cat" in action as a primary source of gaseous chemicals so useful for chemical synthesis.

The cat cracker gases are first processed to remove the ethylene and propylene; the C_4 fraction then goes to an extraction plant where butadiene is removed (the butadiene serves as a source of hexamethylene diamine used in nylon synthesis, as we will see in Chapter 11. After the butadiene has been removed, this C_4 fraction contains 10 to 35 per cent isobutylene plus normal butenes plus some butane. The high reactivity of isobutylene again comes into play in the reaction for its separation. This consists in absorption in diluted sulfuric acid (about 67 per cent H_2SO_4), a reagent that permits the normal butenes to pass through unchanged. Absorbed isobutylene is then removed from the acid by treatment with steam. Washing of the gas, compression, and redistillation yield a product that is 98 to 99 per cent pure.

$$H$$
Isoprene ($H_2C=C-C=CH_2$) is also a product from
$$CH_3$$
the cat cracker, although a minor one. It belongs with a group of C_5 hydrocarbons that are low-boiling liquids (boiling points 30–45° C.). It is recovered from the mixture by extractive distillation, a process in which an extractive solvent runs downstream in a distilling column and accomplishes a selective removal of the desired component in the ascending vapor stream. For isoprene recovery, a mixture of acetone and water serves as the extractive solvent.

Redistillation yields isoprene with 92 to 95 per cent purity, which is sufficient for Butyl rubber production. However, for synthetic natural rubber (same as tree rubber; see Chapter 10) the purity required is much higher than this, and a direct synthesis is employed.

THE STRUCTURE OF BUTYL

The structure of the Butyl polymer is compounded of three facts:

1. The amount of isobutylene units is very large, and of isoprene units, small, the ratios being about 98/2 to 99/1.

2. The isobutylene units seem to be largely fused together through a head-to-tail combination, thus,

$$
-\underset{\underset{\text{CH}_3}{|}}{\overset{\overset{\text{CH}_3}{|}}{\text{C}}}-\text{CH}_2-\left[-\underset{\underset{\text{CH}_3}{|}}{\overset{\overset{\text{CH}_3}{|}}{\text{C}}}-\text{CH}_2-\right]_n-\underset{\underset{\text{CH}_3}{|}}{\overset{\overset{\text{CH}_3}{|}}{\text{C}}}-\text{CH}_2-\text{ etc.}
$$

While the isoprene units are interspaced in the form

$$
-\text{H}_2\text{C}-\overset{\overset{\text{H}}{|}}{\text{C}}=\underset{\underset{\text{CH}_3}{|}}{\text{C}}-\text{CH}_2-
$$

which occurs randomly in the ratio given in 1.

3. The molecular weight is very high, in the range of 300,000 to 400,000. Some polymers have been made with molecular weights near one million. It is apparent, then, that the n value in 2 above must be in the range of 5000 to 6000.

The "backbone" of the Butyl molecule appears to be made up largely of the repeating arrangement:

$$
-\underset{\underset{\text{X}}{|}}{\overset{\overset{\text{X}}{|}}{\text{C}}}-\text{CH}_2-\underset{\underset{\text{X}}{|}}{\overset{\overset{\text{X}}{|}}{\text{C}}}-\text{CH}_2-\underset{\underset{\text{X}}{|}}{\overset{\overset{\text{X}}{|}}{\text{C}}}-\text{CH}_2-\text{ etc.}
$$

where X is the $-\text{CH}_3$ group.

What does this chain look like in reality? X-ray studies reveal a structure like this:

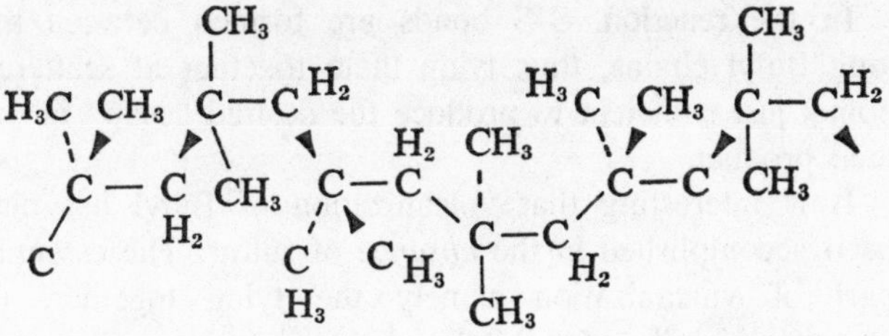

The wedge represents a bond projecting forward; the dotted line, a bond projecting backward, in which the methyls are coiled around the backbone like the threads of a screw, thus like a helical spring. It is this structure that gives Butyl its compactness and apparently explains its great resistance to permeation by gases—hence the ability of tire inner tubes to retain air.

The small amount of residual unsaturation—present in the backbone due to introduction of isoprene units $(-CH_2-C=C-CH_2-)$ in the amount of 1 to 2 per CH_3

98 isobutylene units—is of great importance because this induces the reactivity that permits vulcanization, or "cure," of the Butyl polymer. This leads to a tough final product that is free of stickiness.

Vulcanization

Vulcanization of Butyl is conducted according to a variety of recipes, one of which is the following:

> 100 parts Butyl
> 5 parts zinc oxide
> 1–2 parts sulfur
> 1–2 parts ultra-accelerator*
> temperature 300–340° F.

* Ultra-accelerators speed the reaction with sulfur, which in this case is particularly slow due to the geometry of the molecule and its low content of double bonds.

In the reaction, S–S bonds are formed between the long Butyl chains, thus tying them together at scattered points just sufficient to produce the desired "snap" in the final product.

It is interesting that vulcanization of Butyl has also been accomplished in the *absence* of sulfur. The essential part of vulcanization—namely the tying together, or "cross-linking," of Butyl chains—is, however, still achieved. In the latter case organic molecules are used for the purpose, and they seem to serve just as well.

TABLE X—PROPERTIES OF BUTYL RUBBER AND COMPARISON WITH RELATED MATERIALS

Air Retention

ORIGINAL AIR PRESSURE (PSI) *Inner tubes of*		AIR LOSS (PSI)		
		1 wk.	*2 wk.*	*1 month*
(a) Natural rubber	28	4.0	8.0	16.5
(b) Butyl	28	0.5	1.0	2.0

One sees here that natural rubber tubes lose air pressure at a rate *eight* times greater than Butyl tubes.

TABLE XI—MECHANICAL AND ELECTRICAL PROPERTIES OF RUBBERS

	Butyl	Gum Natural Rubber
Density, g/cc 25° C.	0.91	0.92
Specific heat Cal/g/° C.	0.464	—
Dielectric strength Volts per mil thickness	600	500
Dielectric constant at 1000 cycles, 10 volts		
dry	2.11	2.46
wet	2.10	2.76
Power factor 1000 cycles, 10 volts		
dry	0.04	0.04
wet	0.05	0.16

	T.S.*	Elonga-tion %	T.S.*	Elonga-tion %
Orig. sample	2500	880	3460	1050
After exposure 2–4 weeks at 25° C. in				
a. 37% HCl	2800	860	2700–1800	700
b. 95% H₂SO₄	cleaved	—	decomposed	
c. 70% HNO₃	1600	900	decomposed	
d. 30% NaOH	3100	860	4200	850

* T.S. = tensile strength, psi.

Tables X and XI reveal several important differences between Butyl and natural rubbers:

1. Natural rubber has a significantly higher tensile strength than Butyl, and its elongation at the breaking point is about 15 per cent more.
2. Natural rubber is notably more susceptible to oxidative destruction than Butyl. In fact, the resistance of Butyl to the action of 70 per cent nitric acid is remarkable.† This resistance, of course, is due to its low content of C=C bonds.
3. Strong hydrochloric acid has little effect on Butyl, but notably lowers the tensile strength of natural rubber. Fifty per cent sodium hydroxide, on the other hand, increases the tensile strength of both rubbers.

Recent Developments

Since about 1960, the Enjay Chemical Company has been producing Butyl not only as solid material in sheets and blocks, but also as an aqueous "latex." The latex is a

† The writer vividly recalls a demonstration at a chemical convention in 1940, when Dr. Per K. Frolich of the Esso laboratories displayed the new Butyl rubber, and compared its behavior in hot nitric acid with several other rubbers, including natural. Only Butyl survived the test.

thick creamy material with the remarkable content of 50 to 55 per cent dispersed rubber polymer. The polymer is maintained in its colloidal dispersion by an anionic emulsifier that imparts high stability against coagulation by acids, bases, and other electrolytes. The pH may be varied widely from 1 to 13; precipitation is very slight or absent until a very high alkalinity is developed, of the order of 1 to 1.5 normal, at which point coagulation occurs rather rapidly. Calcium, magnesium, and zinc ions are without effect. Even freezing and thawing several times produce only slight coagulation.

Aside from strong alkali precipitation, the common way of producing a coagulum is simple evaporation from thin layers, whereupon a translucent rubber film appears. As with the earlier Butyls, the latex Butyl may be vulcanized either with sulfur or with organic agents.

This new Butyl latex is of great interest for coatings of various types and is coming into use for textile dips, emulsion paints, roof and leather coatings, and for special waterproof papers.

The manufacturers have not revealed the process by which these emulsions are produced.

SUMMARY

Butyl rubber, derived altogether from petroleum hydrocarbons and one of the earliest successful man-made rubbers, has become an outstanding material in our supply of rubbery materials. Used at first almost entirely for tire inner tubes, it now enjoys widespread use as a general rubber. Its most unusual characteristics are high resistance to oxidative destruction, including hot air, ozone, and nitric acid, and its great retentivity for gases under high pressure. This implies its successful use in tire tubes, balloons, high-pressure rubber tubing, and the like. A highly stable latex of 50 to 55 per cent rubber solids has recently come onto the market.

D. STYRENE-BUTADIENE RUBBER, A SUBSTITUTE THAT SAW US THROUGH THE WAR

Put yourself for a moment back in December 1941 when the course of World War II suddenly propelled the United States into conflict with the Japanese military power. After the great air attack upon Pearl Harbor, the Japanese army rushed southward through the peninsula and the islands of southeast Asia. These faraway places ordinarily seemed rather unimportant to the man in the street, until suddenly realization swept the country that practically all our rubber came from there! Now the man at the wheel began to wonder how long his wheels would turn if rubber could not be gotten for them. America too was finally in the war in a grim struggle for survival!

Listen to the words written by P. W. Litchfield, chairman of the board of the Goodyear Tire and Rubber Company, on December 31, 1941:

Today the Japanese are driving desperately for control of the rich resources of Malaya and the Netherlands Indies, an area which yields *95 percent* of the world's supply of crude rubber. Meanwhile, reports indicate that the British defenders, falling back from Penang on the Malayan peninsula, have destroyed stocks of rubber and rubber processing machinery in the evacuated sections, to prevent their use by the enemy. One need not be an alarmist to discern the ominous note of this developing situation. Few greater calamities could be visited upon us than a world without an adequate supply of rubber. In America such a blow would be felt more keenly than elsewhere because we are the *largest of all consumers* of rubber, and dependent upon it for the maintenance of our way of life. [My italics.]

American rubber consumption at that time was of the order of 800,000 tons of tree rubber per year. Mr. Litchfield continued by pointing out that a year before (1940), rubber authorities, in view of the jeopardy of the spreading of war, had urged several important national actions:

1. To provide immediately a nationalized emergency reserve of crude rubber of 300,000 to 400,000 tons in excess of current commercial needs.
2. To inaugurate a program of conservation, including the collection of larger supplies of scrap rubber for reclaim, and the placing of an embargo on exportation of crude rubber or rubber scrap.
3. To encourage the expansion of our facilities for the production of synthetic rubbers.

For the purpose of our story, the third point is most interesting, because at that time synthetic rubbers were few and extremely limited in quantity. Du Pont—through the work of Carothers, Hill, Collins, and Kirby—had begun turning out the remarkable product "neoprene" in 1936, but its production was only about 20,000 tons per year. Thiokol rubber was also on the market, but—like neoprene—it was a specialty rubber not suited for tires. Butyl rubber (Section C above) was a brand-new product, available only in small quantity; although it was very good for inner tubes, it was not yet suited for the outer casing. Noble as these synthetic efforts were, they were not sufficient for the sudden necessity of producing tire rubber on a massive scale.

The answer lay in an altogether different direction, in "GR-S," a product from the copolymerization of *butadiene* and *styrene*. Strangely enough, these two hydrocarbons were far from being abundant and common in the United States. Polystyrene (Chapter 7, Section C), introduced by Dow Chemical in the late thirties, was gaining recognition, but butadiene was a rarity. But both were well known to the German chemical industries, at that moment also arrayed against us on the other side of the Atlantic.

For many years (in fact, from the time of World War I) German scientists had experimented with butadiene and its derivatives, and with styrene, and had built up an impressive experience with these materials. One of their moderately successful rubbery products was "Buna-S," butadiene-styrene copolymer formed by the action of sodium metal (*na* in the "Buna"). We now took a lesson from the pages of their chemistry books. The theory was good, but there were many difficult steps between the words and the working processes.

EMULSION POLYMERIZATION OF UNSATURATED HYDROCARBONS

For better control of reaction conditions, and in particular to absorb the considerable heat liberated during polymerization of olefinic compounds, the technique of aqueous emulsion polymerization had been explored by the Germans, and was developed to a high point by American chemists and rubber technologists during the war period. The essential features of an emulsion polymerization are the following:

1. A soap or other suitable emulsifying agent is dissolved in water.
2. Polymerization "catalysts" or "initiators" are added along with other agents that control polymer growth ("modifiers").
3. The olefinic compounds to be polymerized are added—in the case of butadiene gas (boiling point, 0° C.) this must be condensed to a liquid by chilling, or pumped into the sealed reaction system under pressure.

4. The reaction mixture is sealed up to prevent loss of volatile materials, and is agitated thoroughly to emulsify the hydrocarbons in the water system; the polymerization begins in the emulsion, and the rubbery polymer forms a creamy "latex" that is stable so long as the soap or emulsifier remains operative. Constant temperature is maintained during the polymerization by appropriate heating or cooling.

5. After the polymerization reaction has proceeded to the proper point, the process is arrested by addition of a so-called "shortstop," usually hydroquinone. Carbon black and other fillers and extenders may be added at this point as a slurry, after which the emulsion is destroyed by addition of salt or acid. The coagulated polymer product, along with its fillers and extenders, comes down as "crumbs." These are washed, dried, and pressed into bales, which are then ready for shipping to the rubber fabricators.

The typical polymerization reactants were:

THE MUTUAL GR-S RECIPE

Material	Amount	
Soap solution containing 3% Ivory flakes, or similar saturated soap	160	parts
Styrene, freshly distilled	25	parts
Butadiene	75	parts
Dodecyl mercaptan	0.5	parts
Potassium persulfate	0.4	parts

The sealed reaction mixture was agitated continuously at 50° C. for a period of twelve hours, at which point about 80 per cent of the monomers had been converted to polymer. The polymer composition was 20 to 22 per cent styrene, the balance being butadiene plus a trace of initiator and modifier. The product, on account of its formation at elevated temperature, was called "hot rubber."

Before long it was learned that a superior rubber would be formed at lower temperature; however, the reaction time then had to be increased greatly to accomplish the same yield. The remedy for this was to find more active initiators than the persulfate; in time, hydroperoxides of organic compounds came into play along with metal ions, such as the ferrous-ferric pair. Extensive experimentation produced various combinations that could produce rapid polymerizations at much lower temperatures. The result was the formation of "cold rubber," much of which was made at a temperature of only 5° C. (41° F.).

Mechanism of the Polymerization, and Structure of the Polymers

$$\text{Butadiene} \quad (H_2C = \overset{H}{C} - \overset{H}{C} - CH_2) \quad \text{and} \quad \text{styrene}$$

$(C_6H_5 - \overset{H}{C} = CH_2)$ in the *absence* of initiators do not polymerize at ordinary temperatures. However, when peroxy compounds are added, their decomposition furnishes free radicals. These activate the monomers in a reaction that changes the double bonds present.

$$R-O-O-R \text{ (a peroxy compound)} \xrightarrow{\text{decomposition}} 2R-O\cdot$$

I. O—O bond breaks   II.

The free radicals generated in this process attack the olefins, e.g., butadiene.

$$R-O\cdots\rightarrow \overset{\overset{\displaystyle H}{|}}{\underset{\underset{\displaystyle H}{|}}{C}}=\overset{\overset{\displaystyle H}{|}}{C}-\overset{\overset{\displaystyle H}{|}}{C}=\overset{\overset{\displaystyle H}{|}}{C} \longrightarrow R-O-\overset{\overset{\displaystyle H}{|}}{\underset{\underset{\displaystyle H}{|}}{C}}-\overset{\overset{\displaystyle H}{|}}{C}=\overset{\overset{\displaystyle H}{|}}{C}-\overset{\overset{\displaystyle H}{|}}{C}\cdot$$

$$\quad\quad\quad\quad\text{III}\quad\quad\quad\quad\quad\quad\quad\quad\text{IV}$$

Note the rearrangement of double bonds in the butadiene, the consumption of one of the double bonds, and the formation of a new free radical (IV) with an unpaired electron. The free radical now attacks a second butadiene molecule:

$$RO-\overset{\overset{\displaystyle H}{|}}{\underset{\underset{\displaystyle H}{|}}{C}}-\overset{\overset{\displaystyle H}{|}}{C}=\overset{\overset{\displaystyle H}{|}}{C}-\overset{\overset{\displaystyle H}{|}}{C}\cdot\cdots\rightarrow\overset{\overset{\displaystyle H}{|}}{\underset{\underset{\displaystyle H}{|}}{C}}-\overset{\overset{\displaystyle H}{|}}{C}=\overset{\overset{\displaystyle H}{|}}{C}-\overset{\overset{\displaystyle H}{|}}{C}\longrightarrow$$

$$\text{IV}$$

$$RO-\overset{\overset{\displaystyle H}{|}}{\underset{\underset{\displaystyle H}{|}}{C}}-\overset{\overset{\displaystyle H}{|}}{C}=\overset{\overset{\displaystyle H}{|}}{C}-\overset{\overset{\displaystyle H}{|}}{\underset{\underset{\displaystyle H}{|}}{C}}-\overset{\overset{\displaystyle H}{|}}{\underset{\underset{\displaystyle H}{|}}{C}}-\overset{\overset{\displaystyle H}{|}}{C}=\overset{\overset{\displaystyle H}{|}}{C}-\overset{\overset{\displaystyle H}{|}}{C}\cdot$$

$$\text{V}$$

The new free radical V attacks another butadiene molecule, adds to it, forms another free radical, and so forth, and the final result is the formation of a very long chain of butadiene molecules joined end to end, thus:

$$RO-\overset{\overset{\displaystyle H}{|}}{\underset{\underset{\displaystyle H}{|}}{C}}-\overset{\overset{\displaystyle H}{|}}{C}=\overset{\overset{\displaystyle H}{|}}{C}-\overset{\overset{\displaystyle H}{|}}{C}-\left(\overset{\overset{\displaystyle H}{|}}{\underset{\underset{\displaystyle H}{|}}{C}}-\overset{\overset{\displaystyle H}{|}}{C}=\overset{\overset{\displaystyle H}{|}}{C}-\overset{\overset{\displaystyle H}{|}}{C}-\right)_{\underline{n}}\cdot$$

$$\quad\quad\quad\quad\quad\quad\quad\quad\quad\quad\quad\quad\quad\quad\text{VI}$$

In the presence of a second olefin, e.g., styrene, the growing chain V reacts occasionally with styrene, as shown, yielding VII,

$$RO \left(\begin{array}{cccc} H & H & H & H \\ -C-C=C-C- \\ H & & & H \end{array} \right)_n \left(\begin{array}{cccc} H & H & H & H \\ C-C=C-C- \\ H & & & H \end{array} \right) \begin{array}{cc} H & H \\ C-C \cdot \\ H & \end{array}$$

VII

and a styrene unit is incorporated in the chain to form VII, which in turn reacts with more butadiene or more styrene. Because the final GR-S polymer contains about 21 per cent styrene, the chain composition can be represented as

$$ROC \begin{array}{cccc} H & H & H & H \\ -C=C-C- \\ H & & & H \end{array} \left(\begin{array}{cccc} H & H & H & H \\ C-C=C-C \\ H & & & H \end{array} \right)_6 \begin{array}{cc} H & H \\ -C-C \cdot \\ H & \end{array}$$

VIII

with seven butadiene units on the *average* to one styrene unit. The unpaired electron at the end of VIII can be tied up by pairing with a second molecule of VIII, thereby bringing the chain growth to a stop. This kind of chain termination process was described previously in the case of polyethylene (Chapter 7, Section D).

The proper termination of chain growth is one of the vital factors in a successful polymerization; either the growth terminates too soon, and a low polymer that is sticky and not rubbery is formed, or the molecular growth becomes enormous, and the desired "workability" of the rubber is lost. The use of traces of *mercaptans* (compounds with the formula R-S-H), in the recipe was found to exert the desired control over chain growth. The molecular weights of satisfactory GR-S rubbers lie in the range of 100,000–500,000.

In addition to this problem of molecular size, two other factors enter in to vary the nature of the final product and its desirability as a commercial rubber.

1. The butadiene monomers do not always join end to end, but sometimes form branches by 1, 2-addition, thus:

$$-\overset{\displaystyle H}{\underset{\displaystyle H}{C}} - \overset{\displaystyle H}{C} = \overset{\displaystyle H}{C} - \overset{\displaystyle H}{\underset{\displaystyle H}{C}} - \overset{\displaystyle H}{\underset{\displaystyle \underset{\displaystyle H}{\underset{\displaystyle /}{C}} \diagdown CH_2}{C}} - \overset{\displaystyle H}{\underset{\displaystyle H}{C}} - \left(\overset{\displaystyle H}{\underset{\displaystyle H}{C}} - \overset{\displaystyle H}{C} = \overset{\displaystyle H}{C} - \overset{\displaystyle H}{\underset{\displaystyle H}{C}} - \right)_{\underline{n}}$$

2. The structure at the double bonds may be "cis"

$$\left(\begin{array}{cc} \overset{\displaystyle H}{\diagdown} & \overset{\displaystyle H}{\diagup} \\ C & = C \\ \diagup & \diagdown \\ -CH_2 & CH_2- \end{array} \right)$$

or it may be "trans"

$$\left(\begin{array}{cc} \overset{\displaystyle H}{\diagdown} & \overset{\displaystyle CH_2-}{\diagup} \\ C & = C \\ \diagup & \diagdown \\ -CH_2 & H \end{array} \right)$$

("cis" means on the same side; "trans" means across, or on opposite sides), and emulsion polymerization seems unable to control the results. In other words, a random distribution of cis and trans arrangements may result. GR-S rubber possesses mostly trans double bonds; about 80 per cent of the butadiene units are linked end to end, that is by 1, 4-addition, while 20 per cent are linked 1, 2, thereby forming branches in the chain. Those rubbers formed at low temperature ("cold rubber") have a higher degree of chain order and less branching than the hot rubbers.

COMPARISON OF GR-S AND TREE RUBBER

The use of GR-S (more recently called SBR*) as a substitute for tires arose out of dire necessity, and not from preference. Nevertheless, as improvements were made in all the factors of formation, vulcanization, and fabrication, SBR came to be widely used as a component of automobile tires even after the war when abundant natural rubber again became available. At present, of the total tonnage of rubber consumed in the United States, 40 to 50 per cent is SBR. The judgment of rubber fabricators on SBR versus tree rubber is expressed generally this way:

SBR is superior to most grades of natural rubber in cleanliness and uniformity and its cost is comparable. Outside of use in tire casings, SBR is superior in aging, heat resistance, and resistance to wear. It is also superior to natural rubber in resistance to ozone; hence, it is used in electrical applications where ozone is present. However, SBR is inferior in tensile strength, workability, tear resistance, cut growth, and heat build-up. It also has less tack or adhesive character. The high heat build-up in SBR rubbers makes them unsatisfactory for use in the casing of large tires, for instance in trucks and earth-moving machinery. In smaller automobile tires, SBR rubbers used as tire treads have shown remarkable wear resistance, even though the tensile strength is somewhat lower than in natural rubber. (Automobile tires running 30,000–35,000 miles now are fairly common—an event that was undreamed-of twenty years ago, and this is due largely

* Styrene Butadiene Rubber.

to the improved SBR in the treads.) The vulcanization process for SBR requires less sulfur, but greater amounts of accelerator. The reinforcing action of carbon black for SBR is much greater than for natural rubber. Special carbons have been devised to increase this reinforcement. Because the two rubbers are compatible, they are frequently intermixed and vulcanized together, whereby new products embracing the better features of each can be produced.

The important mechanical properties of Hevea (tree rubber) and SBR are summarized in the table below. Note the great improvement of tensile strength produced by addition of the carbon black to the SBR product.

Mechanical Properties of SBR and Tree Rubber

SBR
VULCANIZED POLYMERS

	No Added Carbon	With Carbon Black 33%
Per cent Elongation	400–600	400–600
Tensile strength, psi	200–400	2500–4000
Per cent rebound	65	40–50

TREE RUBBER
VULCANIZED POLYMERS

	No Added Carbon	With Carbon Black 33%
Per cent Elongation	750–850	550–650
Tensile strength, psi	2500–3500	3500–5000
Per cent rebound	75	45–55

Unquestionably GR-S, or "SBR," is good enough to be an important ingredient in the rubber fabricator's workshop for a long time to come. Furthermore, its ready availability from petrochemical hydrocarbons—which are now cheap and abundant—is a great stabilizing factor in the price structure of modern rubber.

E. POLYBUTADIENE RUBBER

Butadiene ($H_2C{=}C{-}C{=}CH_2$, with H H above the central carbons) is a highly reactive gas that may be polymerized directly to useful rubbery materials (elastomers) or converted to other compounds suitable for formation of polymers. In Chapter 11 its role in nylon synthesis will be explained, and in Chapter 12 its new role in production of chloroprene, and hence for neoprene synthesis, will be described. As an ingredient for the synthesis of SBR, butadiene has already received attention in Section D of this chapter.

The cis polymer of butadiene should resemble cis polyisoprene (Chapter 10), which is the base for natural tree rubber, and it does. However, the butadiene polymer, very good in some respects, e.g. abrasion resistance, lacks some of the desirable characteristics of natural rubber and of SBR. Hence it is rarely used commercially by itself; more commonly it is compounded with natural rubber or with SBR in order to produce blended polymers that are commercially desirable. For this purpose, considerable amounts of polybutadiene are produced and used; in 1966 production was about 175,000 tons.

Butadiene was first produced by E. Caventou in 1863 by thermal cracking of fusel oil vapors; three years later, the structure of butadiene was established by Berthelot in a synthesis from ethylene and acetylene. Despite this early origin in the workshops of organic chemistry, butadiene was not recognized as a polymerizable material until 1910 when the Russian Lebedev caused it to form a rubbery material by application of heat alone. Shortly afterward (1911), the German Harries independently arrived at the same result. Neither product had any commercial value. During World War I, butadiene was polymerized by the Germans by use of sodium metal. The product (Buna) was a poor substitute for rubber and was abandoned. Nevertheless, chemists of this time were intrigued by the possibilities of using butadiene for rubber synthesis; the result was that it and related materials, namely

$$\text{isoprene} \quad H_2C=C-\overset{\displaystyle H}{\underset{\displaystyle CH_3}{C}}=CH_2,$$

$$\text{dimethyl butadiene} \quad H_2C=\underset{\displaystyle CH_3}{C}-\underset{\displaystyle CH_3}{C}=CH_2$$

$$\text{piperylene} \quad H_2C=\overset{\displaystyle H}{C}-\overset{\displaystyle H}{C}=\overset{\displaystyle H}{C}-CH_3$$

and

$$\text{chloroprene} \quad H_2C=C-\underset{\displaystyle Cl}{\overset{\displaystyle H}{C}}=CH_2$$

received intensive investigation as possible monomers for rubber synthesis. Like butadiene, all of these materials possess a unique structural unit

$$\underset{/}{\overset{\backslash}{C}}=\underset{|}{C}-\underset{|}{C}=\underset{\backslash}{\overset{/}{C}}$$

which is known as a conjugated diene. This was recognized as having special value for production of rubbery polymers. Ironically, the last of these materials to be discovered, chloroprene, was the first to be polymerized to a good commercial rubber (neoprene, Chapter 12).

METHODS FOR POLYMERIZING BUTADIENE

Although a great variety of agents will induce butadiene to polymerize, three in particular are important:

(a) Peroxides, which induce polymerization through formation of free radicals that attack double bonds, as shown in Section D above. This process is readily handled by the technique of emulsion polymerization. On the other hand, peroxides adequate for the purpose are formed by contact of oxygen with butadiene. For this reason one has to exclude oxygen quite thoroughly from cylinders of butadiene liquefied under pressure, or from other vessels in which butadiene is stored. Some of the peroxides formed, if they are concentrated during distillation, may explode violently when heated. For these reasons, it is clear that one should be concerned about the presence of oxygen.

(b) Alkali metals and their compounds.

(c) The Ziegler-type catalysts based on the alkyl aluminums, e.g. triethyl aluminum, in combination with titanium or vanadium halides. (See polyethylene, Chapter 7, Section D.)

In the case of (b), sodium metal has already been mentioned in its role of forming Buna rubber. A later development was the use of a solid-surface catalyst developed by A. A. Morton of the Massachusetts Institute of Technology. The material was a complex mixture of sodium compounds, principally sodium isopropoxide and allyl sodium ($H_2C = CH - CH_2Na$) both of which must be strictly anhydrous. The polymer produced, unlike the peroxide-formed polymer, was rich in the 1, 4 addition product; it was also principally the trans isomer and had a very high molecular weight (about 7,000,000).

The soluble Ziegler catalysts produce primarily the cis isomer, which is rubbery in the conventional sense, whereas the trans isomer is harder and crystalline. These structures may be pictured in the formulas below:

$$
\begin{array}{c}
\text{H}_2\ |\ \text{H}_2 \qquad\qquad |\qquad\qquad \text{H}_2\ |\ \text{H}_2 \\
\text{H}\ \underset{2}{\diagdown}\ \underset{3/4}{\text{C}+\text{C}}\ \underset{1\diagdown 2}{|}\ \text{H}\ |\ \text{H}\ \underset{2}{\diagdown}\ \underset{3/4}{\text{C}+\text{C}}\ \underset{1\diagdown 2}{|}\ \text{H} \\
{}_{1}\text{C}=\text{C}\ |\ {}_{1/}\text{C}=\text{C}\ |\ {}_{1/}\text{C}=\text{C}\ |\ \text{C}=\text{C}\ 3 \\
-\text{C}/\quad \text{H}\ |\ \text{H}\quad {}_{3}\text{C}+\text{C}_4\quad \text{H}\ |\ \text{H}\quad \text{C}-\text{ etc.} \\
\text{H}_2 \qquad\qquad \text{H}_2\ |\ \text{H}_2 \qquad\qquad \text{H}_2
\end{array}
$$

trans 1, 4-polybutadiene

$$
\begin{array}{c}
\text{H}_2\ {}_1 \quad {}_4\text{H}_2\ |\ \text{H}_2 \quad \text{H}_2\ |\ \text{H}_2 \quad \text{H}_2 \\
-\text{C}\ \underset{2}{\diagdown}\ \underset{3/}{\text{C}+\text{C}}\ \underset{1\diagdown 2}{|}\ \underset{3/}{\text{C}+\text{C}}\ \underset{1\diagdown 2}{|}\ \underset{3/4}{\text{C}}-\text{ etc.} \\
\text{C}=\text{C}\ |\ \text{C}=\text{C}_4\ |\ \text{C}=\text{C} \\
\text{H}\qquad \text{H}\ |\ \text{H}\qquad \text{H}\ |\ \text{H}\qquad \text{H}
\end{array}
$$

cis 1, 4-polybutadiene

The extraordinary character of the trans polymer has shown up in its use in a novel kind of heat engine devised by Professors G. Natta, M. Pegoraro, and L. Szilagyi at the Institute of Industrial Chemistry, Politecnico di Milano. Of all synthetic elastomers this substance displays the greatest shrinkage on heating; its fibers contract as much as 5 per cent at 76° C. Below this temperature they return to normal length. Using oriented fibers of the trans polymer attached to an unbalanced wheel, the inventors succeeded in producing rotation of the wheel when the fibers were alternately heated and cooled. The device is admittedly still in a primitive state, but may turn out to have unique applications.

The cis isomer has been the subject of lively controversy as to priority in its synthesis. Several companies have been involved in extensive legal suits in the matter of their patent claims. Phillips Petroleum claimed the first synthesis of polymer containing as much as 85 per cent cis isomer in 1959, but Goodrich-Gulf, Firestone, and Montecatini of Italy are all closely involved.

Professor Natta claims the first synthesis of 99 per cent pure trans polymer (1955) using the Ziegler-Natta catalyst (specially prepared alkyl aluminum compound with titanium salts), and he also claims high-purity cis isomer by use of homogeneous catalysts.

However, several American and foreign companies are now actively producing polybutadiene elastomers with a high cis content (80 per cent or more), and they are entering into rubber formulations on a considerable scale. One of these companies is Goodyear with a product called "Budene." Some of its properties and its behavior when compounded with natural rubber and SBR rubber are in Table XII.

TABLE XII—PROPERTIES OF COMMERCIAL CIS-POLYBUTADIENE (GOODYEAR "BUDENE") COMPOUNDED WITH NATURAL RUBBER, AND WITH STYRENE-BUTADIENE RUBBER ("SBR")*

No. 1 smoked tree rubber sheet	←——— Composition ———→				
	100%	75%	50%	25%	Zero %
Budene 501	zero	25	50	75	100
Tensile strength, psi	4400	3950	3640	3050	2650
Elongation, %	600	610	650	650	655
300% modulus, psi	1670	1550	1150	870	820
Ring abrasion test (Goodyear) cc loss	4.25	3.12	0.59	0.32	0.25
Accelerated aging 100° C., 70 hours					
Tensile retained %	32	35	48	73	76
Elongation retained %	36	37	39	48	53

SBR polymer†	100%	75	50	25
Budene 501	zero	25	50	75
Tensile strength, psi	3700	3510	2940	2450
Elongation, %	590	640	575	520
300% modulus, psi	1520	1560	1200	1100
Abrasion test, cc loss	4.15	3.26	2.52	1.81
Accelerated aging				
Tensile retained, %	84	75	70	84
Elongation retained, %	48	46	45	68

* All polymers named were compounded with carbon black and vulcanized by standard procedures; antioxidants added afterward.
† Goodyear Plioflex.

These data plus others on similar polymers make it clear that for polybutadiene rubber (Budene) the tensile strength is inferior to that of natural rubber and SBR. However, Budene shows excellent abrasion resistance, suffering far less deterioration (volume loss) in this respect than the others. Also, it transfers this resistance to abrasion to other mixtures of which Budene is a part. In the case of natural rubber, the aging properties are improved by addition of Budene, meaning that for a given polymer mixture the per cent loss of tensile strength and elongation after aging is less in the mixture than in the pure rubber.

It is also clear from the table that properties of inter-mixed polymers vary in a complex way with the composition, e.g. the tensile strength of Budene with 25 per cent of SBR added is *less* than either pure Budene or pure SBR, but increases on both sides of this point. In fact, the presence of minimum or maximum values in chemical or mechanical responses is not uncommon in polymer mixtures such as these; accordingly, information like that above is instructive to anyone who would venture to predict the behavior of these systems.

In summary, it has been found that cis-polybutadiene is not suited for general rubber usage, but when blended with other polymers, e.g. natural rubber or SBR, the product is a worthy addition to rubber stocks, especially in regard to improved abrasion resistance. The great difference in properties of the cis and trans isomers as an aspect of stereo-chemistry is also a lesson in the importance of fine points in polymer structure.

Chapter 10

POLYISOPRENE, THE MIRACLE STRETCH

HOW TREE RUBBER GREW IN THE LABORATORY

Beyond the primal requirements for survival on this planet, there is a higher level of culture that calls for good transportation, communication, and recreation. These also have been quite well attained—if not universally, at least in much of the Western world. Because of the demand for convenient and reliable transportation, *engines* and *energy* are necessary on a massive scale, and petroleum has an important place in the energy picture.

Inspection of the transportation mechanism shows that it stands on three legs: engines, energy, and rubber. Without huge quantities of tough durable rubber, our highway vehicles, large and small, would soon be disabled. The natural agricultural source, *Hevea brasiliensis,* is a very special breed of living thing confined to the rainy tropics—Ceylon, Malaya, Indonesia, Indochina, Liberia and similar places. The output of natural rubber at various times has been uncertain, and in recent years inadequate to satisfy the unrelenting demand for more and more rubber in the machine age.

That kind of deficiency problem again found its solution in the chemical research laboratory—synthesis first of *rubbery* materials,* and finally the crowning achievement of

---

* For some thirty years people have been exposed to the term "synthetic rubber," which is innocent enough, but a little misleading. Tree rubber was not made in the laboratory until 1955; the previous products were synthetic "rubbery materials." They did not rightfully belong in the same category as synthetic Vitamin B_1, Vitamin C, indigo, etc., natural products that were fully duplicated in the laboratory.

all—synthesis of rubber itself, the same product as formed by the tree.* The starting material for this synthesis is isoprene, a hydrocarbon which was a rarity before the war, selling for three dollars or more per pound. Although isoprene is not a natural component of petroleum, chemists have recently devised processes for making it from petroleum that are very ingenious and also quite inexpensive. In 1961 the Goodyear Tire and Rubber Company announced completion of plans for a large plant in Texas that would produce isoprene from propylene by the following reactions:

$$2 \underset{\substack{| \\ \text{H} \\ \text{propylene}}}{(\text{H}_3\text{C}-\text{C}=\text{CH}_2)} \xrightarrow[\substack{\text{(propyl aluminum} \\ \text{catalyst)}}]{\text{dimerization}}$$

$$\underset{\text{2-methyl-1-pentene}}{\text{H}_2\text{C}=\overset{\overset{\text{CH}_3}{|}}{\text{C}}-\text{CH}_2-\text{CH}_2-\text{CH}_3}$$

$$\xrightarrow[\text{H}_3\text{PO}_4]{\text{isomerize}} \underset{\substack{| \\ \text{H}}}{\text{H}_3\text{C}-\overset{\overset{\text{CH}_3}{|}}{\text{C}}=\text{C}-\text{CH}_2-\text{CH}_3}$$

$$\xrightarrow[\text{in presence of HBr}]{\text{thermal cracking}} \underset{\substack{| \\ \text{H} \\ \text{isoprene}}}{\text{H}_2\text{C}=\overset{\overset{\text{CH}_3}{|}}{\text{C}}-\text{C}=\text{CH}_2} + \underset{\text{(methane)}}{\text{CH}_4}$$

Cost of the isoprene was at a figure that permitted production of the company's "Natsyn" rubber polymer at a

* Tree rubber is not an absolutely uniform product—in fact, far from it. Its properties vary according to the methods of gathering and processing, particularly with coagulation of the latex and smoking of the coagulum. It also varies somewhat from one plantation to another and with changes in climatic conditions. Accordingly, rubber synthesis can only produce an assumed underlying structural pattern.

price of twenty-five cents per pound, fully competitive with tree rubber. The result is that the "new" rubber, *polyisoprene,* a natural synthetic,* has its roots in petroleum, not in the soil. In the great host of petrochemicals, it occupies first place (for the present at least!) as the most outstanding achievement among the adventures of chemists in turning muck into miracles.

Although many of the best heads in chemistry wrestled with the mysteries of rubber—Tilden, Harries, Staudinger, Carothers, Flory, Mark, Marvel, Natta, and Ziegler, to name but a few—more than a hundred years elapsed in the elusive pursuit of its synthesis. What was so difficult about rubber synthesis? What is required to make rubber in the laboratory?

The next section will give some of the answers.

NATURE OF THE PROBLEM

In 1860 Greville Williams established that isoprene was the chief product obtained by the dry distillation of natural rubber; hence it was presumably involved as a structural unit in rubber. In 1884 W. A. Tilden succeeded in producing isoprene in quantity by the cracking of turpentine,† and then went on to convert it to a rubbery mass by the action of metallic sodium. Chemists tried to find some

* The names applied to the new product vary with the particular manufacturer; "Ameripol SN" for "American polymer synthetic natural" (Goodrich), "Coral" (Firestone), "Natsyn" (Goodyear), "Polyisoprene" (Shell).

† Later, Tilden established the correct structure for isoprene as 2-methyl-1, 4-butadiene,

$$\begin{array}{c} \text{H} \\ \text{HCH} \\ | \\ H_2C = C - C = CH_2 \\ \text{H} \end{array}$$

"right" combination of influences that would cause isoprene to polymerize properly and form rubber. But no one
succeeded, and it appeared, in fact, that nearly everything
else could polymerize better than isoprene. On numerous
grounds, however, several men thought that isoprene had
all that was needed—only the right activator was required
to set off the polymerization. Their thoughts were sobered,
however, by the realization that isoprene need not merely
polymerize—it must polymerize in a very special, orderly
fashion in order to duplicate fully the structure of tree
rubber. The latter had been much investigated and, as a
result of "tear-down" studies, analyses, and X-ray and infrared examinations, rubber chemists felt confident that
purified tree rubber has the following structure:

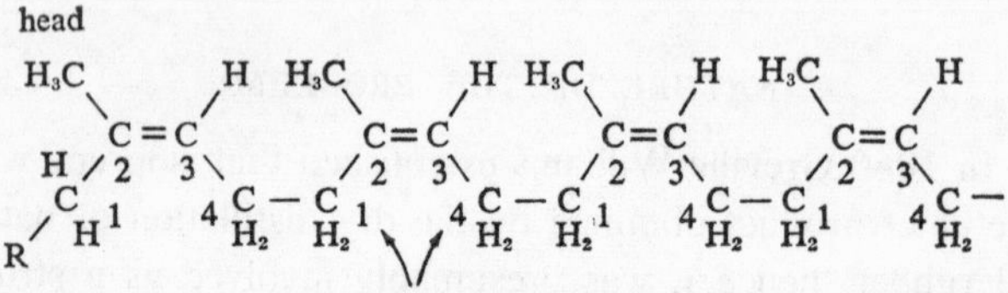

Note that the sequence of carbon atoms 1, 2, 3, 4 is re-
peated indefinitely, and that the CH_3 group marked "Head"
always stands as indicated, adjacent to the *4* position of the
group to its left, and *away* from the *1* position of the group
to its right. This arrangement, as we have noted before, is
called head to tail, head to tail, head to tail, etc. Note too
that the CH_2 groups at the *1* and *4* positions stand *down-*

ward from the $C=C$ group.

There is an alternate possibility, like this:

head   head
```
  H        H₂  H₂          H       H₂   H₂
 HCH   4  C — C           HCH   4  C — C
   \  3  /    1\ 2  H       \  2  3 /    1\ 2  H
   2 C = C        C = C      C = C          C = C 3
     /    H    / 3\ 4   1/   H      /   H          \  4
   — C_H₂      HCH    C — C        HCH          C —
   1           H     H₂    H₂       H           H₂
              head         head
```

polymer B   trans form

Here the groups stand opposite each other with respect to the C=C group, and therefore form a trans arrangement. CH_3 and H are likewise either opposite (trans) or adjacent (cis) to each other.

Because tree rubber has the cis configuration and the 1, 2, 3, 4 units are linked uniformly in the head-to-tail positions, those who try to synthesize rubber must join isoprene units 1 to 4, 1 to 4, 1 to 4, a few thousand times at least, and then make sure that CH_2 groups attached to C=C are always cis to each other. This may seem simple enough, but let us consider how many other possibilities there are.

Examine first the molecule of isoprene, and remember that in the polymerization one of these, A, will be joined to a second one, B, which will in turn be joined to a third, C, and so on.

```
              H
             HCH    H
               \    /
A.      H₂C  = C  — C = CH₂
          1    2    3    4
```

isoprene

(B and C are the same as A)

The reactive positions of the molecules are *across* the double bonds, namely 1 and 2, 3 and 4, and 1 and 4, and the union of A to B will occur in such a manner as to link the reactive positions of A to B, and then B to C, C to D, etc. With regard to geometry alone (and not to mechanism, which is a little more involved!) let us proceed to tie together A, B, C, and D. One readily recognizes the following possibilities:

I. 1 and 4/1 and 4/1 and 4/1 and 4/, etc.
    This arrangement is head to tail, head to tail, with carbons 1 and 4, 1 and 4 joined successively in a long chain.

II. 1 and 4/4 and 1/1 and 4/4 and 1/, etc.
    This arrangement is head to head, tail to tail, with carbons 4 and 4, 1 and 1 joined successively in a long chain.

III. 1 and 2/1 and 2/1 and 2/1 and 2/, etc.

IV. 3 and 4/3 and 4/3 and 4/3 and 4/, etc.

Despite these numerous combinations, they are at least orderly with continuous repetition of structural units. But consider next the possibility of disorder in the linkages; for instance:

V. 1 and 4/1 and 4/4 and 1/3 and 4/1 and 2/1 and 2/, etc.

The degree of possible disorder here is, of course, enormous, and a random helter-skelter combination of isoprene molecules could give this result.

Let us now draw out the molecular combinations corresponding to I, II, III, and IV.

I.

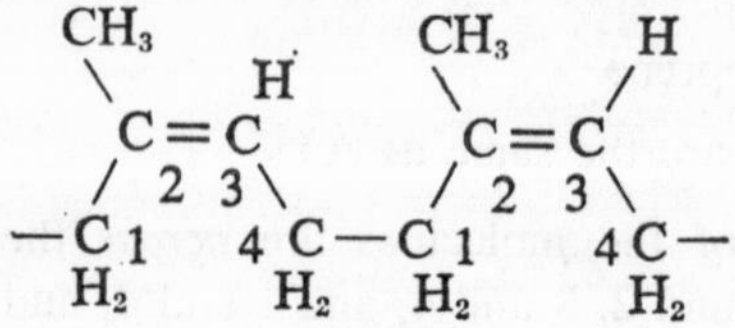

cis head to tail

II.

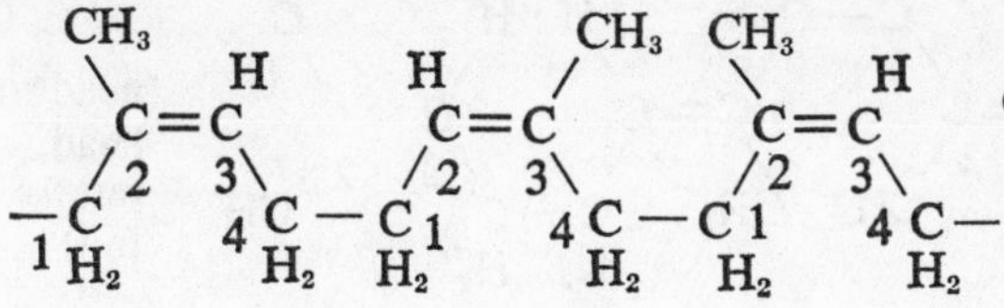

cis head
to head
tail to
tail

III.

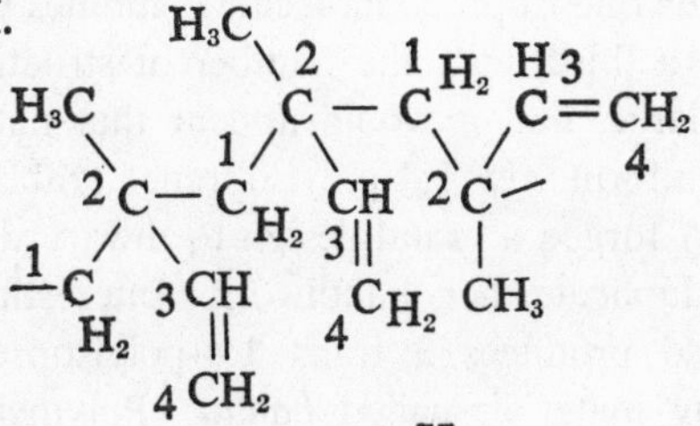

1,2/1,2 union

IV.

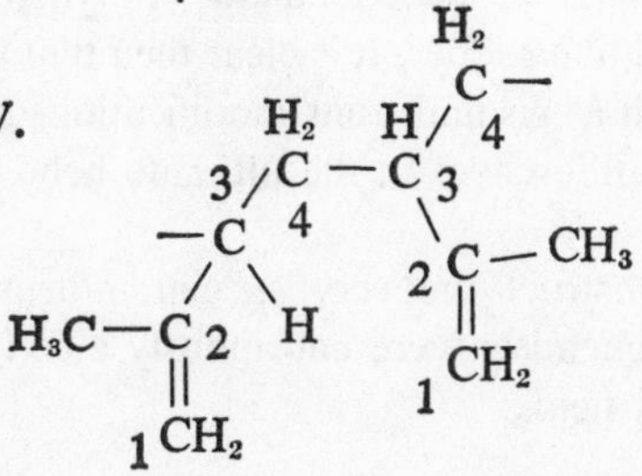

3,4/3,4 union

The structures I and II above are in the cis configuration, but it is equally probable that they could be trans, thus

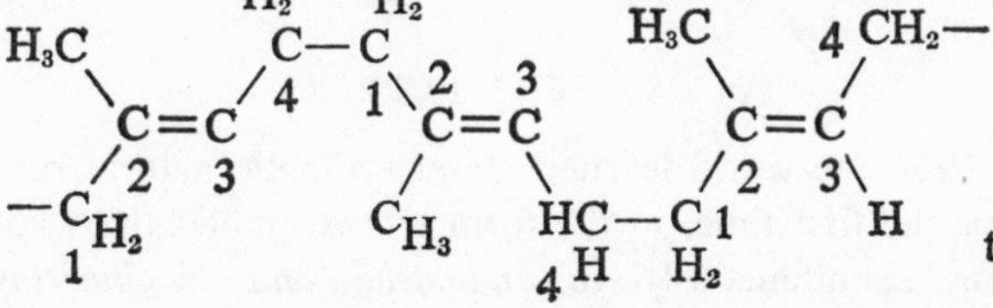

trans

$$
\begin{array}{ccccccc}
& \text{H}_2 & \text{H}_2 & & & \text{H}_2- & \text{trans}\\
& \text{C}-\text{C} & & \text{H} \quad \text{H} & & \text{C} &\\
\text{H} & {}^{/}1 \quad 1\backslash & {}^{3/} & \backslash & & {}^{/}1 &\\
\text{C}=\text{C} & & {}_2\text{C}=\text{C} & & \text{C}=\text{C} & & \text{(head to}\\
{}^{/}3 \quad 2\backslash & & {}^{/} & \backslash & {}^{/}3 \quad 2\backslash & & \text{head,}\\
-\text{C} & \text{CH}_3 & \text{CH}_3 & {}_4\text{C}-\text{C} & & \text{CH}_3 & \text{tail to}\\
\text{H}_2\, 4 & & & \text{H}_2 \quad \text{H}_2\, 4 & & & \text{tail)}
\end{array}
$$

Accordingly, when one isoprene molecule combines with a second and then a third, etc., the number of structural variations is very large, and it would appear that nature in producing a uniform cis 1,4-polyisoprene (rubber) (Polymer *A* above) forged a grand design to thwart all of man's efforts to duplicate her handiwork. Interestingly enough, nature also produces a trans 1,4-polyisoprene, but this is a horny material, called *balata* (Polymer *B* above), and is not at all like rubber. It is clear then that fine points of structure, such as cis and trans modifications of a basic unit, make large differences in the ultimate behavior of molecules.

In the efforts to construct the very special molecules that comprise rubber, chemists were enormously aided by progress in two related fields:

1. The recent work of Professor Ziegler and his colleagues in polymerizing ethylene at low pressure by use of aluminum organic compounds. (See Chapter 7, Section D.)
2. The study of the peculiar reactions of alkali metals, particularly lithium, on unsaturated hydrocarbons.

POLYISOPRENE RUBBER

In 1956 the world learned about synthetic natural rubber for the first time, in the form of two publications appearing simultaneously in *Industrial and Engineering*

Chemistry. One of these emanated from Firestone, the other from Goodrich Rubber Company.* The number of people involved in these two reports (twenty-eight and -nine) is a fair measure of the magnitude of their accomplishments.

How was it done?

Listen to the words of Stavely and his Firestone team.

Isoprene of high purity was further purified just prior to use by refluxing over sodium, followed by distillation; it was then passed over a silica column, after which it was *kept out of contact with air and moisture.* [Italics mine.]

The catalyst was lithium prepared by melting the metal under petroleum jelly and subjecting the molten mass to high speed agitation (stirrer at 18,000 r.p.m. for 30 minutes at 200° C.). The mixing vessel was stainless steel under an atmosphere of *helium gas.* The final dispersion is about 35% metal with particle diameters about 20 microns (20×10^{-3} mm.).

The polymerization recipe employs isoprene, 100 parts, and lithium, 0.1 part, at a temperature of 30–40° C. To the isoprene (in a very dry glass bottle filled with nitrogen) the lithium catalyst is added, after which a loose-fitting cap is attached and the mixture boiled vigorously to purge out possible contaminants, particularly oxygen and water. Finally the cap is sealed tightly and the bottle is fastened on a wheel immersed in a constant temperature water bath and rotated. After a short induction period, the mixture thickens and finally becomes solid. When the polymerization is finished, the polymer is recovered by washing in isopropyl alcohol and acetic acid to remove the lithium. After water washing, antioxidant is added and the product is dried in a vacuum oven.

* The Firestone group, F. W. Stavely and twenty-seven associates, *Industrial and Engineering Chemistry* (1956), p. 778; The Goodrich group, S. E. Horne and eight associates, *Ind. Eng. Chem.* 48 (1956), p. 784.

The authors made the further observation that "the most important factors influencing the structure of the final product are the purity of the components, and the *exclusion of moisture, oxygen* and *air* and *oxygen containing materials.* As the purity of the monomer increases, it becomes much more reactive, even with *traces* of catalyst, until finally its polymerization may proceed with explosive violence. If not properly controlled, the heat evolved may degrade the polymer, even to the point of charring." [Italics mine.]

They also observed that lithium appears to be a unique catalyst* in that it strongly favors the formation of cis 1, 4-polymer to the exclusion of trans 1, 4- and 1, 2-isomers (a trace of 3, 4 polymer was also formed). On the other hand, metals such as sodium, potassium, cesium, and rubidium gave mixtures of cis and trans 1,4-polymers, as well as the 1, 2- and 3, 4-isomers.

The new product, nicknamed "Coral" rubber by the Firestone workers, appeared to be practically identical to natural rubber in its chemical and physical characteristics, including its mechanical performance in the form of tires in road tests. On the other hand, it seemed to be more sensitive to sunlight than tree rubber, while its rate of oxygen absorption in the unvulcanized state was less—a good feature. Molecular weights of Coral and natural rubber were of the same order, approximately 250,000.

And thus the miracle was accomplished. In retrospect it seemed almost simple. But note the extraordinary care for detail and for purity of materials!

The Goodrich team of Horne and his associates described their product in great detail, but gave no specific information on the polymerization recipe, except to say

* Later publications on the subject of isoprene polymerization revealed that organolithium compounds (lithium alkyls) were fully as effective as lithium metal in forming a cis 1,4-polyisoprene practically identical to tree rubber.

that "catalyst systems based on polyolefin information purchased from Karl Ziegler have been applied to isoprene monomer, and modifications have been developed such that either cis or trans 1,4-polyisoprene can now be prepared at will." (Note statement that either polymer was accessible.) Careful analytical studies by infrared and X-ray diffraction methods showed that the Goodrich product, which they called "Ameripol SN," was remarkably similar to tree rubber. Molecular weights of products formed or milled in various ways were high, of the order of 200,000 to 600,000, therefore in the same range as in tree rubber. Ameripol, however, was attacked *more* rapidly by oxygen than natural rubber, and in this respect it was sharply different from Coral, the Firestone product. Nevertheless, the Goodrich product, after vulcanization and compounding, shaped up into tires that were as tough and durable in extended road tests as those made from natural rubber.

Two years later (1958) a second team of Firestone researchers, led by Adams and his associates, reported their successful polymerization of isoprene with triethyl aluminum and titanium tetrachloride catalyst.* Full details of the process were revealed in their production of a polymer which contained 96 per cent cis 1,4-polyisoprene—a remarkable achievement.

Their catalyst was much the same as that used earlier by Ziegler for low-pressure ethylene polymerization, but they found that the ratio of triethyl aluminum to $TiCl_4$ had a critical influence in determining structure and molecular weight of the polymer. (Best ratio was one mole to one mole in a petroleum ether solvent of high purity.) Not until the proper catalyst composition was developed did they succeed in forming the desired product with char-

* H. Adams, R. Stearns, W. Smith, and V. Binder. *Industrial and Engineering Chemistry*, 50 (1958), 1507.

acteristics like natural rubber. Again, extraordinary attention to detail, exclusion of oxygen and water, and extremely high purity of reactants were prime requirements in the successful recipe. Because the metal catalyst flocculated in the solvent, vigorous agitation was required during the polymerization. However, the authors wrote "at 7° C. the polymerization was so rapid, that after one hour, increased viscosity of the solution caused the catalyst to remain suspended after shaking." In twelve hours, the polymerization was completed, and the product was worked up after preliminary soaking in methanol to remove the catalyst. The authors also made the interesting discovery that the polymerization could be greatly increased in velocity by use of chlorinated solvents in place of petroleum ether. O-dichlorobenzene led to a polymerization that was complete in one hour at 50° C.

After formation of the primary polymer, further tests were made on the vulcanized material compounded as for tire manufacture. The mechanical behavior of the finished material was very much like that of natural rubber.

HOW DOES ISOPRENE POLYMERIZE?

In the sections on polyethylene and polypropylene (Chapter 7, Section D, and Chapter 8, Section D) we discussed mechanisms for polymerization of ethylene and propylene by alkyl aluminum catalysts of the type developed by Ziegler and Natta. In a general way, these mechanisms probably pertain as well to a diene like isoprene as they do to the monomers. However, it is clear that each new monomer reaction involves subtle factors for achievement of the precise stereo effect desired in the ultimate polymer. In particular, the complexity of the alkyl aluminum–titanium chloride catalysts makes it hazardous to lay out any brief mechanism for its action; hence none will be attempted.

On the other hand, the lithium-induced polymerization has a beautiful simplicity (on the surface at least!). Professor Henry Gilman, eminent organic chemist and specialist in metal reactions,* has explained the lithium process in the following manner.

Pointing out first that lithium metal has an individuality all its own (despite its membership in the alkali metal family), Professor Gilman writes,

When lithium enters the realm of organic chemistry, its behavior is more like that of an alkaline earth than of an alkali metal. Sodium and other alkali metals form *ionic* bonds with carbon. The alkaline earths, having two electrons in their outer shell, are less eager donators of electrons and form *covalent* bonds with carbon. Each partner in such a bond contributes one electron and the electron pair is shared between them. Lithium also forms a *covalent* bond with carbon but it is a covalent bond with a peculiar configuration, as will be seen.

Speaking next of the rubber polymer and its unique cis 1,4-configuration, he continues:

Recently, with the help of organolithium compounds and with lithium metal itself, investigators at a number of research centers have succeeded in imitating closely the cis head-to-tail structure of natural rubber. One good explanation is that lithium in the organolithium initiator mobilized two unsaturated bonds in the isoprene monomer [see *Figure 10*]. The organic portion of the initiator becomes bound to a carbon on the "tail" of the isoprene and the lithium to a carbon on the "head" of the monomer. The lithium is now in position to perform the same operation on the next isoprene, attaching the *tail* of this molecule to the *head* of the first and attaching itself to the *head* of the now incipient chain. The chain there-

* Henry Gilman and John Eisch, "Lithium," *Scientific American*, January 1963, p. 89.

fore grows in the desired cis-1,4 configuration. Lithium performs this feat better than sodium because of its higher charge density, and because of its smaller size. It can fit more easily between the two double-bonded units of the original isoprene molecule, so that the concentrated positive charge

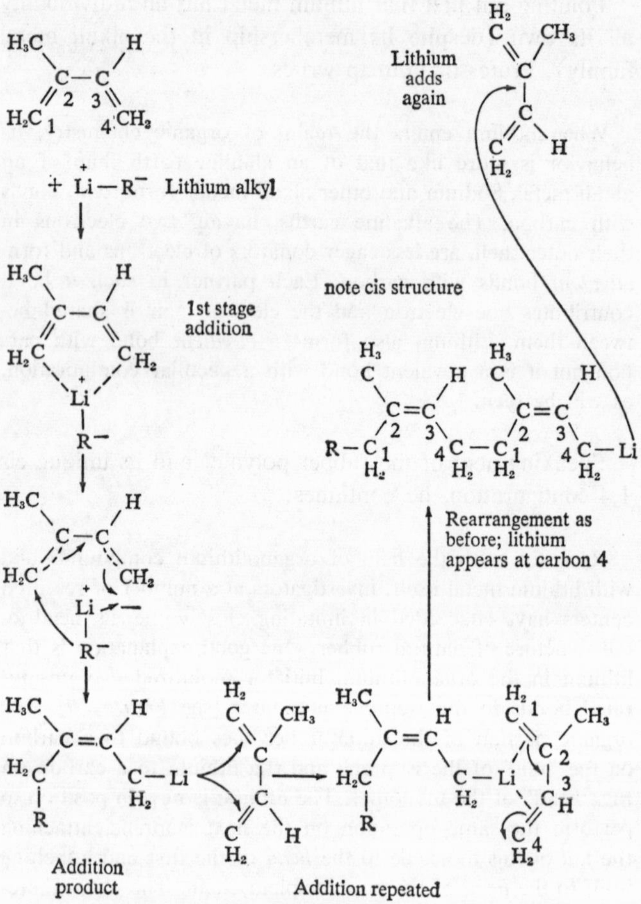

FIGURE 10
Reaction of lithium-alkyl with isoprene.

attracts the mobile double-bond electrons, holding the molecule in the proper position for producing the *cis* structure as
each unit is added to the chain. [Italics mine.]

(Note his particular comment on the *high charge density*
of the lithium atom, and its *small* size, these being key
factors in its unique action.)

The process described here apparently repeats itself three
thousand times or more to form a polymer that ultimately
has a molecular weight of several hundred thousand. One
marvels that the product formed is so much like the desired
biochemical structure, considering that there are so many
devious sidetracks into which the reaction could slip.

Chapter 11

THE NYLONS 6 AND 6/6 ALMOST TWINS

The formation of a linear polyamide structure of great molecular weight that had excellent fiber-forming character was revealed by W. H. Carothers of the Du Pont Company in a series of notable U.S. patents issued during 1937 and 1938. The type of structure involved was what organic chemists call an amide, made up of the atom group in which a carbon chain corresponding to R is con-

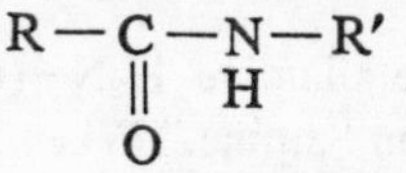

$$R - \underset{\underset{O}{\|}}{C} - \underset{\underset{H}{}}{N} - R'$$

nected to a different carbon chain R' through a carbon-nitrogen bond. It is interesting to note here that nature makes threadlike molecules with amide groups, but these are in the form of proteins. Hair protein (wool) and silk protein are good examples.

Of course, Carothers and his group knew about these natural threads or fibers, but thought it possible to improve on them—at least to synthesize similar materials from simpler starting materials than the amino acids* required for protein synthesis. The result of their efforts was to form molecules with the type of *polyamide* structure shown.

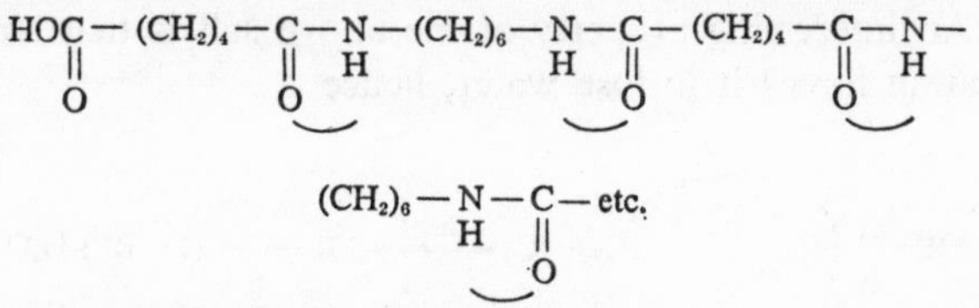

$$HO\underset{\underset{O}{\|}}{C} - (CH_2)_4 - \underset{\underset{O}{\|}}{C} - \underset{\underset{H}{}}{N} - (CH_2)_6 - \underset{\underset{H}{}}{N} - \underset{\underset{O}{\|}}{C} - (CH_2)_4 - \underset{\underset{O}{\|}}{C} - \underset{\underset{H}{}}{N} -$$

$$(CH_2)_6 - \underset{\underset{H}{}}{N} - \underset{\underset{O}{\|}}{C} - etc.$$

* The isolation of *pure* amino acids from a food protein is a complex operation, and the isolated material is therefore too costly for ordinary uses.

Each amide group is underlined. Note the repeating structures

$$-\underset{H}{N}-(CH_2)_6-\underset{H}{N}- \quad \text{and} \quad -\underset{\parallel}{C}-(CH_2)_4-\underset{\parallel}{C}-$$
$$\qquad\qquad\qquad\qquad\qquad O \qquad\qquad\qquad O$$

which in the final product are joined hundreds of times to form a material with molecular weight in excess of 10,-000. These structures are derived from two reacting materials, adipic *acid,*

$$HO\underset{\parallel}{C}-(CH_2)_4-\underset{\parallel}{C}-OH$$
$$\quad O \qquad\qquad\qquad O$$

and hexamethylene diamine $H_2N-(CH_2)_4-NH_2$, an organic *base,* called an "amine." When the acid and base are first mixed, the natural consequence is formation of a salt. If we picture one R-COOH acid group and one amino group $R'-NH_2$ reacting at a time, the salt formed is

$$\left[R-\underset{\parallel}{C}-\bar{O}\right]\left[\underset{H}{\overset{H^+}{\underset{|}{HN}}}-R'\right]$$
$$\qquad O$$

This salt is fairly soluble in water, so a polymer (giant molecule) made up of many such saltlike groups could hardly make a practical fiber because it would wash away.

An interesting property of the above salt is that strong heating forces it to lose water, hence

$$R-\underset{\parallel}{C}-O \quad \overset{H^+}{\underset{|}{HN}}-R' \xrightarrow{\text{heat}} R-\underset{\parallel\;\;|}{C}-\underset{O\;\;H}{N}-R'+H_2O$$
$$\qquad O \qquad\quad H$$

$$-HOH$$

and the new structure formed possesses the amide group. It is precisely this process that leads to the formation of nylon from the acid and the base, thus

Adipic acid + hexamethylene diamine ⟶ poly "salt"
Poly "salt" + heat = H_2O + polyamide

In contrast to the salt, the polyamide is not soluble in water. Carothers in his patents on the process* describes variations in the fundamental process where acids and amines with different lengths of carbon chains are employed. Here is one description:

> The most useful salts for the preparation of fiber forming polyamides are those derived from diamines of formula $H_2N - CH_2 - R - CH_2 - NH_2$ and diacids of formula $HOOC - CH_2 - R' - CH_2 - COOH$ in which R and R' are *single* bonded hydrocarbon chains having at least two carbon atoms. Of this group of salts, those in which R and R' represent $(CH_2)_{x \text{ or } y}$ (x and y are 2,3,4,5, etc.) form a select class since they are especially useful in the preparation of fiber forming polyamides of high quality. Polyamides derived from this class of salts are easily obtained at an appropriate viscosity for spinning and have a type of crystallinity which enables them to be cold drawn with facility. Moreover, these polyamide fibers are all characterized by high tenacity, high orientation, lack of sensitivity to humidity, good elastic recovery, resistance to most solvents and chemical

* Anyone having access to a patent library will find a fascinating story in the lucid explanations which Carothers gives in the series of patents listed below (all of which were assigned to the Du Pont Company).
  U.S. patents by W. H. Carothers

2,071,250 Feb. 16, 1937	2,130,523 Sept. 20, 1938
2,071,251 Feb. 16, 1937	2,130,947 Sept. 20, 1938
2,071,252 Feb. 16, 1937	2,130,948 Sept. 20, 1938
2,071,253 Feb. 16, 1937	

Some inventors and chemists would be well satisfied in a whole lifetime to produce seven patents as outstanding as these! Carothers, however, went on to produce a total of fifty-five before his life was prematurely ended at age forty.

reagents, good dyeing properties and good aging characteristics in the air even at moderately elevated temperatures.
[From U.S. Patent No. 2,130,947]

Here, indeed, was a twentieth-century Aladdin's lamp
lighting the way to a new world of synthetic fibrous materials, and to clothing with a hitherto unknown durability. Shortly afterward (in 1939), as everyone is well aware,
the Du Pont Company announced the commercial availability of the new material under the name "nylon," the
first *man-made* fiber in the world. In the form of ladies'
stockings, nylon swept the country, and before long it was a
household word denoting a magic material of notably superior quality. Nylon soon appeared in numerous fabrics
including the cord for high-grade tires, and in threads
known best to men as fishlines that remain strong year
after year, because nylon is free from rotting even when
it is wet most of the time. Soon thereafter, for the same
reason, nylon became the favorite material for fish nets
used in heavy-duty commercial fishing, and for boat ropes
exposed to sea or lake water. The structural strength and
durability of nylon are also good enough so that numerous
mechanical devices like gears and pulleys have been fabri-
cated from it with great success.

Shortly after the nylon made from adipic acid and
hexamethylene diamine appeared, an interesting variant of
it came into being, that which was made from "caprolactam." Caprolactam is a ringlike molecule with the
structure

It is an unusual compound because of its seven-membered ring. The ring may be opened up between the carbon and nitrogen, after which a recombination of the reactive ends leads to a *linear* polymer with the following structure:

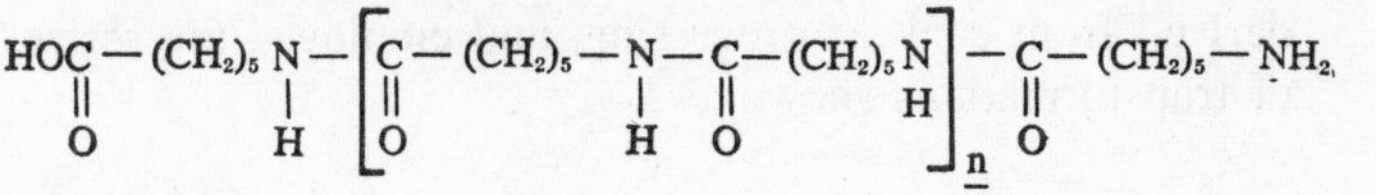

$$\text{HOC} - (CH_2)_5 \ N - \left[\begin{array}{c} C - (CH_2)_5 - N - C - (CH_2)_5 N \\ \| \qquad\qquad | \quad \| \qquad\quad H \\ O \qquad\qquad H \quad O \end{array} \right]_n - C - (CH_2)_5 - NH_2,$$

where n is a large number, 50 or more

This giant molecule is a *poly*amide because it contains many

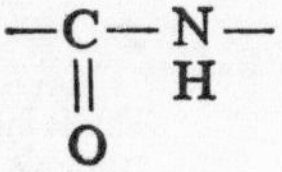

$$\begin{array}{c} -C-N- \\ \| \quad H \\ O \end{array}$$

groups, and as such it resembles the original nylon. However, its amide structure is derived altogether from a *single* repeating unit, whereas the original nylon has in it two repeating units, those derived from adipic acid and hexamethylene diamine. On this account, the nylon derived from caprolactam is known in technical circles as Nylon 6 while that from the acid and amine is known as Nylon 6/6 (each reactive part, as you can see, contains 6 carbon atoms).

Nylon 6/6 is widely used in the United States, while Nylon 6 is the more popular brand in Europe and elsewhere, particularly in Japan, where the caprolactam is made on a large scale. Nylon 6/6 melts at 265° C.—about fifty centigrade degrees higher than Nylon 6. It is harder, more rigid, but not as tough as Nylon 6.

FROM WHAT INGREDIENTS ARE NYLONS MADE?

The value of nylon is even more greatly appreciated when one considers the variety of chemical reactions required for making the monomers—those materials that interact directly to give the giant linear molecules required either for Nylon 6/6 or Nylon 6. The two materials will be described separately.

Nylon 6/6. The original process began with benzene derived from coal-tar processing, and employed the series of transformations shown.

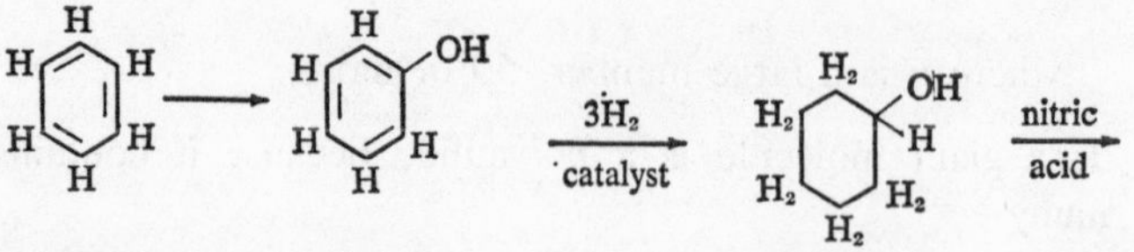

benzene   phenol   cyclohexanol

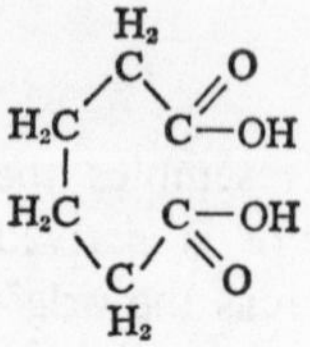

This is ingredient I for the nylon synthesis. The second ingredient, hexamethylene diamine, was derived from it.

I. adipic acid

| ammonia

ammonium salt of adipic acid

| heat and dehydration

N≡C—(CH₂)₄ C≡N   (adiponitrile)

H₂ | + catalyst

II.   H₂N(CH₂)₆—NH₂   (hexamethylene diamine)

Later, processes were developed for direct oxidation of cyclohexane (by use of nitric acid) to form adipic acid, the cyclohexane (see Chapter 4) being derived from benzene by catalytic addition of hydrogen. During the fifties cyclohexane became available from petroleum at a favorable price, so now we can consider that adipic acid is a petrochemical.

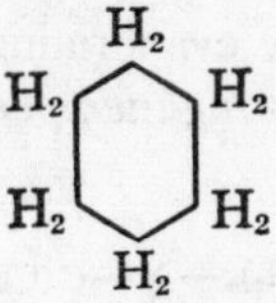

$$H_2C \underset{H_2}{\overset{H_2}{\bigcirc}} H_2$$

The production of hexamethylene diamine (ingredient No. 2) took a fascinating turn via a series of reactions based on butadiene—a petrochemical derived from butane in natural gas. (See also Houdry's biography, Chapter 5, Section D.) The reactions employed are the following:

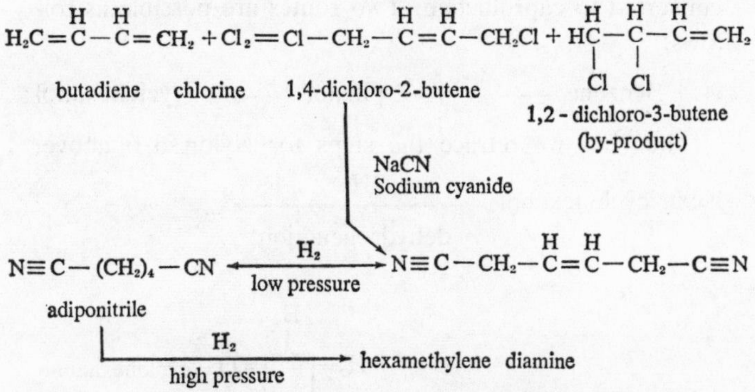

$$H_2C = \overset{H}{C} - \overset{H}{C} = CH_2 + Cl_2 = Cl - CH_2 - \overset{H}{C} = \overset{H}{C} - CH_2Cl + HC - \overset{H}{\underset{Cl}{C}} - \overset{H}{\underset{Cl}{C}} = CH_2$$

butadiene   chlorine   1,4-dichloro-2-butene

1,2 - dichloro-3-butene
(by-product)

NaCN
Sodium cyanide

$$N\equiv C - (CH_2)_4 - CN \xleftarrow[\text{low pressure}]{H_2} N\equiv C - CH_2 - \overset{H}{C} = \overset{H}{C} - CH_2 - C\equiv N$$

adiponitrile

$$\xrightarrow[\text{high pressure}]{H_2} \text{hexamethylene diamine}$$

A key feature in the above scheme is the production of 1, 4-dichloro-2-butene, which is highly reactive to two molecules of sodium cyanide, whereupon two C atoms are added to the original four to make the needed six. (The by-product 1, 2-dichlorobutene is not wasted, because it can be converted by alkali to chloroprene, the monomer for neoprene synthesis.)

SUMMARY

Butadiene is converted to $H_2N-(CH_2)_6-NH_2$ II
Cyclohexane is converted to $HOOC-(CH_2)_4-COOH$ I
I + II = Nylon "salt" (in water)

Water is removed by evaporation to form dry "salt"

"Salt" in autoclave at *high temperature* gives polyamide:

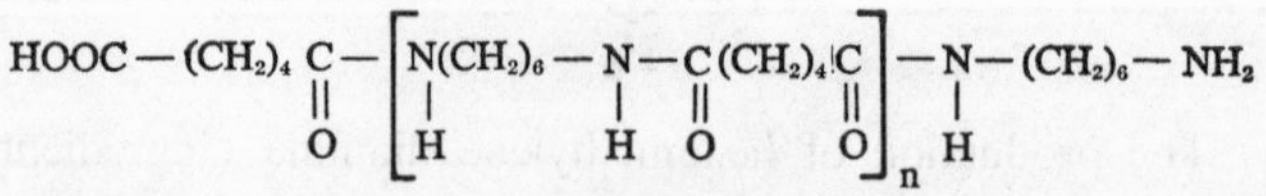

$$HOOC-(CH_2)_4 \underset{O}{\overset{\parallel}{C}} - \left[\underset{H}{\overset{|}{N}}(CH_2)_6 - \underset{H}{\overset{|}{N}} - \underset{O}{\overset{\parallel}{C}}(CH_2)_4 \underset{O}{\overset{\parallel}{C}} \right]_n - \underset{H}{\overset{|}{N}} - (CH_2)_6 - NH_2$$

Nylon polymer (6/6) Melting point 255° C.

Nylon 6. This product requires the formation of the key starting material, cyclohexanone oxime, which in turn is converted to caprolactam. Two routes are possible as follows:

A.   Benzene ⎯⎯⎯⎯⟶ phenol ⎯⎯⟶ cyclohexanol

Thus far, we retrace the steps for Nylon 6/6 above.

Next, cyclohexanol $\xrightarrow[\text{dehydrogenation}]{-2H}$

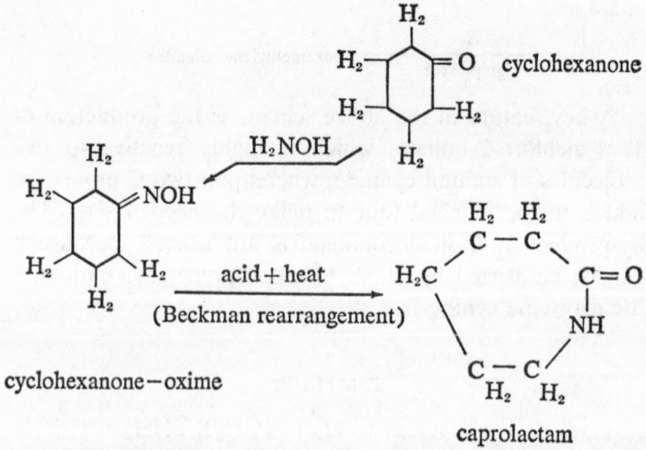

cyclohexanone

cyclohexanone−oxime

caprolactam

This was the original route to caprolactam.

B.   The new route to caprolactam (discovered by E. Müller, 1959):

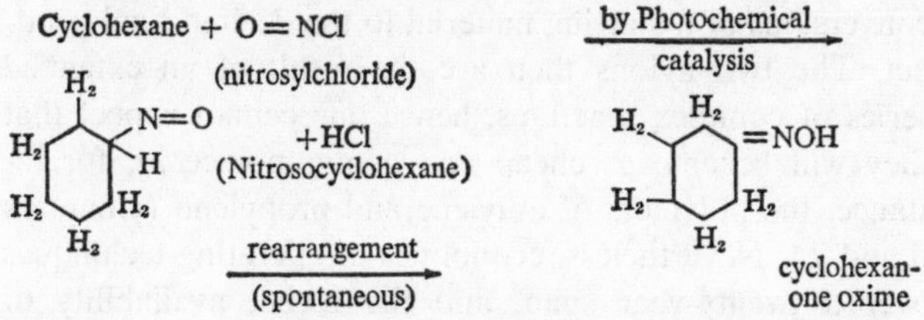

Cyclohexane + O = NCl
(nitrosylchloride)

by Photochemical
catalysis

+HCl
(Nitrosocyclohexane)

rearrangement
(spontaneous)

= NOH

cyclohexan-
one oxime

This rearranges to form caprolactam* as described before.

In this route to cyclohexanone oxime, the key material is nitrosylchloride. It is formed by a series of reactions which begin with ammonia and air:

a. $2NH_3 + 3O_2$ (partial oxidation) $= N_2O_3 + 3H_2O$
b. $N_2O_3 + 2H_2SO_4 = 2[O = NOSO_3H] + H_2O$
c. $O = N - OSO_3H + HCl = O = N - Cl + H_2SO_4$

The HCl needed for stage *c* is continuously replenished by HCl formed when nitrosylchloride reacts with cyclohexane. Thus, the consumed materials in the overall process are ammonia and air. (It is, however, necessary to re-

* The polymerization of caprolactam occurs by catalysis with alkali, thus:

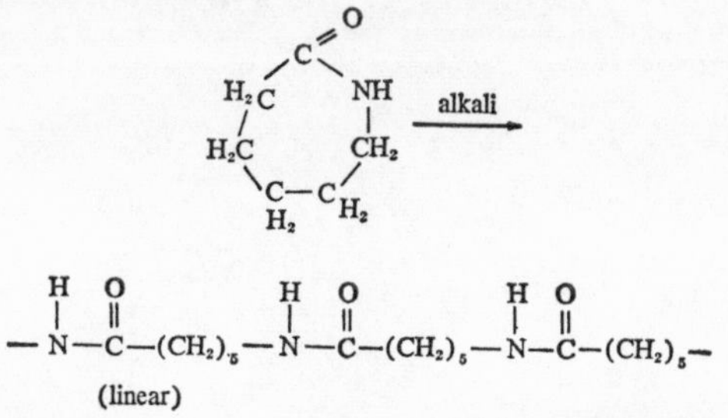

alkali

— N — C—(CH₂)₅—N — C—(CH₂)₅—N — C—(CH₂)₅—
(linear)

Nylon 6 Melting p. 225° C.

move water from the system to provide the necessary high concentration of acid.)

The above processes admittedly are not simple direct conversions of a starting material to the desired final product. The two nylons then are the result of an extended series of complex reactions, hence one cannot expect that they will become as cheap and commonplace as, for instance, the polymers of ethylene and propylene (Chapters 6 and 7). Nevertheless, economies in operating techniques over a twenty-year span, and the recent availability of cyclohexane from petroleum have contributed to cost reduction and the availability of both nylons on a high scale.

The mechanical and electrical properties of nylon are listed and compared with other polymers in Chapter 4. The chemical properties, including resistance to corroding agents, are much alike for the two nylons, but it is interesting to note that Nylon 6/6 is more heat-resistant than Nylon 6; its melting point is about 265° C. versus 225° C. for the latter.

Chapter 12

RUBBER FROM ROCKS AND FROM
NATURAL GAS

Before examining these pages, the reader might well take a backward glance at the pages of automotive history dated about 1905. At that time an adventurous driver who took his car out after dark first made sure that his "carbide" generator was stoked up and working properly. This was to assure him of a supply of acetylene gas to operate his headlights. The acetylene was generated by the reaction of water on calcium carbide, a hard rocky substance made by the fusion of calcium oxide and carbon in an electric furnace.

$$CaC_2 + H_2O = H - C \equiv C - H + Ca(OH)_2$$
calcium carbide   acetylene   calcium hydroxide

Acetylene, a high-energy gas and a fine fuel for head lamps (when it did not explode), was also widely used in oxyacetylene welding, an industrial operation that speeded up greatly the construction of mammoth steel structures like skyscrapers and ships. The latter use continues to this day, but, fortunately for the driver, acetylene head lamps have retired to the museums!

Turn now to 1931, the year when the chemical world learned of an extraordinary synthetic achievement—the formation of a man-made polymer with excellent rubbery character. The source? Acetylene! The men who did this were Wallace Carothers, Ira Williams, Arnold Collins, and James Kirby of the Du Pont research laboratories. Their discovery was announced in an article that stands as a masterpiece of scientific revelation: "A New Synthetic Rubber: Chloroprene and its Polymers."[*]

Back of the researchers lay several years of difficult experimentation with highly reactive chlorine compounds and a notable episode of cooperation with academic scientists, one of whom, Father Julius Nieuwland, was a pioneer investigator in acetylene chemistry at the University of Notre Dame. Nieuwland had already shown how acetylene could be converted in good yield to two exciting but dangerous hydrocarbons:

vinyl acetylene $\quad H_2C \supset C - C \equiv C - H$ (VA), and

with an H above the third carbon.

divinyl acetylene $\quad H_2C \supset C - C \equiv C - C \supset CH_2$ (DVA)

with H below the second and fifth carbons.

Carothers and his research men then took vinyl acetylene, converted it by reaction with hydrochloric acid to the new compound chloroprene, $H_2C=C-C=CH_2$, and polymerized this to a rubbery material to which they gave the name "polychloroprene."

with Cl and H below the second and third carbons.

In a simple, lucid manner that nevertheless carried the impact of this dramatic discovery, Carothers described the experiments that led to this great advance in synthetic chemistry.

Study of the reactions of vinyl acetylene has led to the synthesis of a series of analogs of isoprene.[†] One of these is

[*] This article was published in the *Journal of the American Chemical Society*, 53 (1931), 4203.

[†] For structure and reactions of isoprene, refer back to Chapter 9.

2-chlorobutadiene ("chloroprene"). This compound is especially interesting for the following reasons: It is easily prepared in quantity in a state of purity; it differs structurally from isoprene only in having a chlorine atom instead of a methyl group; like isoprene it reacts with itself to yield a synthetic rubber; but the transformation occurs with much greater velocity than in the case of isoprene, and the product is distinctly superior to natural rubber in some of its properties. The following example is typical of the spontaneous polymerization of chloroprene. About 40 ccs. of chloroprene is placed in a 50 cc. glass bottle, closed with a cork stopper, and allowed to stand at laboratory temperature in the absence of direct light. After 24 hours the viscosity of the sample has increased considerably; after four days it has set to a stiff, colorless, transparent jelly, which still contains a considerable amount of chloroprene. As the polymerization proceeds further, this jelly contracts in volume and becomes tough and dense. After ten days all the chloroprene has polymerized.

. . . The product is a colorless or pale yellow transparent, resilient, elastic mass resembling completely vulcanized soft rubber. It has a tensile strength of about 140 Kg/cm^2 and an elongation at break of about 800%. It is not plastic, that is, it does not sheet out smoothly on the rolls of a rubber mill nor break down on continued milling. It is not thermoplastic. It swells strongly but does not dissolve in carbon tetrachloride, benzene, nitrobenzene or ether. Compared with natural rubber the tendency of this material to imbibe gasoline and lubricating oil is very slight. When a stretched sample is immersed in liquid air for a moment and then struck with a hammer, it shatters into fibrous fragments—the same behavior as already observed with natural rubber.

Carothers continues with several additional observations on chloroprene and its polymers:

Oxygen is an exceedingly powerful catalyst for the transformation of chloroprene into the polymer. Samples of chloroprene distilled in high vacuum and sealed off in glass tubes with no exposure to air show an appreciable increase in viscosity only after a period of 1–2 months, and the transformation to polymer is incomplete after 12 months. Since it is practically impossible to prepare chloroprene without exposing it to air at some time during the preparation, it seems probable that even the products distilled in high vacuum are not altogether free from catalyst. But the amount of oxygen necessary to produce an optimum catalytic effect is quite small—at ordinary temperatures the presence of a volume of air equal to about 10% of the volume of the chloroprene sample causes the transformation to polymer to be complete in eight to ten days. Large quantities of oxygen do affect however the character of the final product, which instead of being colorless or slightly yellow, is dark brown and considerably harder and stiffer than the usual products. Substances that generally function as antioxidants act as powerful inhibitors for the transformation chloroprene into the polymer. The presence of 0.1% catechol will permit a sample to remain fluid for several months.

In contrast to natural rubber, polychloroprene was found by its discoverers to be much more resistant to the action of ozone, and to oxygen at elevated temperature and pressure. The ozone test is a critical one for rubbers intended for insulation around electric motors, because a sparking motor produces ozone which in time degrades the insulation. The resistance to solvents on the part of polychloroprene led to its use in rubber tubing intended to convey gasoline, fuel oils, and similar fluids that ordinarily would cause swelling and ultimate dissolution of conventional rubber tubes. Polychloroprene was found also to be more resistant to degradation than natural rubber with respect to hydrogen chloride, hydrogen fluoride, and strong alkalis.

THE STRUCTURE OF POLYCHLOROPRENE

Carothers and his colleagues formulated the structure of polychloroprene as a giant molecule containing successive monomer units, as follows:

$$\left[\begin{array}{c} \text{H} \quad\quad \text{H} \;\; \text{H} \\ -\text{C}-\text{C}=\text{C}-\text{C} \\ \text{H} \;\; | \quad\quad \text{H} \\ \quad\;\; \text{Cl} \\ 1 \;\; 2 \;\; 3 \;\; 4 \end{array}\right] - \left[\begin{array}{c} \text{H} \quad\quad \text{H} \;\; \text{H} \\ \text{C}-\text{C}=\text{C}-\text{C} \\ \text{H} \;\; | \quad\quad \text{H} \\ \quad\;\; \text{Cl} \\ 1 \;\; 2 \;\; 3 \;\; 4 \end{array}\right] - \left[\begin{array}{c} \text{H} \quad\quad \text{H} \\ \text{C}-\text{C}=\text{C}-\text{CH}_2- \\ \text{H} \;\; | \quad\quad \text{H} \\ \quad\;\; \text{Cl} \\ 1 \;\; 2 \;\; 3 \;\; 4 \end{array}\right]_n$$

The evidence for this kind of structure depended on two primary chemical facts:

1. The chlorine atoms were very firmly fastened to the polymer, and were not removed by hot water, dilute alkalis and the like; hence they were assumed to be part of a "vinyl" system, namely $-\text{C}=\text{C}-$.
$$\text{Cl}$$

2. Degradation of polychloroprene by hot nitric acid produced a considerable amount of a 4-carbon acid, succinic acid. This compound could only arise from a structure that contained a string of four carbon atoms separated by a carbon-carbon double bond.

In the above formula, if one counts along the chain of carbons, 3, 4, 1, 2/, 3, 4, 1, 2/, etc., he encounters a C=C group at every fourth carbon atom. The nitric acid reaction splits the molecule at these double bonds and yields a series of four carbon fragments, each of which becomes succinic acid, $\text{HOOC}(\text{CH}_2)_2\text{COOH}$, as a result of picking up oxygen from the nitric acid.

Carothers made the additional observation that the long chain of successive carbon atoms could not adequately account for the behavior of the polymer in respect to its resistance to solvent action. Stringlike molecules, such as polystyrene and polyethylene, ultimately succumb to the action of hydrocarbon solvents; molecules that resist penetration by solvents must be cross-linked as part of a giant network, thus:

$$\begin{array}{c}
A-A-A-A-A-A-A-A- \\
\quad | \qquad\qquad | \qquad\qquad | \\
A-A-A-A-A-A-A-A- \\
\qquad | \qquad\qquad | \\
A-A-A-A-A-A-A-A-
\end{array}$$

The vertical lines represent atom groups that link together the long chains. Carothers supposed that these cross-links could be in part oxygen, or $C-C$ bonds derived from the interaction of doubly-bonded carbons. As we have seen before in the case of polystyrene, cross-linking to the extent of only 1 per cent can increase profoundly the resistance of a polymer to solvent penetration. The effect of the cross-linking that occurs spontaneously in the polymerization of chloroprene is to produce a rubber that is "prevulcanized," as Carothers has already pointed out.

Carothers also called attention to the problem of establishing the cis or trans nature of the C/C double bonds in the polymer, which at the time was unknown. Subsequent studies showed that the polymer was mostly trans, that is, it had the configuration

The polymerization process, induced as it had been by oxygen reaction and free radical processes, led to the trans structure that is shown.

Shortly after its discovery, polychloroprene was in production by the Du Pont Company and the world came to know of it by the name "neoprene." Du Pont produced 920 tons of it in 1938, but by 1956 was able to produce 155,000 tons. In the mid-sixties production in the United States exceeded 200,000 tons annually. In retrospect, the development of this rubbery polymer appeared simple and direct, yet there is no question that success only came from ingenious and painstaking operation at every step of the way.

It was only after many years that other researchers succeeded in producing polychloroprene in the cis modification, thus

$$
\begin{array}{ccccccccc}
\mathrm{Cl} & & \mathrm{H} & \mathrm{Cl} & & \mathrm{H} & \mathrm{Cl} & & \mathrm{H} \\
\diagdown & & \diagup & \diagdown & & \diagup & \diagdown & & \diagup \\
& \mathrm{C}\!\!=\!\!\mathrm{C} & & & \mathrm{C}\!\!=\!\!\mathrm{C} & & & \mathrm{C}\!\!=\!\!\mathrm{C} & \\
\mathrm{H}\diagup & & \diagdown\mathrm{H} & \mathrm{H}\diagup & & \diagdown\mathrm{H} & \mathrm{H}\diagup & & \diagdown\mathrm{H} \\
-\mathrm{C} & & \mathrm{C}\!-\!\mathrm{C} & & & \mathrm{C}\!-\!\mathrm{C} & & & \mathrm{C}- \\
\mathrm{H} & \text{cis} & \mathrm{H}\ \ \mathrm{H} & & \text{cis} & \mathrm{H}\ \ \mathrm{H} & & \text{cis} & \mathrm{H}
\end{array}
$$

This was accomplished by Drs. Aufdermarsh and Ferguson, also of the Du Pont Company. They arrived at this cis structure by use of magnesium and tin organocompounds in a series of complex stages. The final result was a product that was a soft amorphous gum, quite different from the original rubbery product in 1931.

MONOMERS FOR THE SYNTHESIS OF NEOPRENE

According to the methods devised by Nieuwland, acetylene of high purity was caused to form vinyl and divinyl acetylenes. The necessary catalyst for the purpose was a cuprous ammonium compound prepared by reaction of cuprous chloride with ammonium chloride in the presence of metallic copper and hydrochloric acid. The acetylene gas was passed into the aqueous cuprous mixture until absorption ceased, after which the mixture was allowed to "age" for several days. The vinyl and divinyl acetylenes formed in the reaction were then distilled out of the mixture at reduced pressure and, after water removal, were redistilled. Their structures are the following:

$$H_2C = C - C \equiv CH \qquad H_2C = C - C \equiv C - C = CH^2$$
$$\overset{H}{|} \qquad\qquad\qquad \overset{H}{|}$$

vinyl acetylene   divinyl acetylene

Nieuwland warned that these vinyl acetylenes were extremely dangerous to handle, and should be used promptly and not be allowed to stand around. They polymerize spontaneously and take up oxygen from air to form explosive peroxides.

Carothers next showed that the vinyl acetylene would react with concentrated hydrochloric acid at 25–30° C., provided again that cuprous chloride and ammonium chloride were present. The overall reaction is summarized thus:

$$HC \equiv C - C = CH_2 + HCl = H_2C = C - C = CH^2$$
$$\qquad\qquad \overset{H}{|} \qquad\qquad\qquad\qquad \overset{H}{|}$$
$$\qquad\qquad\qquad\quad (Cu_2Cl_2) \qquad\qquad Cl$$

(chloroprene)

It is interesting to see that butadiene may also be used as a source of chloroprene by addition first of chlorine and then removal of HCl by use of alkali.

$$2H_2C = C - C = CH_2 + 2Cl_2 = HC - C - C = CH_2 \qquad \text{3,4 dichloro-} \atop \text{1-butene}$$

I

+

$$H_2C = C - C = CH_2 \quad \xleftarrow[\text{alkali}]{- HCl} \quad H_2C - C = C - CH_2$$

chloroprene   II

1,4-dichloro-
2-butene

Muskat and Northrop at Northwestern University worked extensively on the chlorination of butadiene in 1930, and succeeded in preparing both compounds I and II in pure form and good yield. But it was some time later that the successful conversion of compound I into chloroprene was worked out. Compound II, as we have already seen in Chapter 11, is a material that goes into the synthesis of nylon.

Meanwhile, acetylene itself has become the object of synthesis from natural gas. The combustion of methane with insufficient oxygen, or the high-temperature cracking of methane, produces acetylene in significant amounts. The reaction is notably *endothermal;* that is, much energy must be put into the system to form the acetylene.

$$2CH_4 \xrightarrow[\text{O}_2]{\text{heat}} HC \equiv CH + 3H_2$$

(Hydrogen is partly converted to water)

This process is gaining steadily in industrial prominence to the point where as much acetylene is made from methane as from calcium carbide.

SUMMARY

Polychloroprene, or neoprene, is a historic first—the first synthetic rubbery material to become commercially successful and to maintain its place in the rubber world. Neoprene is not the same as tree rubber, but resembles it chemically in many ways. However, it is chemically more resistant than tree rubber to solvent penetration and to oxidation.

Neoprene may be synthesized either from acetylene or from butadiene. The acetylene in turn may come from calcium carbide or from natural gas; the butadiene is derived almost entirely from petroleum. Accordingly, neoprene is a polymer of petrochemical parenthood.

The uses of neoprene continue to expand. They lie largely in solvent-resistant tubing and stoppers, soles and heels for shoes, impregnated paper and leather for gaskets, and sealing materials.

A novel use little heard of by the public is the use of neoprene in elasticized concrete and mortar. Neoprene latex is added to concrete and mortar to improve adhesion, impact resistance, and acid resistance. A large use is for cement mixes for ship-deck compositions, where it improves adhesion to steel and gives increased flexibility against the stress of ship vibration.

These versatile uses plus the fact that neoprene can be synthesized readily from cheap abundant materials make it probable that neoprene will be prominent in the rubber world for a long time to come.

Chapter 13

MORE VALUES FROM THE AROMATICS

HOW AROMATIC HYDROCARBONS UNDERLIE
MANY NEW SYNTHETICS

Aromatic hydrocarbons and other ring compounds containing nitrogen, sulfur, or oxygen have long enjoyed popularity as bases for dyes, medicinal products, explosives, insecticides, antiseptics and the like. They are now coming into increasing prominence as ingredients for building giant molecules—those used for structural purposes as films, fibers, and molding compounds. In particular, the aromatic rings are beneficial for the construction of polymers that withstand temperatures above 400° C. (where aliphatic compounds begin to undergo thermal cracking) and are resistant to intense radiation—conditions that must be faced by objects traveling in outer space.

Fortunately, aromatic compounds are available from two great sources, coal and petroleum. Coal was the original source via the coking process performed by the steel industry, and coking operations continue to produce distillates that are a rich source of aromatics. However, petroleum has recently become a major source of benzene, toluene, and the xylenes. An important factor in the employment of aromatics for precise synthesis of extraordinary structures is the high purity attainable commercially at reasonable prices. For instance, the Phillips Petroleum Company produces para-xylene of 99.5 per cent purity by combined distillation and fractional crystallization. Likewise from high-purity benzene the Dow Chemical Company has been able to prepare styrene of the required purity (more than 99 per cent) for production of sparkling-clear polystyrene resins.

Despite one hundred years of progress in unraveling the secrets of aromatic character since the days of August Kekule in Germany, some of the mysteries still remain. Nearly every issue of a journal of organic chemistry reveals some new facet of aromatic character, or an application of aromatics for synthetic purposes. Many of the latter are for the production of high polymers that have unusual chemical stability and resistance to decomposition or melting.

A few of these novel aromatic-based giant molecules are described below.

A.   *The Paracyclophanes and Poly-para-xylylene*

Leading characters in a drama that finally produced the extraordinary substance

$$\left[-\begin{matrix} H \\ C \\ H \end{matrix} - \bigcirc - \begin{matrix} H & H \\ C - C \\ H & H \end{matrix} - \bigcirc - \begin{matrix} H \\ C \\ H \end{matrix} - \right]_{\underline{n}} \quad I$$

$\underline{n} = 1000$ or more

known as poly-para-xylylene were scattered widely from England to California. Professor M. Szwarc, in Manchester, England, was involved in determining the energy for dissociation of the C—H bond by cracking toluene and xylene at high temperatures; C. J. Brown and A. C. Farthing, of Imperial Chemical Industries, also in Manchester, became deeply interested in the by-products of the Szwarc reaction, which included polymers and a strange substance of high melting point (285° C.), which they found to have the structure

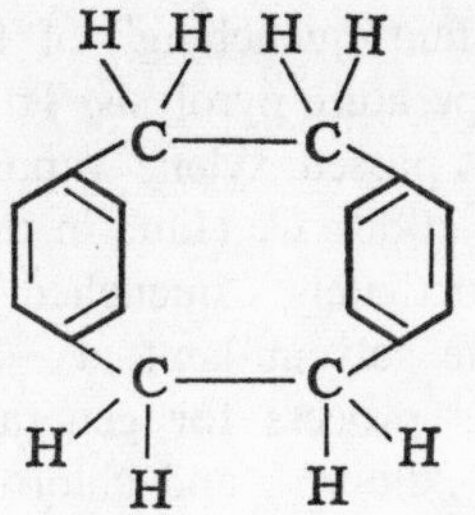

II

(In II the benzene rings face each other as in a sandwich.)
Professor Donald Cram at the University of California
was busy with syntheses aimed at producing macro rings;
he made compound II and others like it but with additional C atoms between the rings (for these he coined the
generic name "paracyclophanes"); Louis Errede and Billy
Landrum, in New Jersey at the Kellogg Company, contrived an improved process for isolating the products of
the pyrolysis of para-xylene, and succeeded in capturing
a new diradical, so-called "para-xylylene" which was formulated as

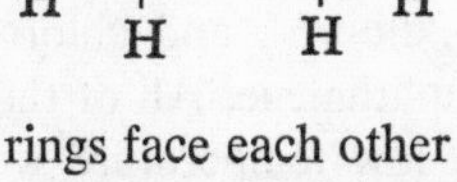

III

Errede and Landrum found that para-xylylene could
be stored as such, but only at very low temperature—its
half-life in xylene was only twenty-one hours at −78° C.,
but it could be kept indefinitely at −190° C. They found
that III would polymerize spontaneously to a giant molecule of high melting point (over 300° C.) simply by allowing its cold solution to warm to room temperature. As
the polymer formed, it precipitated readily from the
monomer solution because of its extraordinary insolubility
—a factor related to its chemical stability.

What Errede and Landrum had devised was a novel

technique of "instant quenching" of the products of a fast-flow high-temperature pyrolysis. To form and preserve para-xylylene they passed xylene vapors at low pressure through a tube at 1000° C. (time in the tube was 1/100 second) and immediately "quenched" the products of cracking in hexane solvent kept at −80° C. Moreover, they extended this process for generating para radicals like III to methyl-, fluoro-, and chloro-xylenes, and also to 1, 4-dimethyl naphthalene. All of the radicals thus generated and kept at low temperature would polymerize to high-melting macromolecules when the cold solutions were allowed to warm up to room temperature. For the novelties of their work Errede and Landrum in 1957 received U.S. Patent No. 2,777,005.

Shortly after these preliminary works, the Union Carbide Company undertook commercial development of the p-xylylene polymers. Their products, known as "Parylenes," include that from para-xylene itself (Parylene N) and halogenated para-xylenes (Parylene C is the polymer from chloroparaxylene). The Parylenes are built on the framework shown in I above in which the benzene rings contain H atoms alone or, additionally, halogens or carbon groups. All are characterized by chemical stability, except to oxygen at elevated temperatures,* high melting points, and good electrical insulating properties.

It is interesting to note that one of the Carbide synthesis methods involved the sandwich compound II (Professor Cram's "2, 2 paracyclophane"); II is the main product of pyrolysis of para-xylene at 950° C. in the presence of steam as a diluent. Afterward II is cracked at a lower temperature (550° C.) and the vapors, upon cooling, form the polymer with molecular weight about 500,000.

---

* In poly-para-xylylene susceptibility to oxygen must be regarded as an inherent property, because all of its side chain hydrogens in the CH_2 groups are "benzylic," and the bonding energy to carbon is low.

B.   Polymers of the Type

(The polyphenylene oxides)

In December 1964, officials of the General Electric Company announced a new technique of synthesizing high polymers by a process called "oxidative coupling." The process, devised by Dr. Allan Hay, was called "the most exciting discovery in polymer chemistry since Nylon."

The principal polymer available via the route explored by G.E. is that derived from 2, 6-dimethyl phenol (2, 6-xylenol), and the reactions are shown in the scheme below.

Various R groups can be substituted for the CH_3 groups. The compound IV is designated "PPO" for short.

The reaction proceeds at ordinary temperature with

oxygen, but requires the presence of a complex catalyst derived from cuprous copper and an amine. (Since the discovery of the cuprous catalyst, others have been found to work as well, e.g. potassium ferricyanide). A quinone-type product is a minor accompaniment of the reaction, and in a few cases is the predominant product depending on the nature of the R groups in the starting material.

The nature of the polymerization reaction and products formed is well explained by the inventor himself in the following quotation:

We have now discovered a new method for polymerization of certain monomers—polymerization by oxidative coupling. Formally, at least, the method can be classed as a condensation polymerization.

When 2, 6-dimethylphenol is oxidized with oxygen in the presence of an amine complex of a cuprous salt as catalyst, a high molecular weight polyether or a diphenoquinone is obtained. The reaction is exothermic and extraordinarily rapid, being over in a few minutes at room temperature, if the reaction mixture is vigorously stirred. Under certain conditions, colorless polymers with intrinsic viscosities as high as 3.4 decil/g have been obtained. The polymer is soluble in chlorinated hydrocarbons such as chloroform and s-tetrachloro-ethane and aromatic solvents such as pyridine, nitrobenzene, and toluene, and evaporation of a solution of the polymer leaves a transparent, tough, flexible film. The polymer has a softening temperature in the neighborhood of 190° C.

This is an extraordinary result because of the extreme facility of the reaction and because it represents not only the first synthesis of a high-molecular-weight polyphenylene ether, but the first example of a polymerization that occurs by an oxidative coupling reaction utilizing oxygen as the oxidizing agent.*

* *Research Laboratory Bulletin,* General Electric Company, Winter 1964/65.

Properties of the new polymer include outstanding mechanical strength over a wide temperature range, e.g. resistance to alternate immersion in boiling water and liquid nitrogen ($-200°$ C.). Because of its resistance to water at high temperature it has probable uses in hot-water and steam piping.

C. *Polycarbonates and Polysulfones based on Bisphenol-A.*

Bisphenol-A, already a major aromatic chemical as a result of its use in the epoxy resins and glues (Chapter 8, Section C), will take on increased importance due to its incorporation in the new carbonate and sulfone polymers. The structure of bisphenol-A is:

$$HO-\!\!\bigcirc\!\!-\overset{\overset{\displaystyle CH_3}{|}}{\underset{\underset{\displaystyle CH_3}{|}}{C}}-\!\!\bigcirc\!\!-OH \qquad VI$$

The carbonate polymers have the general structure

$$ROC-\left[O-\!\!\bigcirc\!\!-\overset{\overset{\displaystyle CH_3}{|}}{\underset{\underset{\displaystyle CH_3}{|}}{C}}-\!\!\bigcirc\!\!-O-C-\right]_{\underline{n}}$$

and are derived by a reaction of bisphenol-A with phosgene ($COCl_2$) or with a carbonate ester, e.g. dimethyl or diethyl carbonate. The polymer reaction is a *condensation,* i.e. one in which two interacting functional groups are linked only by expulsion of a second product. Two examples are shown.

(a) Bisphenol—A in alkaline solution plus phosgene

$$X \cdot HO-\text{⟨⟩}-\underset{\underset{CH_3}{|}}{\overset{\overset{CH_3}{|}}{C}}-\text{⟨⟩}-OH + XCOCl_2 \xrightarrow{\text{heat}} NaCl$$
$$+ NaOH$$

$$H\left[O-\text{⟨⟩}-\underset{\underset{CH_3}{|}}{\overset{\overset{CH_3}{|}}{C}}-\text{⟨⟩}-O-\underset{\underset{O}{\|}}{C}- \right]X$$

VII

(b) Bisphenol—A plus alkyl carbonate esters

$$X \cdot HO-\text{⟨⟩}-\underset{\underset{CH_3}{|}}{\overset{\overset{CH_3}{|}}{C}}-\text{⟨⟩}-OH + X \cdot RO\underset{\underset{O}{\|}}{C}-OR \xrightarrow[\substack{\text{alkaline} \\ \text{catalyst}}]{\text{heat}}$$

polymer VII + 2X $\cdot$ ROH ⭡

In (a) the by-product sodium chloride has to be removed by water washing, whereas in (b) the by-product
is a volatile alcohol like methyl or ethyl, which can be
removed by distillation at reduced pressure. Molecular
weight of the products is influenced considerably by the
amount of alkali, temperature, and time of the cook.

An interesting secondary reaction takes place if the
polymer is subjected to alkali at high temperature. The
ester group rearranges and the carbonate carbon enters
the benzene ring.

The result is formation of aromatic polyethers that have
acid groups in the rings, thus have reactive sites that permit cross-linking to be done. The cross-linking can, in
fact, be accomplished by internal reactions of the polymer, so that what was originally a thermoplastic material
may be converted by this rearrangement into a thermosetting polymer.

These polycarbonate products were studied extensively by Hermann Schnell in Germany during the mid-fifties; he started with alkyl diphenols of the type

and prepared carbonate ester polymers. In the case of $n = 1$, the polycarbonate was a product melting above 300° C. Increase in the value of n brought about a lowering of melting point; likewise change of structure to

as for bisphenol-A lowered the melting point. Nevertheless, because of the availability of bisphenol-A, and other desirable properties of the polymer, including oxidation resistance, the polymer from bisphenol-A was considered a very desirable one.

Polycarbonates produced in Germany by Schnell's process are called "Merlon"; in the United States, at nearly the same time as Schnell's work, General Electric's Daniel Fox produced polycarbonates from bisphenol-A with molecular weight about 25,000. The G.E. product has been named "Lexan," and is growing in importance.

Lexan and Merlon have been produced in clear transparent sheets that have enormous impact strength. They withstand hammer blows and rifle bullets and for these reasons are coming into use for bulletproof windows, protective shields, etc., where great resistance to rupture is required. These polymers are generally quite resistant to deterioration by corrosive agents except concentrated or hot alkalis.

Sulfone polymers from bisphenol-A are materials with the formula

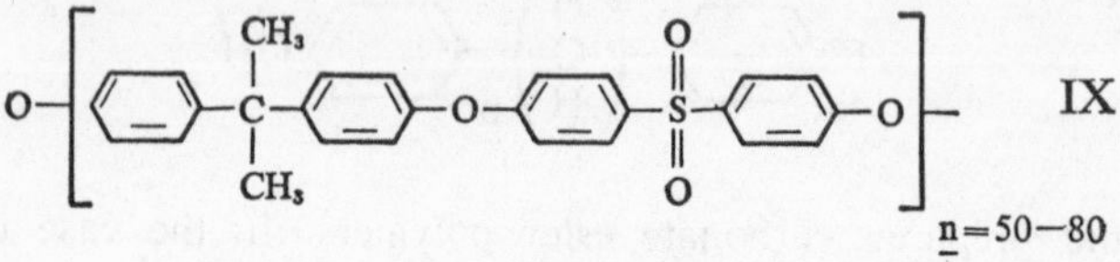

The presence of the bisphenol unit is seen on the left side of the formula, whereas the sulfone group

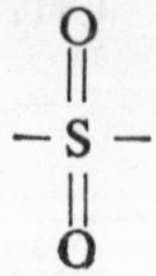

links together two rings on the right side, and contributes to them notable resistance to oxygen. As an ether the polysulfone product is resistant also to alkali degradation, thus differs from the polycarbonates.

The Union Carbide Company in 1967 completed a plant to produce ten million pounds per year of the new product, to which they have given the name "polysulfone."

The polymer is a thermoplastic material which is able to withstand rapid temperature changes from -70 to $+150°$ C.

D.   Cyclic Nitrogen as a Link in a Polymer Chain; the Polyimides

In the effort to construct high polymers which were made up altogether of rings, with no intervening CH, CH_2, or CH_3 groups (which always carry a certain susceptibility to oxygen), Du Pont chemists developed products based on the compound pyromellitic anhydride.

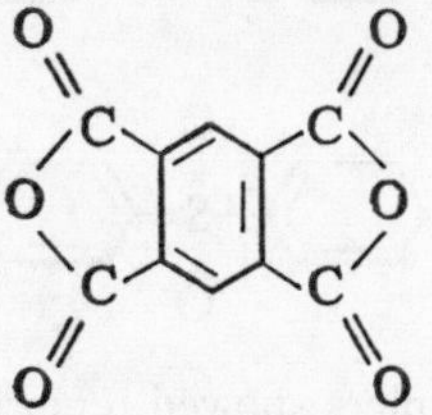

X

This compound, which is a near relative of the well-known phthalic anhydride, is, however, much less common and is not so readily accessible.

When X is made to react with a diamine ($H_2N-R-NH_2$) in an anhydrous solvent and later (following removal of the solvent) heated to $300°$ C., an imide polymer is formed that has the interesting structure

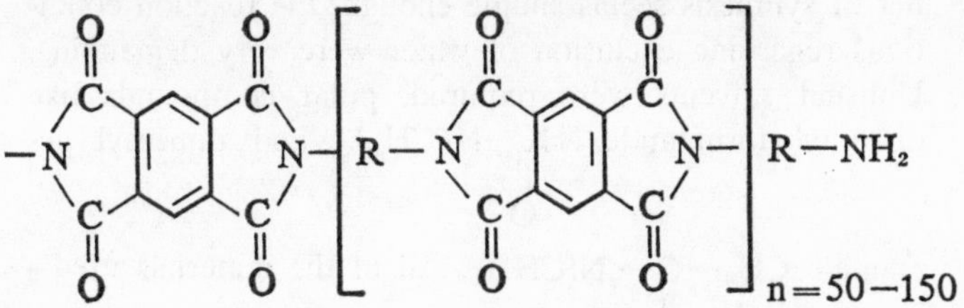

$n = 50 - 150$

XI

If the R portion is itself a ring, then the entire polymer becomes a series of connected rings and will manifest the stability characteristic of them. Du Pont chemists, in particular Sroog, Edwards, and Endrey, prepared polymers of the type XI in which the R group was varied to include the following:

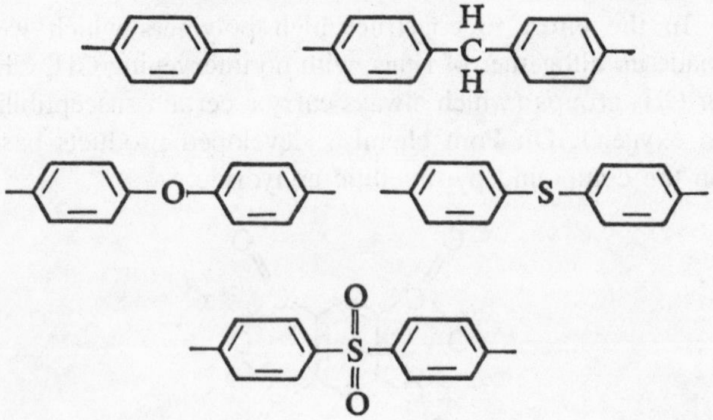

The resulting polymers showed remarkable thermal stability; many were unmeltable up to 800° C. and would withstand month-long exposure to air at 300° C. Likewise, they were resistant to acids, bases, and oxidizing agents. Common solvents have little effect upon them. They do dissolve in concentrated sulfuric and fuming nitric acids at room temperature, but slowly disintegrate in such solutions.

Method of Preparing Polyimides. Although the manner of synthesis seems simple enough, the reaction conditions regarding exclusion of water were very demanding. Unusual solvents were required, polar compounds like dimethyl formamide, $HC-N(CH_3)_2$, and dimethyl ac-

$$HC-N(CH_3)_2$$ with $\overset{\|}{O}$

etamide, $CH_3-C-N(CH_3)_2$. All of the materials used—

$$CH_3-C-N(CH_3)_2$$ with $\overset{\|}{O}$

the acid anhydride, the diamine, and the solvent, as well
as the reaction vessel—had to be rigorously freed of water
in advance, otherwise the process failed to give the desired
product. With these provisions for exclusion of moisture,
the acid anhydride was simply stirred into the diamine solvent mixture while the temperature was held in the range
15–75° C. The investigators noted that above 75° C. the
primary reaction was ineffective in forming products of
sufficiently high molecular weight.

Polymer concentrations up to 40 per cent in the solvent
are possible, whereupon the viscosity becomes considerable. To form the final product, the primary polymer is
freed of solvent and in the form of a thin film is heated
to 300° C. whereupon loss of water occurs to form the
imide. The color, which is at first pale yellow, deepens
to an orange at the elevated temperature; this color appears to be an inherent property of the polymer.

The reactions involved can be shown as follows:

(1) First stage: Formation of Amide-Acid (para-
phenylene diamine as example)

"Polyamic acid"   XII   etc.

(2) Through an interaction of COOH and NH groups, polymer XII loses water as indicated by the dotted lines, and forms imide polymer like XI.

The products of these reactions, by suitable variation of the amino components, compose a series that the Du Pont Company calls "Kaptons." The conditions of manufacture require a high price, twenty-five to thirty dollars per pound, but the Kaptons are coming into use for specialty purposes due to their extraordinary properties.

Modifications of the Polyamic Acids and Polyimides. (a) Compounds of the type XII known as polyamic acids are interesting in themselves, for they are high polymers that dissolve in a variety of solvents—alkalis in particular. Du Pont chemists found advantages in them again by conversion to film-forming insoluble materials through reaction of the acid group with metals, in particular silver, copper, iron, cobalt, nickel, and chromium. In this way additional color was imparted and very stable materials were formed. The incorporation of metals was not by simple salt formation, but by use of "complexing" agents to form so-called chelates.

(b) Dianhydrides different from the pyromellitic anhydride, X, may be used to advantage in the formulation of polyimides. One of these is the complex material benzophenone tetracarboxylic dianhydride ("BTDA"),

This compound is now produced in quantity by the Gulf Oil Corporation. Despite its apparent complexity it is more readily prepared than pyromellitic anhydride through ingenious reactions beginning with o-xylene. The latter, of course, is now one of those readily available hydrocarbons of the benzene series.

Imide polymers from compound XIII would have a structure with repeating units as shown.

XIV

The somewhat angular or "bent" structure of this polymer, compared to the strictly linear arrangement of the Kaptons, is a distinguishing feature.

Polymers of this type using "BTDA" as the anhydride ingredient are now under active development. If their thermal and mechanical properties are as good as the Kaptons, they may have some advantage as to price because of their origin from xylene. Certainly the benzophenone core should provide great chemical stability and resistance to oxidation.

E.   *An Aromatic with a Teflon Touch*

$$\text{Teflon,} \quad \left(\begin{array}{cc} F & F \\ -C - C - \\ F & F \end{array} \right)_n$$

the slippery polymer of tetrafluoroethylene, has its aromatic counterpart in a new product derived from a fluorinated xylene. In this respect the latter is a relative of poly-para-xylylene, already described in *A* above, and which possesses great heat stability. Teflon is likewise noted for its heat stability, as witnessed by its recent flowering in the household as a coating for frying pans and baking vessels.

What then for a polymer that combines benzene rings with $-\overset{\displaystyle F}{\underset{\displaystyle F}{C}}-\overset{\displaystyle F}{\underset{\displaystyle F}{C}}-$ groups?

The answer lay in a new process for producing

$$\overset{\displaystyle F}{\underset{\displaystyle F}{HC}}-\langle\overline{}\rangle-\overset{\displaystyle F}{\underset{\displaystyle F}{CH}}$$

so-called α, α, α', α' tetrafluoro-para-xylene. The compound could not be made from xylene directly; its synthesis depended on reaction of terephthaldehyde

$$O=\overset{\displaystyle H}{C}-\langle\overline{}\rangle-\overset{\displaystyle H}{C}=O$$

with a new reagent, sulfur tetrafluoride, developed recently by Du Pont chemists.

Union Carbide researchers applied the pyrolysis technique of Szwarc and Errede and Landrum to the tetrafluoro compound, or to a halogen derivative like

$$\underline{x}-\overset{\displaystyle F}{\underset{\displaystyle F}{C}}-\langle\overline{}\rangle-\overset{\displaystyle F}{\underset{\displaystyle F}{C}}-\underline{y}$$

where *x* was chlorine or bromine, and *y* was the same, or

hydrogen. Pyrolysis at 800–1000° C. produced diradicals of the type

$$\cdot\underset{F}{\overset{F}{C}}\!-\!\left\langle\ \right\rangle\!-\!\underset{F}{\overset{F}{C}}\cdot$$

and these upon cooling to room temperature linked together to give the polymer

$$\underset{F}{\overset{F}{C}}\!-\!\left\langle\ \right\rangle\!-\!\underset{F}{\overset{F}{C}}\quad\left(\!-\!\underset{F}{\overset{F}{C}}\!-\!\left\langle\ \right\rangle\!-\!\underset{F}{\overset{F}{C}}\!-\!\right)_{\underline{n}}$$

The product has great thermal stability and chemical inertness and, therefore, will be suited to numerous high-temperature applications. It has not yet appeared as a commercial product. One factor—perhaps the most important—is the matter of cost. The monomers for this kind of polymer are extraordinary materials, so far attainable only by lengthy laboratory synthesis. This situation, however, should not deter chemical and industrial explorers from efforts to develop such materials to full usefulness. One only needs to remember that polyethylene and Teflon itself seemed eons removed from the market place when they were first produced.

The above examples of polymer syntheses via the aromatics $(A - E)$ are only a few of the many that are beginning to make their impress in the realm of giant molecules. In some cases their syntheses involve classical procedures with an ingenious touch; in others novel reactions have been devised. The future is likely to witness a judicious assortment of both, based on availability of materials and reactions of high yield, or the need for truly extraordinary materials where price is the smallest factor.

Chapter 14

IS THERE ANY END?

In the early part of this book we have seen that man, in efforts to improve his lot and with ambitions to go anywhere on earth, into the high atmosphere, and deep into the sea, began to develop industry, engines, and machines, with science as an inevitable accompaniment. In the areas where industry and science flourished there has grown an awareness that man has developed a new talent. He now has not only the ability to *modify* existing products of nature to meet his essential needs, but also to *synthesize* practically anything* he wants, provided only that certain basic things are at hand.

This indeed is a revolutionary thought—that man, through the application of his wits, could make practically anything he wants from only a few essential building blocks. The full impact of this revolutionary thinking has hardly been felt, except in those circles where there is great sophistication in chemical syntheses.

The question that naturally arises is this: What are the essential building blocks from which man can synthesize so much of everything he needs and wants?

The roster of necessary or desirable materials includes nitrogen, oxygen, and sulfur, which occur abundantly in elemental form. Carbon from coal or wood char, hydrogen from water, and sodium and chlorine from common salt, practically complete the list. In addition we should have fluorine from fluoride minerals, silicon from sand on the seashore, and a variety of metals that are generally available.

---

* "Practically anything" is a big-enough order; "everything" is too much to expect at this early date!

Several of the above elements can be fastened directly into complex chemical combinations, but generally some simple preliminary transformations are advantageous. Examples are:

(a) Carbon is converted to carbon monoxide, carbon dioxide, acetylene (via calcium carbide), carbon disulfide by reaction with sulfur, and phosgene by reaction of carbon monoxide with chlorine. Each of these is useful in special ways; acetylene is particularly valuable for a wide variety of syntheses.

(b) Nitrogen is converted to ammonia and nitric acid.

(c) Sulfur is converted to sulfur dioxide and sulfuric acid.

(d) Oxygen is something of a universal reactant and can be put into organic structures in numerous ways —sometimes directly, often through employment of suitable catalysts to assist its precise placement.

Wherever nature produces these simple compounds directly, one takes advantage of the fact; for instance, rich nitrate deposits occur in various places and ammonia is available from coal.

While petroleum, natural gas, and coal remain available, many valuable building blocks are readily obtainable from them. Examples are:

(a) the hydrocarbon gases, methane, ethane, propane, butane, and the corresponding unsaturated hydrocarbons already described in Chapter 6.

(b) the aromatic hydrocarbons, benzene, toluene, the xylenes, naphthalene, anthracene, etc., and others like pentane, hexane, heptane, and cyclohexane.

(c) nitrogen ring compounds, e.g. pyridine and the quinolines.

These key materials are enough. They will be combined in myriad ways for literally endless syntheses, not only to form substances altogether foreign to this planet, but also many wondrous materials of living nature, like the gossamer filament spun out by the common spider, the strange light-radiating pigment of the firefly, or a tough protective coating exuded by a lowly beetle or a jungle plant. Among the synthetics will be increasing numbers of giant molecules useful as building materials, fibers, films, plastics, elastics, and adhesives. The chemists behind these syntheses will develop more subtle and ingenious procedures for the precise construction of complex molecular patterns, making them ever more accessible in economical ways. In addition, so long as the sun shines, photosynthesis will be working to produce forests, agricultural products, and life from the sea; from these sources man will obtain carbohydrates, fats, proteins, steroids, and other complex materials. These are usable either directly or, by ingenious chemical manipulation, they will be transformed into things of beauty and utility from the vantage point of their built-in structures, which are difficult to duplicate in the laboratory.

Synthetic science has come a long way from its humble beginnings in the early 1800s. Now we are in a period of fertile and imaginative developments; the products of the future are probably beyond us to foretell, but the *variety* of synthetic substances available then will be endless.

SELECTED REFERENCES

Chemical Technology of Petroleum, W. A. Gruse and D. R. Stevens (New York: McGraw-Hill, 1960), 3d ed.

A wide-spectrum reference, including the topics of crude-oil composition, origin of petroleum, distillation, refining, cracking, chemical reactions, and chemical products from petroleum hydrocarbons.

Petroleum Processing, R. J. Hengstebeck (New York: McGraw-Hill, 1959).

Includes much practical information on types of equipment, operating procedures, characteristics of products formed in commercial operations, properties of catalysts, etc.

The American Petroleum Industry: 100 Years of Oil in the U.S.A. Two Volumes: "The Age of Illumination 1859–1899"; "The Age of Energy 1899–1959." H. F. Williamson, A. R. Daum, R. L. Andreano, G. L. Klose, and P. A. Weinstein (Evanston, Ill.: Northwestern University Press, first volume, 1959; second volume, 1964).

An extensive history of the development of the petroleum industry.

Encyclopedia of Chemical Technology, Kirk and Othmer (New York: Interscience Publishers).

An excellent source of both general and specific information on practically all matters of chemical significance. Petroleum is well covered, as follows:
   (a) Petroleum; Origin, refinery processes, petroleum products and petrochemicals, Vol. 10 (1st ed., 1953), 89–228.
   (b) Alkylation, Vol. 1 (2d ed., 1963), 882.

(c) Antifreezes, Vol. 2 (2d ed., 1963), 540.
(d) Antioxidants, Vol. 2 (2d ed., 1963), 589.
(e) Butadiene, Vol. 3 (2d ed., 1964), 784.
(f) Butylenes, Vol. 3 (2d ed., 1964), 830.
(g) Catalysis and cracking, Vol. 4 (2d ed., 1964), 535–83.
(h) Ethylene, Vol. 8 (2d ed., 1965), 499.
(i) Hexanes, Vol. 11 (2d ed., 1966), 1.
(j) Hydrocarbons, Vol. 11 (2d ed., 1966),
   Oxidation, 225;
   Resins, 242;
   Survey, nomenclature, reactions, toxicity, etc., 263–306.
(k) Waxes, Vol. 15 (1st ed., 1956), 1–17.

Note that subjects in this encyclopedia are arranged alphabetically, so that it is very easy for the reader to locate quickly what he wants.

An Introduction to the Organic Chemistry of High Polymers, C. S. Marvel (New York: Wiley, 1959).

A brief survey of polymerization processes by an author of high distinction in the field.

The Nature and Chemistry of High Polymers, K. F. O'Driscoll (New York: Reinhold, 1964).

A short survey similar to that of C. S. Marvel.

Introduction to Polymer Chemistry, J. K. Stille (New York: Wiley, 1962).

A larger treatment of the subject than those of Marvel and O'Driscoll; it presupposes a good grounding in organic and physical chemistry.

Giant Molecules, by Herman Mark and the Editors of *Life.* (New York: Time Incorporated, 1966).

A brilliantly illustrated book in the custom of *Life* publishers. It is on an elementary level and contains both history and human interest background on the origin and development of important commercial polymeric materials.

The basic chemistry is authentic, and the author, Mark, is a distinguished polymer scientist. The book is a good starting point to acquire familiarity with polymers and their uses.

"Giant Molecules," *Scientific American,* September 1957.

Practically the whole of this excellent issue (pp. 81–216) was devoted to the subject, which was covered by outstanding scientists in the field, e.g. Professors Debye, Mark, Natta, Tobolsky and many more. The subject level is appropriate for those without advanced chemical experience. Later issues of *Scientific American* have also given good coverage of polymer subjects. These can be found readily in the indexes.

Polymer Chemistry, a series of articles on polymers, along with procedures for laboratory preparation of some common plastic and rubbery products. Authors are Marvel, McKnight, LeRoi, Tobolsky, Sorenson, Price, Bruck, Porter, and Condit: in *Journal of Chemical Education,* Vol. 42 (January 1965), 1–25.

The *Encyclopedia of Chemical Technology* (see above) also covers polymer subjects very thoroughly. One only needs to follow the alphabetical system with its cross indexing to find, for instance, Rubber, Polyethylene, Elastomers, Synthetic, and similar topics in the polymer field.

INDEX